BASIC ELECTRICAL ENGINEERING

By the same authors

HIGHER ELECTRICAL ENGINEERING

BASIC ELECTRICAL ENGINEERING

by

J. SHEPHERD, B.Sc., F.I.E.E.

Senior Lecturer, Department of Electrical Engineering,
University of Edinburgh

A. H. MORTON, B.Sc., M.I.E.E., M.I.E.R.E.

Head of Electrical Engineering Department,
Paisley College of Technology

and

L. F. SPENCE, B.Sc., B.Sc.(Econ.), M.I.E.E.

Principal Lecturer
Department of Electrical Engineering,
Borough Polytechnic

LONDON

SIR ISAAC PITMAN & SONS, LTD.

First published 1958
Reprinted 1961
Reprinted 1964
Reprinted 1967

SIR ISAAC PITMAN & SONS, Ltd.
PITMAN HOUSE, PARKER STREET, KINGSWAY, LONDON, W.C.2
THE PITMAN PRESS, BATH
PITMAN HOUSE, BOUVERIE STREET, CARLTON, MELBOURNE
P.O. BOX 7721, JOHANNESBURG, TRANSVAAL
P.O. BOX 6038, PORTAL STREET, NAIROBI, KENYA

ASSOCIATED COMPANIES
PITMAN MEDICAL PUBLISHING COMPANY, Ltd.
39 PARKER STREET, LONDON, W.C.2
PITMAN PUBLISHING CORPORATION
20 EAST 46TH STREET, NEW YORK, N.Y. 10017
SIR ISAAC PITMAN & SONS (CANADA), Ltd.
(INCORPORATING THE COMMERCIAL TEXT BOOK COMPANY)
PITMAN HOUSE, 381-383 CHURCH STREET, TORONTO

SBN: 273 40256 0

MADE IN GREAT BRITAIN AT THE PITMAN PRESS, BATH
F7

Preface

Nature, and nature's laws lay hid in night,
God said, "Let Newton be" and all was light.
—A. Pope

THE authors hope that this textbook will provide a clear and reasonably concise introduction to electrical engineering. It embodies several new features which we feel will aid the understanding of this growing science. It is designed mainly for the increasing number of students who are studying for the Ordinary National Certificate in Electrical Engineering, and is based on lectures given to such students over a number of years. The work covered will also be found to follow the main lines of the new London University Part I syllabus in Electrical Engineering, and the Intermediate Standard in the City and Guilds of London Electrical Engineering Practice examination.

The rationalized M.K.S. system of units has been used throughout and there is no reference to the older c.g.s. system. This means that the student can concentrate on the system which is now in almost universal use for the teaching of electrical engineering.

The symbols and abbreviations are in conformity with those published by the Institution of Electrical Engineers for use in National Certificate Courses (March, 1955, edition). It is convenient to point out here that all symbols are printed in italics, while the abbreviations for units are in roman type. This should help to avoid confusion when an equation involving both symbols and units is used. Further, the abbreviated unit will in general be suitably spaced from the body of the equation.

A large number of worked examples has been included in the text, as we have found that these help the student to grasp the principles behind them. There is also a wide variety of end-of-chapter examples (with answers) on which the budding electrical engineer may try his newly-acquired skill. Many of these examples come from examination papers of the West of Scotland Committee on Technical Education (labelled O.N.C.), and of London University (labelled L.U.) to whom thanks are given for permission to publish.

Of late there has been a tendency for lecturers to adopt the convention that the e.m.f. induced in a circuit due to a change of flux linkage is proportional to the rate of change of flux (as distinct from *minus* the rate of change of flux). This convention has

v

been tried successfully by the authors and has been found to promote a ready understanding of induced e.m.f., especially in the transformer and the synchronous machine. It has therefore been adopted here.

The dot notation for mutual inductance is also introduced, since it is felt that this enables the systematic treatment of mutual inductance in circuits to be more easily achieved.

A chapter on Electronics introduces this important subject, since many O.N.C. courses now include such an introduction at this level in the National Certificate scheme.

Thanks are due to Mullards, Ltd., for permission to publish valve data, and also to our friend **Mr K. M.** Donaldson, B.Sc., for his assistance in connexion with many of the diagrams.

October, 1957

Contents

CHAPTER 1

Units and Simple Circuits

THE ELECTRON is a particle which is normally associated with an atom, but which can exist independently. It has two important properties: (a) a mass of 9.1×10^{-31} kg; (b) a negative electric charge. The total charge on 6.3×10^{18} electrons is one *coulomb* of charge. Some materials, such as silver, copper, and aluminium have many electrons which are free to drift from one atom to another. These materials are *conductors* of electricity. Other materials such as mica, paper, and air have few free electrons and are *insulators*.

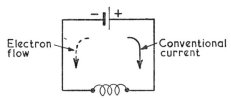

FIG. 1.1. ELEMENTS OF AN ELECTRIC CIRCUIT

If the terminals of an electric battery (Fig. 1.1) are joined by a wire of some conducting material there will be a general drift of electrons round the circuit formed, from the negative battery terminal round the wire to the positive battery terminal. Inside the battery the drift will be from the positive to the negative terminal. The rate of flow of electric charge past any section in the circuit is called the current strength or simply the *current*. The conventional direction of current flow is taken as opposite to the direction of electron drift.

The flow of electrons round a circuit is associated with the transfer of energy from one part of a circuit to another. If the circuit is broken by opening a switch or by a break in the conductor, the current and the energy transfer cease (Fig. 1.2). The speed at which energy is transferred from one part of a circuit to another is approximately the speed of light (3×10^8 metres per second or 186,000 miles per second). The actual speed at which the electrons drift round the circuit is, however, quite small.

1

With a direct current the electron flow is always in the same direction round the circuit. An alternating current is one in which the current direction continually reverses. Irrespective of the current direction however, the energy flow (in the case of simple loads like lamps) is always from the source of electrical energy towards the load.

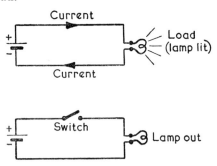

FIG. 1.2. TRANSFER OF ENERGY IN A COMPLETE CIRCUIT

1.1. Mechanical, Thermal, and Electrical Units

The three fundamental units used for measurement are units of length, mass, and time. In the British F.P.S. system the standard units are the foot, the pound, and the second. In the M.K.S. system they are the metre, the kilogramme, and the second.

$$1 \text{ ft} = 0\cdot3045 \text{ m}$$
$$1 \text{ lb} = 0\cdot4536 \text{ kg}$$

The British unit of force is the pound weight (lb (wt)). It is the force required to give a mass of 1 lb an acceleration of $32\cdot2$ ft/sec² (i.e. the acceleration due to gravity).

The M.K.S unit of force is the newton (Nw). It is the force required to give a mass of 1 kg an acceleration of 1 m/sec².

One kilogramme (kg(wt)) is the force required to give a mass of 1 kg an acceleration of $9\cdot81$ m/sec² (i.e. gravitational acceleration).

Note: $9\cdot81$ m/sec² $= 32\cdot2$ ft/sec².

$$1 \text{ kg(wt)} = 9\cdot81 \text{ Nw}$$
$$1 \text{ lb(wt)} = 0\cdot4536 \text{ kg(wt)} = 4\cdot45 \text{ Nw}$$

Mechanical work is measured by the product of force and distance moved in the direction of the force. One foot-pound (ft-lb(wt)) is the work done when a force of one pound moves its point of application a distance of one foot. One joule (J) is the work done when a force of one newton moves its point of application a distance of one metre.

Energy is the capacity for doing work, so that it has the same units as work in all systems.

$$1 \text{ ft-lb(wt)} = 0.3045 \times 4.45 \text{ newton-metres} = 1.36 \text{ joules}$$

The joule is thus a little smaller than the ft-lb(wt).

Torque or turning moment is measured by the product of the force and the perpendicular distance from the line of action of the force to the axis of rotation. It is measured in lb(wt)-ft or newton-metres (Nw-m).

$$1 \text{ lb(wt)-ft} = 4.45 \times 0.3045 \text{ Nw-m} = 1.36 \text{ Nw-m}$$

Power is the rate of doing work, i.e.

$$\text{Unit of power} = \frac{\text{Unit of energy}}{\text{Unit of time}}$$

One horse-power (h.p.) is a rate of work of 550 ft-lb(wt)/sec or 33,000 ft-lb(wt)/min.

1 *watt* (W) is a rate of work of one joule per second.

$$\begin{aligned}
1 \text{ h.p.} &= 550 \text{ ft-lb(wt)/sec} \\
&= 550 \times 1.36 \text{ J/sec} \\
&= 746 \text{ watts}
\end{aligned}$$

Energy may also be measured as the product of the power and the time for which it is applied.

Thus one horse-power-hour (h.p.-h) is the work done when a power of one horse-power is expended for one hour.

$$1 \text{ h.p.-h} = 33,000 \times 60 = 1,980,000 \text{ ft-lb(wt)}$$

Also $1 \text{ watt-sec} = 1 \text{ J}$

A larger unit of electrical energy is required commercially, this being the kilowatt-hour (kWh).

$$\begin{aligned}
1 \text{ kWh} &= 10^3 \times 60 \times 60 \text{ watt-sec} \\
&= 3,600,000 \text{ J}
\end{aligned}$$

where $1 \text{ kW} = 1,000 \text{ watts}$

Thermal energy (heat) is measured in calories, where one *calorie* is the thermal energy required to raise the temperature of one gramme of water through one centigrade degree (C°).

The thermal unit/mechanical unit relationship is found, by experiment, to be

$$1 \text{ calorie (cal)} \equiv 4\cdot185 \text{ joules}$$

The British unit of thermal energy is the *British Thermal Unit* (B.Th.U.) which is the heat required to raise the temperature of one pound of water through one Fahrenheit degree (F°).

By experiment 1 B.Th.U. = 778 ft-lb(wt)

$$= 778 \times 1\cdot36 \text{ J}$$

$$= 1,055 \text{ J}$$

	F.P.S. Unit	M.K.S. Unit	Conversion
Length	Foot (ft)	Metre (m)	1 ft = 0·3045 m
Mass	Pound (lb)	Kilogramme (kg)	1 lb = 0·4536 kg
Time	Second (sec)	Second (sec)	
Force	Pound weight (lb(wt))	Newton (Nw)	1 lb(wt) = 4·45 Nw
Work	ft-lb(wt)	Newton-metre (Nw-m) or joule (J)	1 ft-lb(wt) = 1·36 Nw-m
Torque	lb(wt)-ft	Newton-metre (Nw-m)	1 lb(wt)-ft = 1·36 Nw-m
Power	1 h.p.	1 watt (W)	1 h.p. = 746 W

1.2. Energy and Power Relationships

The following table shows the prefixes and the multiples and sub-multiples into which M.K.S. units are divided.

Prefix	Number of original units denoted	Symbol	Example
Mega	10^6	M	1 Megawatt (MW) = 10^6 watts
kilo	10^3	k	1 kilowatt (kW) = 10^3 watts
milli	10^{-3}	m	1 milliwatt (mW) = 10^{-3} watts
micro	10^{-6}	μ	1 microwatt (μW) = 10^{-6} watts
pico	10^{-12}	p	1 picowatt (pW) = 10^{-12} watts

Since electrical energy must, before use, be transformed into another form of energy, it is important that a thorough understanding of the conversion from electrical units to mechanical and to thermal units is obtained. This enables the efficiency of any piece of equipment to be readily found. The efficiency of any equipment is defined as

$$\text{Efficiency } (\eta) = \frac{\text{Power output from equipment}}{\text{Power input to equipment}}$$

$$= \frac{\text{Energy output in a given time}}{\text{Energy input in the same time}}$$

This is called the "per unit" efficiency. The percentage efficiency is

$$\frac{\text{Power output}}{\text{Power input}} \times \frac{100 \text{ per cent}}{1}$$

For the above formula the input and output must be expressed in the same units.

Example 1.1

Calculate the overall efficiency of a generating station which has a daily output of 1,280 MWh and uses daily 600 tons of coal of calorific value 13,000 B.Th.U./lb.

The problem is the expression of the electrical energy output in B.Th.U.

$$\text{Energy output/day} = \frac{1,280 \times 10^3 \times 3\cdot6 \times 10^6}{1,055} = 4\cdot36 \times 10^9 \text{ B.Th.U.}$$

The input energy per day $= 600 \times 2,240 \times 13,000$ B.Th.U.

$$= 17\cdot5 \times 10^9 \text{ B.Th.U.}$$

Therefore overall percentage efficiency $= \dfrac{\text{Energy output}}{\text{Energy input}} \times 100$ per cent

$$= \frac{4\cdot36}{17\cdot5} \times \frac{10^9}{10^9} \times 100 \text{ per cent}$$

$$= \underline{\underline{25 \text{ per cent}}}$$

Example 1.2

A bath containing 1 gal of water is to be heated by a 90 per cent efficient electric heater so that the water temperature is raised by 50°C in 30 min.

Calculate the electrical energy input to the heater, the average electric power supply and the cost of the energy at 3d. per kWh. (Neglect the heat absorbed by the bath.)

1 gal of water weighs 10 lb.

Mass of water $= 10 \times 0\cdot454 \times 1,000 = 4,540$ gm

Heat required by water $= 4,540 \times 50 \times 4\cdot2$ J

$$= \text{energy output of heater}$$

$$\text{Energy input to heater} = \frac{\text{energy output}}{\eta}$$

$$= \frac{4{,}540 \times 50 \times 4 \cdot 2}{0 \cdot 9} \text{ J or W-sec}$$

$$= \frac{4{,}540 \times 50 \times 4 \cdot 2}{0 \cdot 9 \times 1{,}000 \times 3{,}600} \text{ kWh}$$

$$= 0 \cdot 294 \text{ kWh}$$

Now this energy entered heater in 30 min (0·5 hour).

Average electric power = average rate of energy supplied

$$= \frac{0 \cdot 294}{0 \cdot 5} = 0 \cdot 588 \text{ kW}$$

Cost of energy = $3 \times 0 \cdot 294 = 0 \cdot 882$d.

Example 1.3

A hydro-electric station has a turbine of 85 per cent efficiency and a generator of 95 per cent efficiency. The effective head of water is 500 ft. Calculate the volume of water used when delivering a load of 50 MW for 5 hours. Water weighs 62·5 lb/ft³.

Overall per unit efficiency = $0 \cdot 85 \times 0 \cdot 95 = 0 \cdot 807$

Energy output = 50×5 MWh

$$= \frac{50 \times 5 \times 10^6 \times 3{,}600}{1 \cdot 36} \text{ ft-lb(wt)}$$

$$= 6 \cdot 61 \times 10^{11} \text{ ft-lb(wt)}$$

$$\text{Energy input} = \frac{6 \cdot 61 \times 10^{11}}{0 \cdot 807} = 8 \cdot 2 \times 10^{11} \text{ ft-lb(wt)}.$$

Since the head is 500 ft and 1 ft³ of water weighs 62·5 lb, the energy contributed by each ft³ = $500 \times 62 \cdot 5$ ft-lb(wt)

$$\text{Volume of water for required energy} = \frac{8 \cdot 2 \times 10^{11}}{500 \times 62 \cdot 5}$$

$$= 26 \cdot 3 \times 10^6 \text{ ft}^3$$

Example 1.4

A battery-driven electric vehicle weighing 2 tons has an electric motor and gearing which together have an efficiency of 80 per cent. Calculate the energy storage capacity of the battery required to make possible a 50-mile run on level road, taking the tractive resistance to be 70 lb(wt)/ton. If the maximum speed on the level is 30 m.p.h. calculate the corresponding power supply from the battery and also calculate the power taken from the battery when the vehicle ascends a gradient of 1 in 30 at 15 m.p.h.

Force required to drive vehicle on level = $70 \times 2 = 140$ lb(wt)

Distance travelled = $50 \times 5{,}280 = 2 \cdot 64 \times 10^5$ ft

For a circuit which has a source with an e.m.f. of E volts the energy which is converted in the source per coulomb passing is, by definition, E joules. Hence the energy which is converted per second will be $E \times$ number of coulombs per second.

If the current flowing through the circuit is I amperes, then the number of coulombs passing per second will be I. Hence,

$$\text{energy converted per second} = EI \text{ J/sec}$$

i.e. $$\text{power conversion} = EI \text{ W}$$

In the same way if the p.d. between two terminals is V volts then the energy transferred from one side of the terminals to the other per coulomb passing is V joules.

Therefore $$\text{energy transferred per second} = VI \text{ J/sec}$$

i.e. $$\text{power transmission} = VI \text{ W}$$

where I is the current flowing

If a power flow of VI watts is maintained for t seconds then the total energy transferred will be—

$$\text{energy} = VIt \text{ J}$$

Example 1.6

A motor which is 80 per cent efficient runs from a 250-V supply when delivering a power of 40 h.p. Calculate the current taken by the motor.

$$\text{Power input} = \frac{\text{Power output}}{\eta} = \frac{40}{0\cdot8} = 50 \text{ h.p.}$$

$$\text{Supply current} = \frac{50 \times 746}{250} = \underline{\underline{149 \text{ A}}}$$

1.6. Resistance

When a current flows through a conductor, heat is produced in the conductor. By analogy with mechanical friction, this heating is said to be due to the resistance of the conductor to the passage of current. Experimentally ti is found that the p.d. (V) across the ends of most conductors is directly proportional to the current (I) flowing through them, provided that the physical conditions (particularly the temperature) remain constant (Fig. 1.6).

$$V \propto I$$

i.e. $$V = I \times R \text{ volts} \qquad . \qquad . \qquad . \quad (1.1)$$

where R is a constant, called the resistance of the conductor. From equation (1.1),

$$R = \frac{V}{I}$$

The units of resistance are volts per ampere or (more usually) *ohms* (Ω).

This experimental relationship is known as *Ohm's law.*

The *unit of resistance* (the ohm) is defined as the resistance across which there is a p.d. of one volt when a current of one ampere flows. The symbol for ohm units is the Greek letter omega (Ω).

If there is no source of e.m.f in a conductor, the p.d. across it is sometimes called the "*IR* drop."

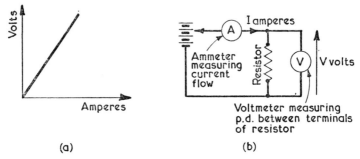

(a)   (b)

Fig. 1.6. Relationship between Current and P.D. for a
Conductor, and Relevant Circuit

If a current of *I* amperes is passed from some generator through the resistor *R*, then

$$\text{p.d. across } R = I \times R = V$$

Therefore   power entering $R = V \times I$ W

$$= I^2R \text{ W}$$

Or since $I = \dfrac{V}{R}$ (from equation (1.1)),

power entering $R = V \times I = \dfrac{V^2}{R}$ W

1.7. Kirchhoff's Laws

Kirchhoff's laws state that—

1. The algebraic sum of all the currents at any point in an electrical network is zero.

2. Round any closed mesh in a network, the algebraic sum of the e.m.f.s acting round the mesh is equal to the algebraic sum of the products of current and resistance (i.e. volt drops) round the same mesh.

An algebraic sum is one in which the sign of the quantity must be taken into account.

Mathematically Kirchhoff's laws may be summarized as—

1. $\Sigma I = 0$ at any point.
2. $\Sigma E = \Sigma V$ round any closed mesh.

The symbol Σ (sigma) denotes "the algebraic sum of all similar terms."

In Fig. 1.7 four conductors are shown meeting at a point O. Choosing as the positive direction of current a current flowing towards the junction, then

$$\Sigma I = I_1 + I_2 - I_3 + I_4 = 0$$

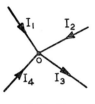

$$\Sigma I = 0$$

FIG. 1.7.
KIRCHHOFF'S
FIRST LAW

In Fig. 1.8 the heavy lines indicate various closed meshes picked from the same network; Kirchhoff's second law may be applied to each (arbitrary current directions are chosen for this illustration). Thus in—

Fig. 1.8 (a) proceeding clockwise (i.e. against I_2 but with I_3)—

$$\Sigma E = -E_2 = \Sigma IR$$

i.e.
$$-E_2 = I_3R_3 - I_2R_2$$

Fig. 1.8 (b) proceeding clockwise—

$$\Sigma E = -E_1 + E_2 = \Sigma IR$$

i.e.
$$-E_1 + E_2 = I_2R_2 - I_1R_1$$

Fig. 1.8 (c) proceeding clockwise—

$$\Sigma E = -E_1 = \Sigma IR$$

i.e.
$$-E_1 = I_4R_4 - I_1R_1$$

Fig. 1.8 (d) proceeding clockwise—

$$\Sigma E = 0 = \Sigma IR$$

$$0 = -I_3R_3 + I_4R_4$$

The counter-clockwise direction could equally well have been chosen in any particular case.

RESISTORS IN SERIES

As an example of Kirchhoff's laws, consider n resistors* connected in series (Fig. 1.9). Then by the first law, the same current flows in each resistor. By the second law—

$$E = IR_1 + IR_2 + IR_3 + \ldots + IR_n$$

* A resistor is a piece of apparatus (e.g. a coil of wire) designed to have a given resistance.

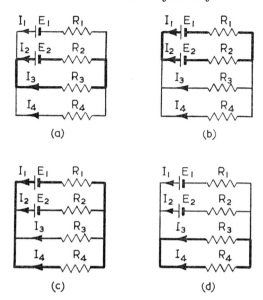

Fig. 1.8. Examples of Closed Meshes

If R_{eq} is defined as the single resistor which allows the same current to flow from the same e.m.f. (Fig. 1.9 (b)) then—

$$E = IR_{eq}$$
$$IR_{eq} = IR_1 + IR_2 + IR_3 + \ldots + IR_n$$
$$R_{eq} = R_1 + R_2 + R_3 + \ldots R_n$$

Hence the equivalent resistance of a number of resistors connected in series is the sum of the individual resistances. For n equal resistors in series $R_{eq} = n \times R$.

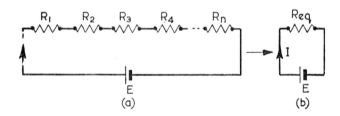

Fig. 1.9. Resistors in Series

RESISTORS IN PARALLEL

In Fig. 1.10 (a) n resistors are shown connected in parallel. By Kirchhoff's first law, applied at point A.

$$I = I_1 + I_2 + I_3 + \ldots + I_n$$

$$= \frac{E}{R_1} + \frac{E}{R_2} + \frac{E}{R_3} + \ldots + \frac{E}{R_n}$$

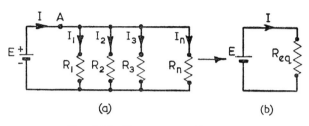

(a)   (b)

FIG. 1.10. RESISTORS IN PARALLEL

Defining the equivalent resistance as for the series connexion, the equivalent circuit of Fig. 1.10 (b) gives

$$I = \frac{E}{R_{eq}}$$

$$\frac{1}{R_{eq}} = \frac{1}{R_1} + \frac{1}{R_2} + \frac{1}{R_3} + \ldots \frac{1}{R_n} \, . \qquad (1.2)$$

For n equal resistors in parallel

$$\frac{1}{R_{eq}} = \frac{n}{R}, \text{ i.e. } R_{eq} = \frac{R}{n}$$

For two resistors in parallel equation (1.2) becomes

$$\frac{1}{R_{eq}} = \frac{1}{R_1} + \frac{1}{R_2} = \frac{R_1 + R_2}{R_1 \times R_2}$$

$$R_{eq} = \frac{R_1 R_2}{R_1 + R_2}$$

If the p.d. across the resistors is V volts, then $V = I \times R_{eq}$ where I is the total current $= I_1 + I_2$

$$V = I \cdot \frac{R_1 R_2}{R_1 + R_2}$$

Current through R_1 is $I_1 = \dfrac{V}{R_1} = I\,\dfrac{R_2}{R_1 + R_2}$ . . .   (1.3)

And the current through R_2 is $I_2 = \dfrac{V}{R_2} = I\,\dfrac{R_1}{R_1 + R_2}$ . .   (1.4)

These equations show how the current divides between two parallel resistors.

1.8. Internal Resistance

In every source there is a loss of electrical energy as heat. For instance, if the source is an accumulator cell as represented in

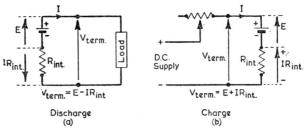

FIG. 1.11. CHARGE AND DISCHARGE OF AN ACCUMULATOR

Fig. 1.11 (a), during discharge chemical energy is converted to electrical as represented by the letter E which indicates that E joules of electrical energy are derived from stored chemical energy for each coulomb passing round the circuit. However, there is a loss of energy corresponding to a heating effect as the current passes through the cell—this is represented by the resistance R_{int} and thus the output potential is less than E.

$$\text{Output potential} = V = E - I R_{\text{int}} \quad . \quad . \quad (1.5)$$

Multiplying both sides by I

$$VI = EI - I^2 R_{\text{int}}$$

$$\text{output power} = \begin{Bmatrix} \text{power from chemical} \\ \text{reaction} \end{Bmatrix} - \begin{Bmatrix} \text{internal power loss as} \\ \text{heat} \end{Bmatrix}$$

Again, if the accumulator were put on charge (i.e. if it were the load supplied with electrical energy from another source as in Fig. 1.11 (b)) and the potential across its terminals were V volts, then for each coulomb passed V joules would be transferred to the accumulator. However, only part (E) of this would become chemical energy, the remainder would heat the accumulator; the charging accumulator may be represented by the same symbols as the discharging accumulator but E is now less than V.

$$V = E + IR_{int} \qquad . \qquad . \qquad . \quad (1.6)$$

It will be noticed from equation (1.5) that if an accumulator is connected to a resistance load (Fig. 1.11 (a)) or to a system where the p.d., V, is less than the e.m.f., E, then the accumulator discharges and the current is given by

$$I = \frac{E - V}{R_{int}}$$

If the accumulator is connected to a supply whose p.d., V, exceeds the e.m.f., E, then the accumulator charges (equation (1.6)) and the current is given by $I = \dfrac{V - E}{R_{int}}$.

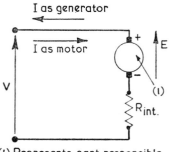

(1) Represents part responsible for energy conversion

FIG. 1.12. E.M.F. AND P.D. OF A MACHINE

An electrical machine may be treated in a similar manner (Fig. 1.12). Every machine has an equivalent internal resistance representing part, at least, of the losses in the machine. Let E be the e.m.f. in a machine (i.e. E joules of energy are converted from a mechanical to an electrical form or vice versa) with the passage of each coulomb through the machine.

Case (a). If $E > V$ then the machine acts as a generator, and hence

$$I = \frac{E - V}{R_{int}}$$

and electric power output $= \left\{ \begin{matrix} \text{net mechanical} \\ \text{power input} \end{matrix} \right\} - \left\{ \begin{matrix} \text{heat losses in} \\ \text{machine} \end{matrix} \right\}$

Case (b). If $V > E$, then the machine acts as a motor and since

$$V = E + IR_{int} \qquad . \qquad . \qquad . \quad (1.6)$$

then

$$I = \frac{V - E}{R_{int}}$$

and electric power input $= \left\{ \begin{matrix} \text{gross mechanical} \\ \text{power developed} \end{matrix} \right\} + \left\{ \begin{matrix} \text{heat losses in} \\ \text{machine} \end{matrix} \right\}$

Example 1.7

A 110-V battery of internal resistance 1 Ω is connected in parallel with a d.c. generator of e.m.f. 115 V and internal resistance 0·5 Ω, to supply a load of 10 Ω resistance. Determine the currents in the generator, battery and load.

Step. 1. Draw in the assumed currents I_1, I_2, and I_3 (Fig. 1.13). The direction in which the currents are assumed to flow is unimportant, since if the wrong direction is chosen, it is indicated by a negative sign in the result.

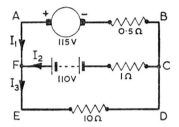

FIG. 1.13. PERTAINING TO EXAMPLE 1.7

Step 2. Since there are three unknown currents three simultaneous equations must be formed.

1st equation—At junction F, $I_1 + I_2 = I_3$ . . . . . (1)

2nd equation—Mesh $BAFCB$ $115 - 110 = I_1 \times 0.5 - I_2 \times 1$

Therefore $5 = 0.5I_1 - I_2$ . . . . . (2)

Note that the I_1 term is positive since I_1 flows round the mesh in the same sense as $BAFCB$, while the I_2 term is negative since I_2 flows in the opposite sense to $BAFCB$. The same applies to the signs of the e.m.f.s.

3rd equation—Mesh $CFEDC$ $110 = 10I_3 + 1 \times I_2$ . . . . (3)

Step 3. Solve the equations.

Substitute for I_3 from equation (1), in equation (3).

$$110 = 10(I_1 + I_2) + I_2$$
$$110 = 10I_1 + 11I_2$$

Therefore $I_2 = \dfrac{110 - 10I_1}{11}$ . . . . . (4)

Substitute this in equation (2).

$$5 = 0.5I_1 - \frac{110 - 10I_1}{11}$$
$$55 = 5.5I_1 - 110 + 10I_1$$
$$165 = 15.5I_1$$

Therefore $I_1 = \underline{\underline{10.65 \text{ A}}}$

Substitute for I_1 in equation (4).

$$I_2 = \frac{110 - 106.5}{11} = \frac{3.5}{11} = \underline{\underline{0.32 \text{ A}}}$$

Substitute in equation (1) for I_1 and I_2

$$I_3 = I_1 + I_2 = 10.65 + 0.32 = \underline{\underline{10.97 \text{ A}}}$$

In this case all current values turned out to be positive showing that the currents would in fact flow in the direction of the arrowheads; had one or all of the currents happened to turn out with a negative sign then that current would actually flow in the opposite direction to that of the arrowhead. If such were the case it would be incorrect to alter the current directions on the diagram on completing the problem, as this would falsify all the equations in the problem.

1.9. Maxwell's Mesh Current Method

It is often convenient when solving more complicated problems involving electrical networks to introduce mesh currents in place of actual conductor currents. A mesh current is assumed to flow in all the conductors of a given closed mesh, the actual current which flows in any one conductor being made up of the algebraic sum of the individual mesh currents which flow through it. Thus if one conductor is common to two meshes there will be two mesh currents through it and the actual conductor current will be the algebraic sum of these two mesh currents. If, in a network, the current through only one conductor is required, it is usually possible to arrange the mesh currents so that only one mesh current flows through the required conductor. If this is done then the number of simultaneous equations needed for the solution is one less than is required by the conductor current method of Example 1.7.

The mesh equations are formed by equating the algebraic sum of the e.m.f.s round any closed mesh, to the algebraic sum of the products of all the mesh currents concerned and the corresponding resistances. The number of mesh currents used must be the same as the number of internal meshes in the network.

Example 1.8

In the circuit shown in Fig. 1.14 find the current in the 10-Ω resistor, and the voltage across it. The internal resistances of the generators may be taken as 0·5 Ω each.

The figure shows that there are three internal meshes, so that three mesh currents are required. These are chosen as shown, so that only i_1 flows through the 10-Ω resistor. The third mesh is taken as the external mesh, *ABCDA*. The mesh equations may then be written down.

Mesh 1, *DAED*.
$$200 = (2 + 10 + 0·5)i_1 - 2i_2 + 0·5i_3$$
Mesh 2, *EBE*.
$$0 = (1 + 3 + 2)i_2 - 2i_1 + 1i_3$$
Mesh 3, *ABCD*.
$$200 - 210 = (0·5 + 1 + 0·5)i_3 + 0·5i_1 + 1i_2$$

Note that the products of $i \times R$ are positive, if the particular mesh current flows in the direction in which the mesh is traversed, and negative if in the opposite direction; a similar rule applies to e.m.f.s.

Simplifying

$$200 = 12 \cdot 5i_1 - 2i_2 + 0 \cdot 5i_3 \quad . \quad . \quad . \quad (1)$$

$$0 = -2i_1 + 6i_2 + i_3 \quad . \quad . \quad . \quad . \quad (2)$$

$$-10 = 0 \cdot 5i_1 + i_2 + 2i_3 \quad . \quad . \quad . \quad . \quad (3)$$

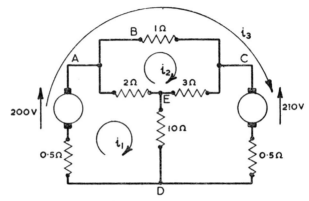

FIG. 1.14. PERTAINING TO EXAMPLE 1.8

Eliminating i_3 from equations (1) and (2), (i.e. by multiplying equation (1) by 2 and subtracting equation (2)) gives

$$400 = 27i_1 - 10i_2 \quad . \quad . \quad . \quad . \quad (4)$$

and eliminating i_3 from equations (2) and (3) (i.e. by multiplying equation (2) by 2 and subtracting equation (3)) gives

$$10 = -4 \cdot 5i_1 + 11i_2 \quad . \quad . \quad . \quad . \quad (5)$$

From equation (4), $i_2 = \dfrac{27i_1 - 400}{10}$

$$= 2 \cdot 7i_1 - 40$$

Substituting for i_2 in equation (5) gives, $i_1 = \underline{17 \cdot 86 \text{ A}}$

Therefore p.d. across 10-Ω resistor is $17 \cdot 86 \times 10 = \underline{\underline{178 \cdot 6 \text{ V}}}$

If the result had been negative the actual current would have been in the opposite direction to that indicated by the mesh arrow i_1.

Note that the actual current through the 200-V generator is $i_1 + i_3$, through the 1-Ω resistor is $i_2 + i_3$, etc.

1.10. Conductor Properties

(a) RESISTIVITY OR SPECIFIC RESISTANCE

By experiment it is found that (a) the resistance of a uniform conductor increases with the length of conductor and (b) the resistance decreases as the cross-sectional area increases.

Hence, $$R \propto \frac{l}{A}$$

where l = conductor length, A = conductor cross-sectional area.

Hence, $$R = \frac{\rho l}{A} \; \Omega \quad . \qquad . \qquad . \qquad . \quad (1.7)$$

where ρ (pronounced "ro") is a constant called the *resistivity* or *specific resistance* of the given conductor material. It is defined as the resistance between opposite faces of a conductor of unit length and unit cross-sectional area.

Since $\rho = R \times \dfrac{A}{l}$, the value of ρ will depend on the units chosen to measure l and A. Common units for ρ are

(a) Ω per cm per cm^2 (often quoted as Ω-cm) for l in centimetres, and A in square centimetres.

(b) Ω per in. per in.^{2} (Ω-in.) for l in inches and A in square inches.

(c) Ω per mile per in.^{2} (this is convenient for the calculation of the resistance of transmission lines).

Instead of specifying the resistivity of a material sometimes the *conductivity* (g) is specified

where $$g = \frac{1}{\rho} \text{ mho/unit length}$$

Example 1.9

An aluminium conductor 1,000 yd. long, and 0·5 in.^{2} cross-section is connected in parallel with a copper wire of equal length. It is found that 0·6 of the total current carried by the two conductors flows through the aluminium wire. Calculate the diameter of the copper wire.

$$\rho_{cu} = 0\cdot7 \times 10^{-6} \; \Omega\text{-in.}$$
$$\rho_{al} = 1\cdot12 \times 10^{-6} \; \Omega\text{-in.}$$

From equation (1.7),

$$\text{resistance of aluminium wire} = R_{al} = 1\cdot12 \times 10^{-6} \times \frac{1{,}000 \times 36}{0\cdot5} \; \Omega$$

$$= 0\cdot0806 \; \Omega$$

Note that since ρ is given in Ω-in., l must be in inches and A in sq. inches.
From equation (1.3) for the current division in two parallel resistances the current in the aluminium wire is given by

$$I_{al} = I \times \frac{R_{cu}}{R_{al} + R_{cu}} \text{ where } R_{cu} = \text{resistance of copper wire.}$$

$$\text{but } I_{al} = 0\cdot6 \; I$$

$$\frac{R_{cu}}{R_{al} + R_{cu}} = 0\cdot6$$

$$R_{cu} = 0\cdot6 \; (0\cdot0806 + R_{cu})$$

$$0\cdot4 R_{cu} = 0\cdot04836$$

$$R_{cu} = 0\cdot121 \; \Omega = \rho_{cu} \frac{l}{A_{cu}}$$

Cross-sectional area of copper wire $A_{cu} = \dfrac{0 \cdot 7 \times 10^{-6} \times 1{,}000 \times 36}{0 \cdot 121}$

$$= 0 \cdot 208 \text{ in.}^2$$

Therefore the diameter of the copper wire $= \sqrt{\left(0 \cdot 208 \times \dfrac{4}{\pi}\right)} = \underline{\underline{0 \cdot 515 \text{ in.}}}$

(b) Temperature Coefficient

Conductors may be divided into three groups, according to the effect of temperature rise on their resistance: (a) Those whose resistance increases with rise in temperature (e.g. copper). (b) Those whose resistance decreases with rise in temperature (e.g. carbon). (c) Those whose resistance is almost unaffected by temperature (e.g. manganin). For the first group it is found that an approximately linear relationship exists between 0°C and 100°C of the form

$$R_2 = R_1\{1 + \alpha_{\theta_1}(\theta_2 - \theta_1)\} \qquad . \qquad . \qquad (1.8)$$

where $R_2 =$ resistance at θ_2°C

$R_1 =$ resistance at θ_1°C

α_{θ_1} is called the temperature coefficient of resistance at θ_1°C.

From equation (1.8),

$$\alpha_{\theta_1} = \frac{R_2 - R_1}{\theta_2 - \theta_1} \cdot \frac{1}{R_1}$$

α_{θ_1} is defined as the change in resistance of a conductor per °C temperature change per ohm of resistance at θ_1°C. Since α_{θ_1} depends on the value of θ_1, it will be different at different temperatures. It is usually quoted at 0°C or 20°C.

If the resistance R_1 of a conductor at θ_1°C is known, and either α_0 or α_{20} is given, then the resistance R_2 at any other temperature θ_2°C may be found as follows—

Let α_{20} be given.

Then from equation (1.8)

$$R_1 = R\{1 + \alpha_{20}(\theta_1 - 20)\}$$

and $\qquad R_2 = R\{1 + \alpha_{20}(\theta_2 - 20)\}$

where $R =$ resistance of the conductor at 20°C

Dividing gives

$$\frac{R_1}{R_2} = \frac{1 + \alpha_{20}(\theta_1 - 20)}{1 + \alpha_{20}(\theta_2 - 20)}$$

Therefore $\qquad R_2 = R_1 \times \dfrac{1 + \alpha_{20}(\theta_2 - 20)}{1 + \alpha_{20}(\theta_1 - 20)}$

If α_0 is given this simplifies to

$$R_2 = R_1 \times \frac{1 + \alpha_0\theta_2}{1 + \alpha_0\theta_1} \qquad . \qquad . \qquad . \quad (1.9)$$

For the particularly important case of copper

$$\alpha_0 = \frac{1}{234\cdot5} \text{ per } °C$$

For copper, equation (1.9) may be written

$$R_2 = R_1 \frac{(1 + \theta_2 \,.\, 1/234\cdot5)}{(1 + \theta_1 \,.\, 1/234\cdot5)}$$

$$R_2 = \frac{R_1(234\cdot5 + \theta_2)}{(234\cdot5 + \theta_1)} \qquad . \qquad . \quad (1.10)$$

Example 1.10

The resistivity of copper at 20°C is $0\cdot7 \times 10^{-6}$ Ω-in. Calculate (a) the resistivity at 45°C and (b) the temperature coefficient at 45°C.

$$\alpha_0 = 4\cdot26 \times 10^{-3} \text{ per } °C$$

(a) Since α is quoted at a different temperature from R_1 and R_2 equation (1.9) must be used.

Resistance of an inch cube at 20°C $= R_1 = 0\cdot7 \times 10^{-6}$ Ω

Let $R_2 =$ resistance of an inch cube at 45°C $(= \rho_{45})$

Then $\rho_{45} = R_2 = 0\cdot7 \times 10^{-6} \times \dfrac{1 + 4\cdot26 \times 10^{-3}(45)}{1 + 4\cdot26 \times 10^{-3}(20)} = \underline{\underline{0\cdot77 \times 10^{-6} \text{ Ω}}}$

(b) From equation (1.8),

$$R_{45} = R_0\{1 + \alpha_0(45 - 0)\} = R_0\{1 + 45\alpha_0\} \qquad . \qquad . \quad (1)$$

and $\qquad R_0 = R_{45}\{1 + \alpha_{45}(0 - 45)\} = R_{45}\{1 - 45\alpha_{45}\} \qquad . \qquad . \quad (2)$

substituting for R_0 in equation (1)—

$$R_{45} = R_{45}(1 - 45\alpha_{45})(1 + 45\alpha_0)$$

$$\alpha_{45} = \underline{\underline{3\cdot58 \times 10^{-3} \text{ per } °C}}$$

1.11. Alternating Quantities

An alternating quantity is one which experiences a complete and definite cycle of reversals which is repeated in time. Alternating current circuits have become more common than direct current circuits since alternating currents and voltages may be more conveniently controlled and since alternating current switches are much simpler to construct than direct current switches.

The time taken for one cycle is called the period (T) and the number of cycles occurring per second is called the frequency (f). When instantaneous values of the alternating quantity are plotted to a base of time the resulting graph is referred to as a wave.

The most important alternating quantities in electrical engineering are those which vary sinusoidally.

A sinusoidal alternating quantity is one whose instantaneous value is varying according to a sinusoidal function of time, e.g. an e.m.f. may be written as $e = E_m \sin \omega t$ or $e = E_m \cos \omega t$, where E_m and ω are constants.

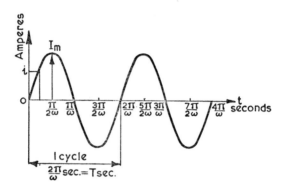

FIG. 1.15. SINUSOIDAL ALTERNATING CURRENT WAVE

It is immaterial whether a sine or cosine function is used; the sine function will be used in the following discussion. It may be noticed that a small letter is used to denote an instantaneous value of a continuously changing quantity. The maximum or peak value of the e m.f. is E_m.

Now ω determines the rate at which e is changing, e.g. 1 cycle will be completed in the time taken for ωt to change from 0 to 2π radians.

If T is the period of the alternating quantity

$$\omega T = 2\pi$$

$$T = \frac{2\pi}{\omega} \text{ sec}$$

$$\omega = \frac{2\pi}{T} \text{ radians per second}$$

ω is called the angular velocity (for a reason to be seen in §5.1)

The frequency, $f = \dfrac{1}{T}$ cycles per second $\qquad . \qquad . \qquad .$ (1.11)

therefore $\qquad \omega = \dfrac{2\pi}{T} = 2\pi f$ radians per second $\quad . \qquad .$ (1.12)

In the same way an alternating current (Fig. 1.15) may be expressed as

$$i = I_m \sin \omega t$$

1.12. Effective (or R.M.S.) Value of an Alternating Current

During any one cycle of an alternating current the current passes through an infinite number of values between $+I_m$ and $-I_m$. The question arises as to what steady or direct current the alternating current is equivalent. The power effect is taken as the basis of

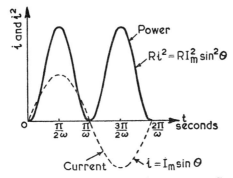

FIG. 1.16. POWER WAVE OF AN ALTERNATING CURRENT

equivalence, and the equivalent direct current is the direct current in amperes which has a power effect the same as the average power effect of the given alternating current. This value is called the *effective value* of the alternating current.

Consider an alternating current $i = I_m \sin \omega t$ flowing through a non-inductive resistance R Ω. Let I be the direct current whose power effect is the same as the average power effect of the alternating current in the same resistance.

Instantaneous power produced$\left.\right\}$ = Ri^2 watts (See Fig. 1.16)
by the alternating current

Average power effect of the$\left.\right\}$ = $R \times$ (mean value of i^2) taken
alternating current $\qquad$ over 1 cycle

This is to be equal to RI^2, the power produced by the equivalent direct current.

$$RI^2 = R \times \text{(mean value of } i^2)$$

therefore $\qquad I^2 = \text{(mean value of } i^2)$

and $\qquad I = \sqrt{\text{(mean value of } i^2)}$

Because of the form of the above expression the effective value I is often referred to as the root mean square (r.m.s.) value.

$$I^2 = \text{mean value of } i^2$$
$$= \text{mean value of } I_m{}^2 \sin^2 \omega t$$
$$= I_m{}^2 \times \text{mean value of } \sin^2 \omega t$$

since $I_m{}^2$ is a constant.
Hence,

$$I^2 = I_m{}^2 \times \text{mean value of } \left(\frac{1}{2} - \frac{\cos 2\omega t}{2} \right)$$

Now the mean value of a cosine wave taken over a whole cycle is zero since the positive and negative loops are equal in area

Therefore $\qquad I^2 = \dfrac{I_m{}^2}{2}$

and $\qquad I = \dfrac{I_m}{\sqrt{2}} \qquad . \qquad . \qquad . \quad (1.13)$

In the same way the effective or r.m.s. value (E) of $e = E_m \sin \omega t$ is given by

$$E = \frac{E_m}{\sqrt{2}} \qquad . \qquad . \qquad . \quad (1.14)$$

According to these results the r.m.s. or effective value of an alternating quantity is defined as that direct quantity which will produce the same heating effect in the same resistance. For "alternating quantity" "alternating voltage" or "alternating current" may be substituted.

In general the average value of an alternating quantity over a half-cycle may be found by dividing the area under the curve (determined by any rule for areas) by the length of the base.

In the same way the r.m.s. value is found by (i) finding the area under the curve of the square of the alternating quantity (ii) dividing the area by the length of the base (iii) taking the square root of the result.

Note: 1. Unless otherwise stated an alternating quantity may be assumed to vary sinusoidally, so that

$$E_{\text{r.m.s.}} = \frac{E_m}{\sqrt{2}} \text{ or } I_{\text{r.m.s.}} = \frac{I_m}{\sqrt{2}}$$

2. Unless otherwise stated it is the r.m.s. value of an alternating quantity which is specified or read from an instrument scale.

3. An alternating current will in general have no net chemical effect since the effect, if any, taking place during the positive half-cycle will be reversed during the negative half-cycle.

4. Similarly there will be no net force between a permanent magnet and an alternating current carrying conductor, e.g. an alternating current in a coil will not deflect a compass needle.

The average value of $i = I_m \sin \omega t$ over a whole cycle is zero, since the average value of $\sin \omega t$ over a cycle is zero. The average value of $i = I_m \sin \omega t$ over a half-cycle is $\frac{2}{\pi} \cdot I_m$. This may be shown as follows—

$$I_{\text{av}} = \frac{1}{\dfrac{\pi}{\omega} - 0} \int_0^{\frac{\pi}{\omega}} I_m \sin \omega t \, \mathrm{d}t$$

$$= \frac{\omega}{\pi} \cdot I_m \cdot \left[-\frac{\cos \omega t}{\omega} \right]_0^{\frac{\pi}{\omega}}$$

$$= \frac{2}{\pi} \cdot I_m \qquad . \qquad . \qquad . \qquad . \qquad (1.15)$$

In the same way

$$E_{\text{av}} = \frac{2}{\pi} \cdot E_m \qquad . \qquad . \qquad . \qquad (1.16)$$

The form factor $= \dfrac{\text{r.m.s. value}}{\frac{1}{2} \text{ cycle average value}} = \dfrac{I_m}{\sqrt{2}} \times \dfrac{\pi}{2I_m} = 1{\cdot}11$

$$\qquad . \qquad . \qquad . \qquad (1.17)$$

i.e. the form factor for sine waves is 1·11.

The form factor gives a measure of the "peakiness" of the wave form. A square wave, which is flatter than a sine wave, has a form factor of 1·0. A triangular wave, on the other hand, is more "peaky" than a sine wave, and has a form factor of 1·15.

Example 1.11

The positive half-cycle of an alternating current is shown in Fig. 1.17. If the negative half-cycle is symmetrical find the r.m.s. value, the average value over half a cycle, and the form factor.

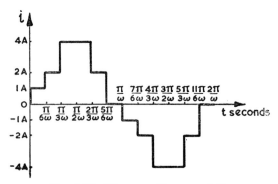

FIG. 1.17. WAVE OF EXAMPLE 1.11.

$$I_{av} = \frac{\text{area under curve of } i}{\text{length of base}}$$

$$= \frac{1\left(\dfrac{\pi}{6\omega} - 0\right) + 2\left(\dfrac{\pi}{3\omega} - \dfrac{\pi}{6\omega}\right) + 4\left(\dfrac{2\pi}{3\omega} - \dfrac{\pi}{3\omega}\right) + 2\left(\dfrac{5\pi}{6\omega} - \dfrac{2\pi}{3\omega}\right)}{\dfrac{\pi}{\omega} - 0}$$

$$= 2 \cdot 167 \text{ A}$$

$$I^2_{r.m.s.} = \frac{1^2\left(\dfrac{\pi}{6\omega} - 0\right) + 2^2\left(\dfrac{\pi}{3\omega} - \dfrac{\pi}{6\omega}\right) + 4^2\left(\dfrac{2\pi}{3\omega} - \dfrac{\pi}{3\omega}\right) + 2^2\left(\dfrac{5\pi}{6\omega} - \dfrac{2\pi}{3\omega}\right)}{\dfrac{\pi}{\omega} - 0}$$

$$= 6 \cdot 833 \text{ A}^2$$

$$I_{r.m.s.} = \sqrt{6 \cdot 833} = \underline{\underline{2 \cdot 62 \text{ A}}}$$

$$\text{Form factor} = \frac{2 \cdot 62}{2 \cdot 167} = \underline{\underline{1 \cdot 21}}$$

EXAMPLES 1

1. Define 1 volt, 1 watt.

Show that the power absorbed by a load is given by the product of the voltage across the load and the current through the load.

A 500-V, d.c. motor of efficiency 95 per cent drives a pump of efficiency 80 per cent. If the pump raises 6,000 gal of water per minute against a head of 76 ft, calculate the input current to the motor.

1 gal of water weighs 10 lb. *(O.N.C.)*

Ans. 272 A.

2. A hydro-electric generating station is supplied from a reservoir of capacity 200,000,000 ft³ at a head of 500 ft.

(a) What is the total available energy in kWh if the hydraulic efficiency be 0·8 and the electrical efficiency 0·9?

Ans. $1·7 \times 10^6$ kWh.

(b) Find the fall in the reservoir level after a load of 12,000 kW has been supplied for 3 hr, if the area of the reservoir is 1 mile².

Ans. 1·83 in.

(c) If the reservoir be supplied by a river at the rate of 40 ft³/sec what does this flow represent in kW, in kWh/day, and in kWh/year? Assume constant head and efficiencies.   (*O.N.C.*)

Ans. 1,225 kW; $2·94 \times 10^4$ kWh/day; $1·07 \times 10^7$ kWh/year

3. Derive from first principles a relation between the B.Th.U. and the kWh.

A diesel-electric generating set gives an output 20 kW. The fuel oil used has a calorific value of 22,000 B.Th.U./lb. The efficiency of the diesel motor is 40 per cent and that of the generator 95 per cent. Calculate the mass of oil required per hour. Also find the electrical energy generated per ton of fuel.   (*O.N.C.*)

Ans. 1 kWh $\equiv$ 3,410 B.Th.U.; 8·17 lb; 5,490 kWh.

4. The daily output of a generating station is 1,600 MWh and the coal consumption is 780 tons/day. If the calorific value of the fuel is 12,500 B.Th.U./lb calculate the thermal efficiency of the station.   (*O.N.C.*)

Ans. 25 per cent.

5. A 500-V, d.c. motor with an efficiency of 85 per cent takes a current of 20 A when coupled to a pump delivering 500 gal of water per minute against a head of 50 ft. Find (a) the efficiency of the pump and (b) the cost of raising 10,000 gal of water if energy costs 0·5d. per kWh.   (*O.N.C.*)

Ans. 66·7 per cent; 1·67d.

6. Calculate the current required by a 1,500-V, d.c. locomotive when drawing a 100-ton load at 30 m.p.h. with a tractive resistance of 10 lb/ton along (a) level track (b) a gradient of 1 in 50. Assume a motor efficiency of 90 per cent.   (*O.N.C.*)

Ans. 44·25 A; 242 A.

7. A bath containing 20 gal of water has four 1·5-kW, 250-V immersion heating elements. Ignoring all losses, determine the time required to boil the water if the initial temperature is 20°C—

(a) If all four elements are connected in parallel.

(b) If all four elements are connected in series.

(c) If the elements are connected two in series in parallel with two in series (series-parallel connexion). The supply voltage is 250 V.

Ans. 5,050 sec; 80,800 sec; 20,200 sec.

8. State Kirchhoff's laws. Derive an expression for the effective resistance of three resistors connected in parallel.

Define specific resistance.

An aluminium wire 5 m long and 2 mm diameter is connected in parallel with a copper wire 3 m long. The total current is 4 A and that in the aluminium

wire is 2·5 A. Find the diameter of the copper wire. The respective resistivities of copper and aluminium are 1·7 and 2·6 $\mu\Omega$-cm units.   (*O.N.C.*)
    Ans. 0·97 mm.

9. Define resistance temperature coefficient.
    It is found that the resistance of a coil of wire increases from 50 Ω to 58 Ω when the temperature rises from 15°C to 55°C. Calculate the temperature coefficient at 0°C of the conductor material.   (*O.N.C.*)
    Ans. 0·00426/°C.

10. A coil is wound with 200 m of copper wire of cross-sectional area 5 mm². During a heat run the current is maintained at a constant value of 15 A and the average temperature rise is from 10°C to 30°C. The resistivity at 20°C and the temperature coefficient at 0°C are $\dfrac{1}{58}$ Ω/m/mm², and $\dfrac{1}{243\cdot5}$/°C respectively.
    Calculate the increase in copper loss.   (*O.N.C.*)
    Ans. 12 W.

11. The moving coil of a permanent magnet instrument has a temperature resistance coefficient of 0·004/°C. A swamping resistance of temperature resistance coefficient 0·0002/°C is to be added such that the overall temperature resistance coefficient is 0·0008/°C. Assuming all measurements are given for 0°C, find the value of the resistance if the coil resistance is 3 Ω.
    Ans. 16 Ω.

12. The resistance of each of the four arms of a Wheatstone bridge $ABCDA$ are $AB = 1,000$ Ω, $BC = 1,000$ Ω, $CD = 749$ Ω, $DA = 750$ Ω. What current will flow through a galvanometer of resistance 500 Ω connected between B and D if a p.d. of 2·0 V is maintained between A and C?
        (*L.U. part question* 1938).
    Ans. 0·485 μA.

13. Write a careful statement of the Kirchhoff laws used in d.c. circuit analysis.
    An accumulator battery of open circuit voltage 100 V and internal resistance 2 Ω is charged through a 20-Ω series resistor from a 200-V supply. A second battery, of open circuit voltage 80 V and resistance 1·2 Ω is then connected in parallel with the first, the two positive terminals being connected together.
    Find, using Kirchhoff's laws, or any other method, the magnitude and direction of all the currents in the network both before and after the connexion of the second battery, and comment on the usefulness of the circuit as a means of charging two batteries simultaneously.   (*L.U.* 1949)
    Ans. 4·55 A; 5·42 A; 4·22 A; 9·64 A.

14. Three batteries P, Q and R consisting of 50, 55 and 60 cells in series respectively, supply in parallel a current load of 100 A. Each cell has an e.m.f. of 2 V, and an internal resistance of 0·005 Ω. Determine the current supplied by each battery and the load voltage.   (*L.U.* 1950)
    Ans. 1·2 A; 35·4 A; 65·8 A; 100·3 V.

15. An alternating current has a wave-shape as follows—

$$0 < \omega t < \frac{\pi}{6} \qquad\qquad i = 0 \text{ A}$$

$$\frac{\pi}{6} \leqslant \omega t < \frac{\pi}{3} \qquad\qquad i = 2 \text{ A}$$

$$\frac{\pi}{3} \leqslant \omega t < \frac{2\pi}{3} \qquad\qquad i = 4 \text{ A}$$

$$\frac{2\pi}{3} \leqslant \omega t < \frac{5\pi}{6} \qquad\qquad i = 2 \text{ A}$$

$$\frac{5\pi}{6} \leqslant \omega t \leqslant \pi \qquad\qquad i = 0 \text{ A}$$

The negative and positive half-cycles are symmetrical. Find the r.m.s. value of the current.   (*O.N.C.*)

Ans. 2·58 A.

16. Calculate, or estimate graphically, the r.m.s. values, average values and form factors of the following wave forms—
(*a*) sinusoidal (*b*) rectangular (*c*) each half-cycle in the form of isosceles triangles. The maximum value of the waves is 10 units in each case.

Ans. 7·07, 6·36, 1·11; 10, 10, 1·0; 5·77, 5, 1·154.

CHAPTER 2

Elements of Electromagnetism

IF A COMPASS needle is placed near a current-carrying conductor such as a long straight wire or a coil, it is found that a deflexion is produced when the current is switched on and that the direction of the deflexion depends on the direction of the current (see Fig. 2.1).

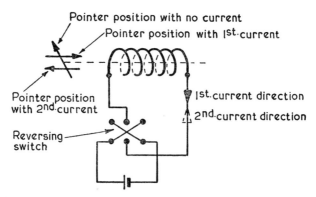

FIG. 2.1. INTERACTION BETWEEN A COIL AND A COMPASS NEEDLE

The space round the conductor where this effect is observed is called the *Magnetic Field* of the conductor. The force on the compass needle, which causes it to deflect, is called the *Magnetic Force*. A picture of the magnetic field may be obtained by placing the compass in a large number of positions near the coil and recording the direction in which the north pole points, in each position. A more comprehensive picture is obtained if the compass is moved successively in the direction of the north pole. If this is done, it is found that for any given starting point a path will be traced out which is a complete loop, having the conductor inside. The path is said to link the conductor.

Fig. 2.2 shows some of the paths so formed round a coil. The direction of the current in the coil is shown by the dot and cross convention, a dot representing a current emerging from the plane of

32

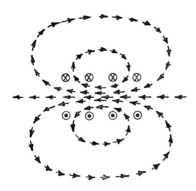

FIG. 2.2. RECORD OF COMPASS POSITIONS IN A PLANE THROUGH
THE AXIS OF A SINGLE-LAYER COIL

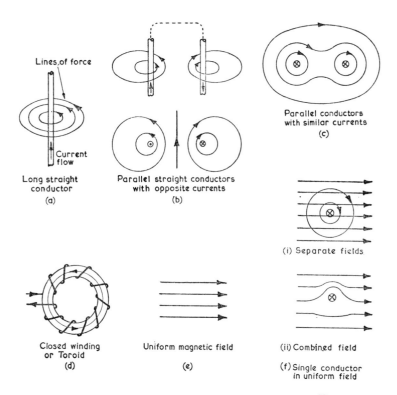

Lines of force

Current flow

Long straight
conductor
(a)

Parallel straight conductors
with opposite currents
(b)

Parallel conductors
with similar currents
(c)

(i) Separate fields

Closed winding
or Toroid
(d)

Uniform magnetic field
(e)

(ii) Combined field

(f) Single conductor
in uniform field

FIG. 2.3. TYPICAL LINES OF FORCE IN ELECTROMAGNETIC FIELDS

33

the paper and a cross representing a current entering the plane of the paper. It will be observed that in the centre of the coil, where the force on the compass needle is strongest, the paths are closest. Thus a magnetic field may be mapped out by a series of lines, whose direction gives the direction in which the north pole of a compass points, and whose spacing gives an indication of the strength of the force on the needle.

It is convenient to imagine a particle which has north polarity only (all actual magnets must have both north and south poles). If this particle were placed at any point in a magnetic field, and were allowed free movement (no inertia or resistance forces) it would experience a magnetic force which would cause it to move round a path similar to that traced out by the compass.

The path is termed a *Line of Magnetic Force*. Fig. 2.3 shows typical lines of force round current-carrying conductors. From these, two important facts may be noted—

(*a*) In an electro-magnetic field, every line of force forms a complete loop linking at least one current-carrying conductor.

(*b*) No two lines of force intersect, since at any point the resultant force on a pole can have only one direction.

2.1. Magnetic Field Strength or Magnetizing Force

Unit magnetic pole is defined as that magnetic pole which when placed one metre from a very long single straight conductor carrying a current of one ampere experiences a force of $1/2\pi$ newtons.

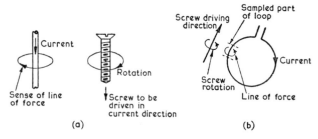

FIG. 2.4. APPLICATION OF THE R.H. SCREW RULE

The strength of the magnetic field at any point is then defined as the magnetic force which would act on a unit pole were such a pole placed at the required point.

The field strength, or magnetizing force, is usually denoted by the symbol H and may be measured in the unit "newtons/unit magnetic pole." The direction and sense of the magnetizing force, H, at any point is given by the direction and sense of the line of force passing through the point considered.

It is useful to have a memory aid which will give the sense of a line of force. Such an aid is the Right-Hand Screw Rule—If it be imagined that a right-hand threaded screw is to be driven in the direction of current flow, then the direction of rotation of the screw will suggest the sense of the lines of force; this is illustrated in Fig. 2.4.

Lines of magnetic force are very useful ideas for helping to visualize the shapes of magnetic fields but it should be remembered that they have no real existence.

2.2. Calculation of Magnetic Field Strength: Work Law

It is found experimentally that, except in the case of some composite magnetic fields containing ferro-magnetic materials

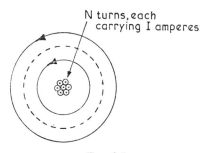

N turns, each
carrying I amperes

Fig. 2.5

(irons), the magnetic field strength is proportional to the current which produces the field. Thus, a unit pole placed one metre from a long straight conductor carrying a current of I amperes will experience a force of $\dfrac{I}{2\pi}$ newtons. Furthermore, if the single conductor were replaced by, say, N conductors each carrying I amperes in the same direction then the total force on the unit pole one metre distant would be $\dfrac{IN}{2\pi}$ newtons (Fig. 2.5).

If the unit pole is carried round the N conductors along a circular path of radius one metre, then at all points the movement of the pole will be in the direction of the magnetic force which is constant at each point along the path.

$$\text{Work done in complete path} = \frac{IN}{2\pi} \times 2\pi \times 1 \quad \text{Nw-m}$$

$$= IN \quad \text{J} \qquad . \qquad . \qquad . \quad (2.1)$$

The work must be performed against the magnetic field if the movement is in opposition to the lines of force and, conversely, if the movement is in the direction of the magnetic field work will be performed by the magnetic force on whatever is restraining the movement of the pole.

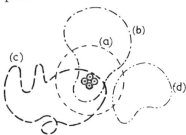

FIG. 2.6. APPLICATION OF THE WORK LAW

In the movement of the unit pole just described it will be seen that the path of the pole linked the N conductors once and exactly completed itself. A very important law called "the work law" applies to all such paths—

The work law states that the net work in joules done on, or by, a unit pole in moving round any single completed path is equal numerically to the "ampere-turns" linked within the path.

It is seen that the law applies to the very simple path of Fig. 2.5. The work law applies, however, no matter what the shape of the complete path is. This is illustrated in Fig. 2.6. Paths a, b, c, are all completed paths which link the N conductors once and thus the net work done in each of these paths will be IN joules. Path d is a typical completed path which does not link any current carrying conductor and thus no net work would be required to move a unit pole exactly once round this path.

The law is applicable for all magnetic fields, irrespective of the shape of the field or of the materials which may be present.

2.3. Field around a Single Long Straight Conductor

A simple application of the "work law" is the calculation of the magnetizing force at a distance r m from a long straight conductor carrying a current I amperes.

Let H_r be the magnetizing force at point P distant r m from the conductor axis (Fig. 2.7); i.e. the force on a unit pole at P equals H_r newtons.

The lines of force are all circular, so that if the pole is moved

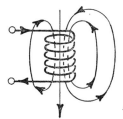

FIG. 2.7. CALCULATION OF   FIG. 2.8. REPRESENTING
        FIELD STRENGTH   MAGNETIC FLUX

round the path of radius r it will always move in the direction of the magnetic force.

Work done on pole in circular path

$$= \text{force} \times \text{distance moved}$$
$$= H_r \times 2\pi r \quad \text{Nw-m}$$
$$= 2\pi r H_r \quad \text{J}$$
$$= \text{ampere-turns (AT) linked (by work law)}$$
$$= I \text{ (since only 1 turn)}$$

Therefore $2\pi r H_r = I$

Field strength at $P = H_r = \dfrac{I}{2\pi r}$ Nw/unit pole . . (2.2)

Examination of equation (2.2) shows that the dimensions of field strength H are amperes/metre (A/m). If there had been more than one turn the dimensions of H would have been ampere-turns/metre (AT/m). Thus an alternative and more convenient unit in which to measure field strength is the ampere-turn/metre (AT/m).

The field strength at a point due to a long straight current carrying conductor is inversely proportional to the distance of the point from the conductor axis.

2.4. Magnetic Flux

When considering magnetic problems it is always advisable to imagine the magnetic field mapped by a large number of imaginary lines of force. For instance the magnetic field around the current-carrying coil of Fig. 2.8 is described by the few lines of force drawn. The lines are imaginary—they represent the paths which would be taken by free north poles if such could exist and were indeed present.

Together with the imaginary magnetic lines there should be visualized a "magnetic effect" in the space surrounding the coil. It is impossible to explain the nature of the "magnetic effect" since it is still present even when the coil is mounted in a large evacuated container. The "magnetic effect" is assumed to be everywhere in the same direction as the lines of force, which are often regarded as indicating the

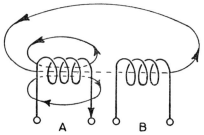

Fig. 2.9. Mutual Flux

boundaries of imaginary tubes of "magnetic effect." An imaginary picture of "magnetic effect" may be formed by considering an elastic material surrounding the coil and assuming that this material is susceptible to magnetic force. When a current passes through the coil the elastic material is strained in the direction of the magnetic forces. The resultant strain or deformation of the elastic material resembles the idea of "magnetic effect."

It will be observed that all the lines of force pass through the coil, in Fig. 2.8, and that all the lines form closed loops. Thus the total "magnetic effect" is assumed to pass through the coil and to complete itself through the space surrounding the coil. This total "magnetic effect" is called *the magnetic flux linking the coil*. The conception of "magnetic flux" assists considerably in describing the manner in which an e.m.f. is set up in an electric circuit by magnetic means.

There are two ways in which magnetic flux may be associated with a circuit or circuits—

(*a*) The flux set up by a coil or circuit may link all or some of the turns of the circuit. Such flux is called self flux (Fig. 2.8).

(*b*) Some or all of the flux set up by one circuit (e.g. coil *A* of Fig. 2.9) may link a second circuit (e.g. coil *B*). Such flux is called mutual flux.

2.5. Induced E.M.F.

Faraday made the very important discovery that when the magnetic flux linking a circuit is changing, an e.m.f. is induced in the circuit.

Referring to Fig. 2.9, if the coil B is moved away from or towards coil A so that the mutual flux through the coil B changes then an e.m.f. will be set up in coil B. The e.m.f. is detectable by connecting a voltmeter across the terminals of coil B. Alternatively, if the current through coil A is increased or decreased, so that the amount of flux linking the stationary coil B is altered, then also an e.m.f. may be observed during the instants when the flux is changing. The magnitude of the e.m.f. is found to be proportional to the number of turns on coil B and is taken as being proportional to the rate of change of flux through the coil.

An e.m.f. is also induced in coil A when the current through it is changing; this is attributed to the changing self-flux within coil A. Assuming that coil A is made of such a heavy copper conductor that it has effectively no resistance, when the current in the coil is constant there will be no potential difference between the coil terminals ($R = 0$, therefore $V = IR = 0$), and a voltmeter connected across them would read zero. But when the current in the coil is either increasing or decreasing the flux linking the coil will be changing and an e.m.f. will be induced in the coil, causing the voltmeter to deflect. When the flux stops changing the voltmeter again reads zero.

It is found that the induced e.m.f., e, is proportional to $N \times$ rate of change of flux, where $N =$ number of turns on the coil examined.

The symbol for magnetic flux is the Greek letter Φ (phi),

$$e \propto N \times \frac{\text{change in } \Phi}{\text{change in } t}$$

where t represents time in seconds

Therefore
$$e \propto N \times \frac{\Delta\Phi}{\Delta t}$$

In the notation of calculus this becomes

$$e \propto N \frac{\mathrm{d}\Phi}{\mathrm{d}t} \propto \frac{\mathrm{d}(\Phi N)}{\mathrm{d}t} \text{, since } N \text{ is a constant}$$

i.e.
$$e = k \times \frac{\mathrm{d}}{\mathrm{d}t}(\Phi N)$$

where k is the constant of proportionality.

The product ΦN is referred to as the *flux-linkages* with the coil or circuit. The relationship between the induced e.m.f. and the rate of change of flux linkages is often called Faraday's Second Law of Electrodynamics. A unit of flux, called the weber (Wb) (pronounced veyber), is chosen so that the constant, k, is unity, when e is in volts. Thus *one weber* may be defined as the magnetic flux which, when linking a single turn coil, induces in the coil an e.m.f. of one volt when the magnetic flux is reduced uniformly to zero in one second. The equation for induced e.m.f. then becomes

$$e = N \times \frac{\Delta \Phi}{\Delta t} \text{ or } N \times \frac{d\Phi}{dt} \text{ or } \frac{d}{dt}(\Phi N) \text{ volts} \qquad . \quad (2.3)$$

From this
$$\Delta \Phi = \frac{e \times \Delta t}{N}$$

so that an alternative unit for magnetic flux is the volt-second.

Example 2.1

Calculate the average e.m.f. induced in a coil of 10 turns if a flux of 0·02 Wb through the coil is reversed in 0·001 sec.

Initial flux linkages = 0·02 × 10 weber-turns (Wb-T)
Final flux linkages = −0·02 × 10 Wb-T
Net flux linkage change = 0·04 × 10 Wb-T

Average e.m.f. induced in coil $= \dfrac{\Delta(\Phi N)}{\Delta t} = \dfrac{0 \cdot 04 \times 10}{0 \cdot 001} = \underline{\underline{400 \text{ V}}}$

2.6. Lenz's Law

This law states that the e.m.f. induced in a circuit by a changing

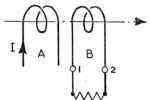

FIG. 2.10. LENZ'S LAW

flux will always be in such a direction that it tends to set up a current which will oppose the change of flux.

For instance, if the coil B in Fig. 2.10 is closed through a resistance while the current in coil A is increased, the flux linking coil B will increase, so giving rise to an e.m.f. in coil B. The e.m.f. will give rise to a current which will oppose the increase of flux. This means that terminal 1 must be driven positive with respect to terminal 2. Lenz's Law is an extension of the Law of Conservation of Energy. The law also applies where the e.m.f is induced by a changing self flux. When the key is pressed in the circuit of Fig. 2.11 the current in the coil will change, so producing a change of self flux linkages and an e.m.f., e, which will oppose the change. The e.m.f. will make terminal A positive with respect to B, to oppose the current change, and thus the current will only gradually rise to the value $\dfrac{V}{R}$, (assuming the coil has no resistance) which it would immediately attain if the coil were not present.

If the switch in Fig. 2.11 has been closed for some time and is then opened, the current and flux linkages in the coil will decrease, so setting up an e.m.f. which must oppose the decrease, i.e. drive the terminal B positive with respect to the terminal A in an attempt to maintain the current through the circuit. Usually the maintenance

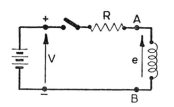 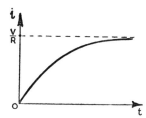

FIG. 2.11. GROWTH OF A CURRENT IN AN INDUCTIVE CIRCUIT

of the current is momentarily accomplished by an arc across the opening switch blades—indicating a high value of induced e.m.f.

Example 2.2

Two coils are placed relative to one another so that when the current in the first coil is 1 ampere a flux of 10^{-3} webers passes completely through the 100 turns of the second coil. The current through the first coil is varied in the following manner—

1. A linear increase from 0 to 10 A in 0·01 sec.
2. A constant current of 10 A for 0·02 sec.
3. A linear decrease from 10 to -5 A in 0·01 sec and thereafter remains constant.

Assuming that the flux in the second coil is proportional to the current in the first coil, plot to scale the waveform of the e.m.f. across the terminals of the second coil. Take a positive e.m.f. in the second coil as the e.m.f. which would produce a current setting up a mutual flux in opposition to the mutual flux from the first coil.

Let subscript 1 refer to quantities of coil 1, subscript 2 to quantities of second coil.

When $i_1 = 1$, $\Phi_2 N_2 = 10^{-3} \times 100 = 10^{-1}$ Wb-T

when $i_1 = 10$, $\Phi_2 N_2 = 10 \times 10^{-1} = 1$ Wb-T

i.e. increase in flux linkages as i_1 increases from 0 to 10 A is 1 Wb-T.

$$e_2 = \frac{\Delta(\Phi_2 N_2)}{\Delta t} = \frac{1}{0·01} = 100 \text{ V}$$

Therefore e.m.f. in second coil in first stage = <u>100 V</u>

This e.m.f. will tend to set up a current which gives a cancellation of the flux change, and thus this is a positive e.m.f.

During the second and fourth stages there will be no flux changes since the currents are constant and therefore the e.m.f.s will be zero.

For the third stage—

$$e_2 = \frac{\Delta(\Phi_2 N_2)}{\Delta t} = \frac{15 \times 10^{-1}}{0·01} = \underline{\underline{150 \text{ V}}}$$

Since the flux is now decreasing, the e.m.f. in the second coil will be negative.

4—(T.824)

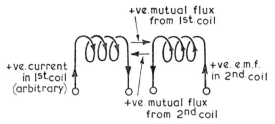

+ve.mutual flux from 1st coil

+ve.current in 1st.coil (arbitrary)

+ve. mutual flux from 2nd coil

+ve. e.m.f. in 2nd coil

Relative directions of +ve. current, flux, and e.m.f.

(a)

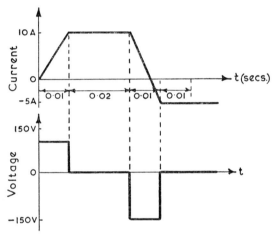

1st.coil current and 2nd.coil e.m.f. waveforms

(b)

Fig. 2.12. Illustrating Example 2.2

Example 2.3

An air-cored solenoid or coil is wound with 1,000 turns in such a way that the flux through the solenoid core is 10^{-4} Wb/A in the coil. If the current through the coil is varied sinusoidally according to $i = 5 \sin 300t$ A, find the voltage which must be applied to the coil assuming that the coil resistance is negligible. Take a positive e.m.f. in the coil as one which tends to give a current setting up a flux in opposition to the positive current flux.

The e.m.f. at any instant will be given by

$$e = \frac{\mathrm{d}(\Phi N)}{\mathrm{d}t} = \frac{\mathrm{d}}{\mathrm{d}t} (10^{-4} \times 5 \sin 300t \times 1,000)$$

$$= 150 \cos 300t \text{ V}$$

When the flux is increasing during the first quarter of the cycle the e.m.f. must be such that it will tend to set up a current opposing the change. Thus the e.m.f. will be positive during this quarter period, i.e. according to the cosine

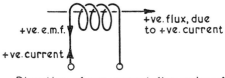

Direction of +ve. current, flux, and e.m.f.

(a)

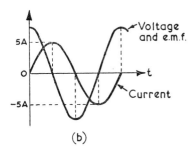

(b)

Fig. 2.13. Pertaining to Example 2.3

law found above. The voltage applied at any instant must be such as to overcome the e.m.f. and set up the required current through the coil.

$$\text{Applied voltage} = V = e + iR$$

However the coil resistance, R, is negligible

Therefore

$$V = e = \underline{150 \cos 300t \text{ V}}$$

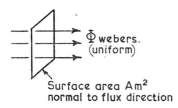

Fig. 2.14. Uniformly Distributed Flux

2.7. Flux Density

If a flux, Φ Wb, passes uniformly and at right angles (i.e. normally) through a surface of area A m², then at each point on the surface there must be a density of flux of $\dfrac{\Phi}{A}$ Wb/m² (see Fig. 2.14). This is called the Flux Density (symbol B).

Thus

$$B = \frac{\Phi}{A} \quad \text{Wb/m}^2$$

or
$$\Phi = BA \quad \text{Wb} \quad . \quad . \quad . \quad (2.4)$$

Considering the area A m^2 of Fig. 2.15 it is obvious that when the plane is parallel to the flux no flux will pass through it.

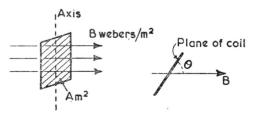

FIG. 2.15. EFFECT OF THE ANGLE BETWEEN PLANE AND FLUX

By geometry then, for a plane inclined by angle θ to the flux direction,

flux Φ through the plane $= BA \sin \theta \quad$ Wb $\quad$. (2.5)

Example 2.4

A circular coil of 100 turns and diameter 3·18 cm is mounted on an axle through a diameter and placed in a uniform magnetic field, where the flux density is 0·01 Wb/m^2, in such a manner that the axle is normal to the field direction. Calculate (a) the maximum flux through the coil and the coil position at which it occurs; (b) the minimum flux and the coil position at which it occurs; and (c) the flux through the coil when its plane is inclined at 60° to the flux direction.

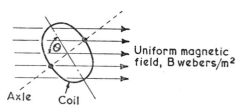

FIG. 2.16. ILLUSTRATING EXAMPLE 2.4

(a) The maximum flux will pass through the coil when the plane of the coil is perpendicular to the flux direction, (Fig. 2.16). Since the field is uniform the total flux through the coil is the product of the coil area and the flux density.

Maximum flux $= B \times$ total coil area

$$= \frac{0·01 \times 3·14 \times 3·18^2 \times 10^{-4}}{4} = 0·795 \times 10^{-5} \text{ Wb}$$

(b) When the plane of the coil is parallel to the flux direction no flux will pass through the coil. This is the minimum flux position and the minimum flux is zero.

(c) Flux through coil $= BA \sin \theta$ . . . . . . (2.5)

$$= 0.795 \times 10^{-5} \sin 60° = 0.69 \times 10^{-5} \text{ Wb}$$

Example 2.5

A rectangular coil 5 cm deep and 10 cm broad has 50 turns and is supported on an axle which lies along one of the shorter sides. The axle of the coil is normal to a large uniform magnetic field in which the flux density is 0·1 Wb/m² and the coil is rotated about this axle at 100 r.p.m. Calculate the maximum e.m.f. and the e.m.f. at an instant when the coil plane makes an angle of 45° with the field direction.

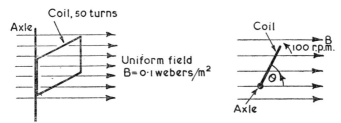

FIG. 2.17. ILLUSTRATING EXAMPLE 2.5

Consider the field direction to be the reference direction and assume that the coil plane is parallel to the reference direction at $t = 0$.

The coil rotates through 2π radians in $\dfrac{1}{100}$ min $= \dfrac{60}{100}$ sec

Angular velocity of the coil $= \omega = \dfrac{2\pi}{0·6} = 10·5$ rad/sec

Let $\theta =$ the angle between the coil plane and the field at an instant t

then $\theta = \omega t$.

At this instant

the flux linkages with the coil $= BAN \sin \theta$ Wb-T

$$= 0·1 \times 0·1 \times 0·05 \times 50 \sin \theta$$
$$= 0·025 \sin \omega t \quad \text{Wb-T}$$

Therefore e.m.f. induced in the coil $= \dfrac{\mathrm{d}}{\mathrm{d}t}$ (flux linkages)

$$= 0·025 \, \omega \cos \omega t$$
$$= 0·025 \times 10·5 \cos \omega t$$
$$= 0·262 \cos \omega t \quad \text{V}$$

The maximum value of the e.m.f. occurs at the instant when $\cos \omega t = \pm 1$

Therefore maximum e.m.f. $= 0·262$ V

At the instant when $\theta = 45°$, $\omega t = \dfrac{\pi}{4}$, $\cos \omega t = 0·707$

Therefore e.m.f. at the instant when $\theta = 45° = 0·262 \times 0·707$

$$= 0·184 \text{ V}$$

It may be noted that a coil rotating in a constant uniform magnetic field has a sinusoidally alternating e.m.f. induced in it.

2.8. Effective Induced E.M.F. in a Single Conductor

Only the e.m.f. induced in a complete loop may ever be measured, but it is sometimes convenient to consider the e.m.f. induced in a single conductor which forms part of a complete circuit. It will be realized (Fig. 2.18) that the connexion of a voltmeter across a single

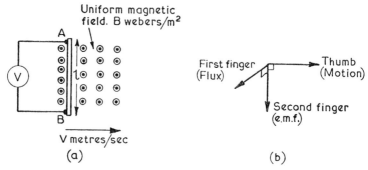

FIG. 2.18. E.M.F. IN A SINGLE CONDUCTOR

conductor automatically completes a circuit, so that the voltmeter reading is the e.m.f. induced in the completed circuit of conductor and voltmeter leads.

Suppose that in the arrangement shown in Fig. 2.18 the conductor and voltmeter are sweeping across the magnetic field with a velocity v m/sec.

The flux entering the loop in one sec $= Blv$ Wb, assuming that there is no flux at the side of the loop, where the voltmeter is placed. Since the loop is of one turn,

$$\text{e.m.f. induced in the loop} = Blv \quad \text{V}$$

Now the voltmeter leads do not contribute directly to the flux entering the loop, i.e. the flux entering the loop is the flux "cut" by the moving conductor, and so it is assumed that the total e.m.f. induced in the loop is the e.m.f. induced in the moving conductor. Therefore

$$\text{e.m.f. induced in the moving conductor} = Blv \quad \text{V} \quad . \quad (2.6)$$

If the movement across the field is continued until there are equal rates for flux leaving the loop on one side and for flux entering on the other then there will be no net change of flux through the loop and no e.m.f. induced in the loop. It is assumed that there will still be an e.m.f. of *Blv* volts induced in the moving conductor, but there will now also be an e.m.f. of *Blv* volts induced in the voltmeter arm, so that the resultant e.m.f. round the loop is zero.

It may be deduced from Lenz's law that the e.m.f. in the moving conductor is given by the following rule—

RIGHT HAND RULE

1. Place the thumb, first finger and second finger of the right hand in a mutually perpendicular manner, as shown in Fig. 2.18 (*b*);

2. Point the thuMb in the direction of the conductor Motion relative to the field.

3. Point the First finger in the Flux direction.

4. Then the sEcond finger will lie in the conductor direction in which the e.m.f. acts.

Alternatively the loop of Fig. 2.18 (*a*) may be held stationary while the flux sweeps past the conductor with velocity *v* m/sec.

Then the e.m.f. induced in the conductor = *Blv* volts.

The relative directions will still be given by the right hand rule provided that the thumb is pointed in the direction of the conductor motion relative to the field. If the circuit moved out of, or into, the plane of the paper, instead of across the plane of the paper, then there would be no e.m.f. in the loop, since no flux would be cut. E.m.f. is induced in a conductor if it moves across a magnetic field but not if it moves parallel to a magnetic field.

Example 2.6

A straight conductor of 10-cm length is moved at 5 m/sec in a uniform magnetic field where the flux density is 1 Wb/m². Calculate the e.m.f. induced in the conductor in the following cases—

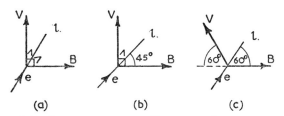

Fig. 2.19. ILLUSTRATING THE RELATIVE CONDUCTOR AND MOVEMENT DIRECTIONS OF EXAMPLE 2.6

(*a*) conductor lying directly across the field and moving normally to itself and the field direction.

(*b*) conductor lying at 45° to the field direction and moving normally to itself and the field direction.

(c) conductor lying at 60° to the field direction and moving at 60° to the plane containing the field and conductor directions.

(a) $\qquad e = Blv = 1 \times 0.1 \times 5 = \underline{\underline{0.5\ V}}$

(b) $\qquad e = Blv \sin\theta = 1 \times 0.1 \times 5 \times 0.707 = \underline{\underline{0.353\ V}}$

(c) $\qquad e = Bl\ (v\sin 60°)\sin\theta = 1 \times 0.1 \times 5 \times 0.866 \times 0.866$

$$= \underline{\underline{0.375\ V}}$$

2.9. Force on a Current-carrying Conductor in a Magnetic Field

In the circuit of Fig. 2.20, let the side ab be moved a small distance Δx at right angles to the uniform magnetic field of B Wb/m^2 in a

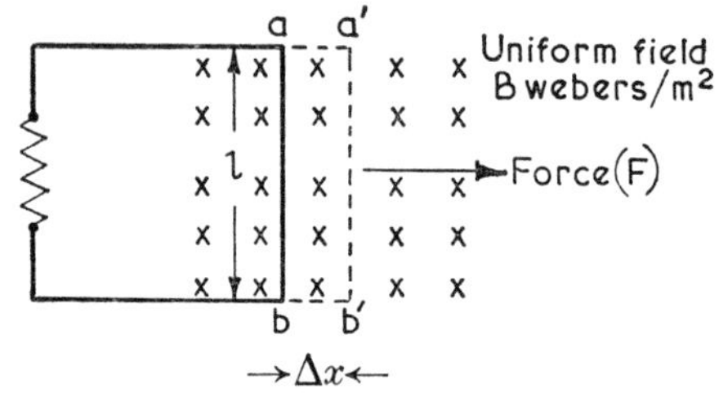

FIG. 2.20. FORCE ON A CONDUCTOR IN A MAGNETIC FIELD

time Δt seconds. Then by equation (2.6) an e.m.f. will be induced in the conductor, given by

$$e = Blv = Bl\frac{\Delta x}{\Delta t}\ \ V$$

This e.m.f. drives a current of i amperes through the external resistor.
Therefore

$$\left.\begin{array}{l}\text{electrical power supply to}\\ \text{resistor during movement } \Delta x\end{array}\right\} = ei\ \ W$$

$$= Bli \cdot \frac{\Delta x}{\Delta t}\ \ J/sec$$

Therefore

$$\left.\begin{array}{l}\text{electrical energy supplied to}\\ \text{resistor during movement } \Delta x\end{array}\right\} = Bli \cdot \frac{\Delta x}{\Delta t} \times \Delta t\ \ J$$

$$= Bli \cdot \Delta x\ \ Nw\text{-}m$$

By the law of conservation of energy, the electrical energy supplied to the resistor must have been derived from the source of mechanical energy which caused the movement Δx. But mechanical work

done $= F \times \Delta x$ Nw-m where F Nw is the force necessary to cause the movement of the coil through the magnetic field.
Therefore

$$F \cdot \Delta x = Bli \cdot \Delta x$$

$$F = Bli \quad \text{Nw} \cdot \qquad \cdot \qquad \cdot \qquad (2.7)$$

This is the force exerted by the mechanical support on the conductor. The force exerted by the conductor on the mechanical support will be equal and opposite.

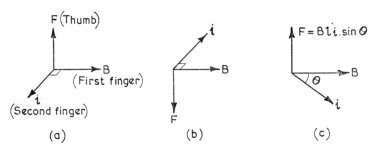

FIG. 2.21. RELATIVE CURRENT, FLUX, AND FORCE DIRECTIONS, ILLUSTRATING THE LEFT HAND RULE

The following results may be deduced or verified experimentally—

(a) The mechanical force exerted by the conductor is always in a direction perpendicular to the plane containing the conductor and the magnetic field direction.

(b) The direction of this force is given by the *Left Hand Rule*, namely,

1. Place the thumb, first finger and second finger of the left hand mutually perpendicular (Fig. 2.21).

2. Point the First finger in the Flux direction.

3. Point the seCond finger in the Current direction.

4. The thuMb then points in the direction of the Mechanical force exerted by the conductor.

(c) If either the current or the field is reversed, the direction of the force is also reversed, but if both are reversed the force remains in the same direction.

(d) The maximum force of Bli Nw is only obtained when the magnetic field and conductor directions are perpendicular.

(e) If the conductor and field make an angle θ with one another then the force is given by

$$F = Bli \sin \theta \quad \text{Nw}$$

Example 2.7

A coil is wound with 15 turns on a rectangular former 10 cm long and 6 cm broad; it is mounted on an axle through the centre line of the coil and parallel to the 10-cm length of the coil. The coil is placed in a uniform magnetic field of 0·2 Wb/m² so that the axle is perpendicular to the direction of the magnetic field and the coil is inclined at 60° to the magnetic field. Find the torque on the coil when a current of 0·5 A is passed through it, and comment on the manner in which the coil torque depends on the inclination of the coil.

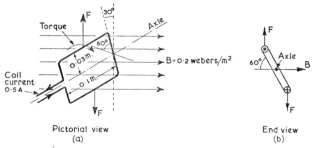

Pictorial view
(a)

End view
(b)

FIG. 2.22. ILLUSTRATING EXAMPLE 2.7

Each conductor in a 10-cm coil side lies normally to the magnetic field irrespective of the inclination of the coil. The directions of the forces may be obtained using the left-hand rule. The force on one coil-side is upwards and the force on the other is downwards as shown in Fig. 2.22(b). These forces give additive torques about the coil axis. Forces also act on the 6-cm sides but these do not produce torque about the axle and may usually be neglected.

Force on each 10-cm conductor $= BIl \sin 90°$ Nw.

$$= 0·2 \times 0·1 \times 0·5 = 0·01 \text{ Nw}$$

Therefore for 15 conductors total force on upper side $= F = 0·15$ Nw
Moment of force about coil axle $= F \times 0·03 \cos 60°$

$$= 0·00225 \text{ Nw-m}$$

Therefore total torque on coil from both upper and lower sides $= 2 \times 0·00225$

$$= \underline{0·0045 \text{ Nw-m}}$$

It will be observed that though the forces on the axial conductors are constant the torque about the axle varies with the coil inclination. As shown in Fig. 2.22(b) the torque will be a maximum when the plane of the coil lies in the direction of the magnetic field; when the plane of the coil is at right angles to the field the torque will be zero and for a position beyond this point the torque will be reversed.

2.10. General Expression for the Torque on a Current-carrying Coil in a Magnetic Circuit

The torque on a rectangular coil may be calculated from the BIi expression as in the previous example. If the coil is not rectangular the calculation of the torque may become very difficult mathematically. The following theory gives an expression from which the torque on a coil may often be calculated very simply.

Consider a coil of N turns lying in a magnetic field and carrying a current of I A. Let T be the torque exerted by the coil about the given axis.

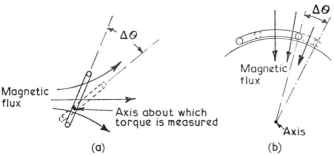

(a)   (b)

FIG. 2.23. TORQUE ON A CURRENT-CARRYING CIRCUIT

Suppose that the torque causes a small rotation of $\Delta\theta$ radians about the axis in a time Δt sec and suppose that due to this movement the flux linking the coil changes by an amount $\Delta\Phi$ Wb

Mechanical work done = e.m.f. in coil $\times$ quantity of electricity passed (by definition of e.m.f.)

$$T \times \Delta\theta = \frac{N\Delta\Phi}{\Delta t} \times I\Delta t$$

therefore
$$T = IN\frac{\Delta\Phi}{\Delta\theta}$$

In the limit when $\Delta\theta \to 0$, i.e. for a stationary coil

$$T = IN\frac{d\Phi}{d\theta} \text{ Nw-m} \qquad (2.8)$$

This is a completely general expression applying to any coil in any magnetic field.

Fig. 2.23 shows two important cases, in the first (a) the axis lies within the plane of the coil and in the second (b) the axis is outside but parallel to the plane of the coil. The latter case may be directly applied to the calculation of the torque in a multi-pole machine.

A similar expression may also be deduced for the linear force on a current-carrying circuit in any magnetic field. The expression is

$$F = IN\frac{d\Phi}{dx} \text{ Nw} \qquad . \qquad . \qquad (2.9)$$

where F is the force in the x direction and $d\Phi/dx$ is the rate of change of flux in the x direction.

Example 2.8

Perform the calculation for example 2.7 by the use of equation (2.8)
The flux linking the coil is given by $BA \sin \theta$ Wb where θ is the angle between the coil plane and the magnetic field.

i.e.
$$\Phi = BA \sin \theta$$

$$\frac{d\Phi}{d\theta} = BA \cos \theta$$

Therefore torque about axis $= IN\, BA \cos \theta$ Nw-m

$$= 0{\cdot}5 \times 15 \times 0{\cdot}2 \times 10 \times 6 \times 10^{-4} \cos 60°$$

$$= \underline{\underline{0{\cdot}0045 \text{ Nw-m}}}$$

2.11. The Fundamental Units of Current and Permeability

In the preceding pages the units of a charge, p.d., e.m.f., flux, etc. are all defined directly or indirectly in terms of the ampere. The ampere itself is defined in terms of fundamental mechanical units.

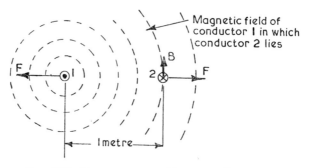

FIG. 2.24. FORCE BETWEEN PARALLEL CONDUCTORS

If a long straight conductor carries a current then a magnetic field is produced in its vicinity. If a second current carrying conductor is placed in the field of the first, then this conductor will experience a force. By Newton's third law, the first conductor will also experience the same force. The ampere is defined in terms of the force between parallel current carrying conductors.

One ampere is the current which, when flowing through each of two long parallel conductors spaced one metre apart *in vacuo*, gives rise to a force between them of 2×10^{-7} newtons per metre run.

Consider a section of the system as in Fig. 2.24. Conductor 2 is a current-carrying conductor in a magnetic field and will exert a force, F,

where $F = B \,.\, l \,.\, I$ Nw
or $F = B \,.\, I$ Nw/m length

If the current is one ampere in the parallel conductors at one metre spacing, then the force (F) on the conductors is by definition 2×10^{-7} newtons/metre length.

Therefore
$$2 \times 10^{-7} = B \times 1$$

Therefore flux density at second conductor $= B = 2 \times 10^{-7} \, \text{Wb/m}^2$. At a distance r metres from a long straight conductor carrying a current I amperes the magnetic field strength H, is given by equation (2.2) as

$$H = \frac{I}{2\pi r} \quad \text{Nw/unit pole or ampere-turns/metre (AT/m)}$$

Thus at the second conductor (1 m distant), the magnetic field strength H due to the current (1 A) in the first is given by

$$H = \frac{1}{2\pi} \quad \text{AT/m}$$

At the second conductor
$$B = 2 \times 10^{-7} \quad \text{Wb/m}^2$$

and
$$H = \frac{1}{2\pi} \quad \text{AT/m}$$

Therefore
$$\frac{B}{H} = 4\pi \times 10^{-7}$$

This ratio $\dfrac{B}{H}$ is called the *permeability* (μ) of the material and is found to be dependent on the nature of the material at the point considered. The above value of $4\pi \times 10^{-7}$ is the value for *vacuo* or air and is taken to be constant for all values of B. It is called the absolute permeability of free space (μ_0). In most other materials μ may be regarded as having the same value as in air or *vacuo*, i.e. $\mu_0 = 4\pi \times 10^{-7}$, but in alloys of iron, cobalt and nickel the permeabilities are very much higher and are not constant but vary with B and H. The permeability μ is usually expressed as a multiple of μ_0. This multiple of μ_0 is called the relative permeability μ_r. Thus

$$\mu = \mu_r \mu_0$$

For air and other non-magnetic materials $\mu_r = 1$. For magnetic materials μ_r is greater than 1, and usually considerably greater. The permeability is often, as here, stated without a unit. Strictly speaking the unit of permeability is one henry per metre (H/m) where one henry is the unit of inductance.

Example 2.9

Derive an expression for the flux density at a point r metres from the axis of a circular conductor surrounded by air and carrying a current of I amperes. Draw a curve showing the variation of flux density from the conductor surface outwards if the current is 10 A and the conductor diameter is 2 mm. See Fig. 2.25.

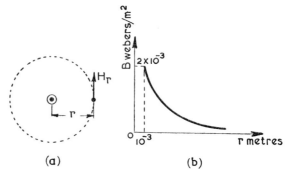

(a)   (b)

FIG. 2.25

$$\left. \begin{array}{l} \text{Field strength at radius } r \text{ m} \\ \text{from conductor axis} \end{array} \right\} = H_r = \frac{I}{2\pi r} \ \text{AT/m (as previously)}$$

$$\text{Flux density at radius } r \text{ m} = B_r = \frac{\mu_0 I}{2\pi r} \ \text{Wb/m}^2 \ (\text{since } \mu_r = 1)$$

$$= \frac{4\pi \times 10^{-7} \times 10}{2\pi r}$$

$$= \frac{2 \times 10^{-6}}{r} \ \text{Wb/m}^2$$

At the conductor surface $r = 1 \text{ mm} = 10^{-3}$ m

$$B_r = \frac{2 \times 10^{-6}}{10^{-3}} = \underline{2 \times 10^{-3} \ \text{Wb/m}^2}$$

The curve of B_r is shown in Fig. 2.25(b).

2.12. Force between Two Long Straight Parallel Conductors

Two long parallel conductors carrying currents I_1 and I_2 amperes, respectively, are laid with a spacing of r metres between centres. This distance is so much larger than the conductor diameters that if the field strength (due to one conductor) is known at the centre of the second conductor, then, to a sufficiently good approximation, the same field strength may be assumed over all the space occupied by the second conductor. (There is a tendency for alternating currents to flow only in the adjacent parts of the conductors. However, if the spacing is large and the frequency low this effect may be neglected) (Fig. 2.26).

Let B_r = the flux density at the second conductor due to the current I_1 in the first.

Then,

$$B_r = \frac{\mu_0 I_1}{2\pi r} \text{ Wb/m}^2$$

The second conductor is then carrying a current of I_2 at right angles to a magnetic field of B_r.

Therefore force on second conductor/unit length $= B_r I_2$ Nw/m

$$= \frac{\mu_0 I_1 I_2}{2\pi r} \text{ Nw/m} \quad . \quad . \quad . \quad (2.10)$$

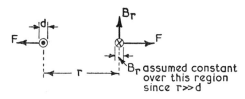

FIG. 2.26. END VIEW OF LONG STRAIGHT PARALLEL CONDUCTORS WITH OPPOSING CURRENTS

This is also the force acting per metre length on the first conductor.

If

$$I_1 = I_2 = I$$

then force/unit length $= \dfrac{\mu_0 I^2}{2\pi r}$ Nw/m $\quad . \quad . \quad . \quad (2.11)$

2.13. Self-inductance

When a current flows through a circuit magnetic self flux linkages are formed, and if these self flux linkages are changing an e.m.f. is induced in the circuit.

Consider a coil or circuit of N turns, in which a current, i, sets up a flux of Φ webers. If there is no iron present, then, self flux linkages, ΦN, are proportional to i.

Therefore, induced e.m.f. $= \dfrac{d}{dt}(\Phi N) \propto \dfrac{di}{dt}$

$$= \text{Constant} \times \frac{di}{dt} \text{ V}$$

i.e. the induced e.m.f. in a single circuit is proportional to the rate of change of current through the circuit. The constant of proportionality is called the *inductance* of the circuit.

The inductance of a circuit is defined as that property of a circuit whereby an e.m.f. appears across the terminals of the circuit when the current in the circuit is changing.

Unit inductance is the inductance of a circuit in which an e.m.f. of one volt is induced when the current through the circuit is changing at a rate of one ampere per second.

This unit inductance is called the *henry* (H)

$$1 \text{ henry} = 1 \text{ volt}/(\text{ampere}/\text{second})$$

Inductance is represented by the symbol L

or
$$e = L\frac{\mathrm{d}i}{\mathrm{d}t} \text{ V} \quad . \quad . \quad . \quad . \quad (2.12)$$

So long as a circuit has no ferro-magnetic material adjacent to it

$$\Phi \propto i$$

i.e.
$$\Phi = ki$$

where $k = \dfrac{\Phi}{i} = $ flux through the circuit per ampere

therefore $e = \dfrac{\mathrm{d}(\Phi N)}{\mathrm{d}t} = kN\dfrac{\mathrm{d}i}{\mathrm{d}t}$ (because k and N are independent of t)

therefore
$$L = kN = \frac{\Phi N}{i} \quad . \quad . \quad . \quad . \quad (2.13)$$

Therefore the *inductance* L may also be stated as the flux linkages per ampere in a circuit. This statement is usually applied when the inductance of a coil is being calculated.

The inductance of a circuit is independent of the circuit current and depends only on (*a*) the geometry of the circuit, (*b*) the number of turns, and (*c*) the permeability of the materials in the vicinity of the circuit. The independence of inductance and current depends on the flux being proportional to the current. In general this is not true of iron-cored coils where the inductance tends to vary with the current.

2.14. Inductance of a Uniformly-wound Toroid

A toroidal winding has a ring as a former and, though it is difficult to wind in practice, it has a simple theoretical magnetic field which is particularly important when a magnetic material is to be tested.

Consider a uniform toroidal coil of N turns carrying i A.

Suppose a unit magnetic pole is moved round a circular path of radius r m within the core (Fig. 2.27). The movement of the pole is everywhere in the direction of the lines of force, i.e. in the direction of the magnetic force, H_r on the pole at radius r m. Applying the work law,

$$\left.\begin{array}{l}\text{Work done on or by unit pole}\\\text{in one complete circle}\end{array}\right\} = \text{Ampere-turns linked}$$

$$H_r \times 2\pi r = iN$$

Therefore $$H_r = \frac{iN}{2\pi r} \text{ AT/m}$$

At inner edge where $r = r_i$ $$H_i = \frac{iN}{2\pi r_i} \text{ AT/m}$$

At outer edge where $r = r_0$ $$H_0 = \frac{iN}{2\pi r_0} \text{ AT/m}$$

Hence the value of H can be calculated at any point within the core and is seen to decrease from the inside towards the outside edge.

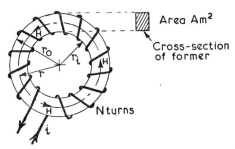

Area Am²

Cross-section of former

N turns

FIG. 2.27. TOROIDAL WINDING ON A RECTANGULAR FORMER

Usually the ring has a diameter much greater than its cross-sectional thickness so that the difference between H_i and H_0 is small and it may be assumed that at each point on the cross-section $H_r = H_m$ where H_m is the field strength at the mean radius.

i.e. $$H_m = \frac{iN}{2\pi r_m} \text{ AT/m}$$

On the same assumption, the flux density at each point on a cross-section may be taken as equal to the flux density B_m at the mean radius where

$$B_m = \mu_0 \mu_r H_m = \mu_0 \mu_r \frac{iN}{2\pi r_m} \text{ Wb/m}^2$$

The total flux in the core $= \Phi = B_m \times A = \mu_0 \mu_r \frac{iNA}{2\pi r_m} \text{ Wb}$

The total flux links all the N turns on the winding

Therefore, self inductance $= L = \dfrac{\Phi N}{i}$

$$= \mu_0 \mu_r \frac{iNA}{2\pi r_m} \times \frac{N}{i}$$

$$= \frac{\mu_0 \mu_r N^2 A}{2\pi r_m} \text{ H} \qquad . \quad (2.14)$$

The inductance, L, may be calculated by the above expression from a knowledge of the number of turns and the linear dimensions of the winding, when the core is non-magnetic. The value of L is then said to be known "absolutely" since it depends only on physical dimensions and number of turns.

2.15. Inductance of a Long Solenoid

Fig. 2.28 shows a few typical lines of force round a solenoid which has a wound length, l, which is much greater than its diameter, d.

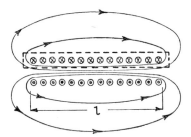

Fig. 2.28. Magnetic Field around a Long Solenoid

Inside the solenoid the lines of force are comparatively crowded while outside there is a considerable spreading of the lines. This suggests that the field strength inside the solenoid is relatively high compared with the field strength outside. Accordingly, the following two simplifying assumptions are found to be tolerably well justified for $l \gg d$.

(a) field strength outside the solenoid is effectively zero

(b) field strength inside the solenoid is everywhere uniform and equal to H AT/m, when the solenoid current is i A in N turns.

Assume that a unit magnetic pole is moved round the rectangular "dashed" path in Fig. 2.28. No work is done during the movement outside the solenoid where the field strength is negligible.

Total work done round closed path = ampere-turns linked

$$\left.\begin{matrix}\text{Work done on or by} \\ \text{unit pole inside solenoid}\end{matrix}\right\} + \left.\begin{matrix}\text{Work done on or by} \\ \text{unit pole outside solenoid}\end{matrix}\right\} = iN$$

Therefore $\qquad\qquad H \times l + 0 = iN$

Therefore field strength inside solenoid $= H = \dfrac{iN}{l}$ AT/m

Assuming the solenoid to have a non-magnetic core,

flux density inside solenoid $= B = \mu_0 \dfrac{iN}{l}$ Wb/m^2

total flux in solenoid $= \Phi = BA = \mu_0 \dfrac{iNA}{l}$ Wb

where A m^2 is the area of solenoid cross-section.

If all the flux links all the turns,

$$\text{self inductance } L = \frac{\Phi N}{i}$$

$$= \mu_0 \frac{iNA}{l} \times \frac{N}{i}$$

$$= \frac{\mu_0 N^2 A}{l} \text{ H} \qquad . \qquad . \quad (2.15)$$

It is only in simple cases such as those dealt with above that the work law may be applied. General methods of determining magnetic field strengths are available but involve more advanced mathematics.

2.16. Mutual Inductance

Mutual inductance is defined as that property of two circuits whereby an e.m.f. appears in one while the current in the other is changing.

If a current i_1 flows in coil 1 a flux is set up and part of this flux, the mutual flux, links the second circuit. Let this flux be Φ_{12} (see Fig. 2.29).

$\Phi_{12} \propto i_1$ assuming no iron present

i.e. $\qquad\qquad \Phi_{12} = K_{12} i_1$

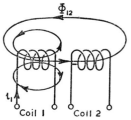

FIG. 2.29. PERTAINING TO MUTUAL INDUCTANCE

where K_{12} is a constant representing the flux from coil 1 which links coil 2 per ampere in coil 1.

The linkages with coil $2 = \Phi_{12}N_2 = K_{12}N_2 i_1$

Therefore   the e.m.f. in coil $2 = \dfrac{d}{dt}(\Phi_{12}N_2) = K_{12}N_2\dfrac{di_1}{dt}$

thus $e_2 \propto \dfrac{di_1}{dt}$

Therefore $e_2 = M_{12}\dfrac{di_1}{dt}$.   .   .   (2.16)

M_{12} is called the *coefficient of mutual inductance.*

Unit mutual inductance will be the mutual inductance between two circuits when an e.m.f. of one volt appears across the terminals of one circuit while the current in the other circuit is changing at a rate of one ampere per second.

i.e.   unit mutual inductance $= 1$ V/A/sec $= 1$ henry (H)

also $M_{12} = K_{12}N_2 = \dfrac{\Phi_{12}}{i_1}\cdot N_2$ H   .   .   (2.17)

i.e. mutual inductance is the mutual flux linkages with the second coil per ampere in the first.

Reversing the problem and assuming that the rate of change of current in the second circuit, $\dfrac{di_2}{dt}$, corresponds with an e.m.f. e_1 appearing across the terminals of circuit 1.

then $e_1 = K_{21}N_1\dfrac{di_2}{dt} = \dfrac{\Phi_{21}}{i_2}\cdot N_1\cdot\dfrac{di_2}{dt}$

where K_{21} is the mutual flux linking coil 1 per ampere in coil 2

Also $e_1 = M_{21}\dfrac{di_2}{dt}$ V   .   .   .   (2.18)

Thus M_{12} refers to the e.m.f. in coil 2 due to current changing in coil 1 while M_{21} refers to the e.m.f. induced in coil 1 due to current changing in coil 2.

Now $M_{12} = K_{12}N_2 = \dfrac{\Phi_{12}}{i_1}\cdot N_2$

and $M_{21} = K_{21}N_1 = \dfrac{\Phi_{21}}{i_2}\cdot N_1$.   .   (2.19)

To find the relationship between M_{12} and M_{21}, suppose the two coils are connected in series so that the same current i A flows through each.

The mutual flux linkages with coil $2 = K_{12}N_2 i$

Therefore, by equation (2.9) force on coil $2 = i \cdot \dfrac{\mathrm{d}}{\mathrm{d}x}(K_{12}\,N_2\,i)$.

Similarly, force on coil $1 = i\dfrac{\mathrm{d}}{\mathrm{d}x}(K_{21}N_1 i)$

By Newton's third law these two forces must be equal

Therefore $i\dfrac{\mathrm{d}}{\mathrm{d}x}(K_{12}N_2 i) = i\dfrac{\mathrm{d}}{\mathrm{d}x}(K_{21}N_1 i)$

Therefore $K_{12}N_2 = K_{21}N_1$

Therefore $M_{12} = M_{21}$ . . . . (2.20)

Mutual inductance is exactly the same in both directions and will henceforward be represented as merely M.

Example 2.10

A ring of wood, of mean diameter 30 cm and of circular section 2 cm in diameter, has two windings; the first, with 500 turns, is uniformly distributed round the core while the second, with 50 turns, is concentrated over a small length of the core. Calculate (a) the field strength in the core when the current in the first winding is 3 A, (b) the rate of change of flux density in the core when an e.m.f. of 0·1 V appears across the terminals of the small coil, (c) the mutual inductance between the two windings. (Fig. 2.30.)

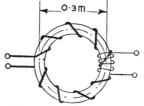

FIG. 2.30. ILLUSTRATING EXAMPLE 2.10

(a) Since the cross-sectional diameter is small compared with the ring diameter it may be assumed that the field strength, H, at all points in the core is equal to that at the mean radius.

Therefore $H = \dfrac{iN_1}{2\pi r_m} = \dfrac{3 \times 500}{2\pi \times 0.15} = \underline{1{,}592\ \text{AT/m}}$

(Note that a current in the small coil would not have set up a uniform or easily calculable field strength in the core.)

(b) E.m.f. induced in the second coil $= 0.1$ V

Therefore rate of change of linkages with the second coil $= 0.1$ Wb-T/sec

$$= \dfrac{\mathrm{d}}{\mathrm{d}t}(\Phi N_2)$$

Therefore rate of change of flux through the second coil

$$= \dfrac{1}{N_2} \times \text{rate of change of flux linkages}$$

$$= \dfrac{1}{50} \times 0.1$$

$$= 0.002\ \text{Wb/sec}$$

Therefore rate of change of flux density in the core $= \dfrac{1}{A} \cdot \dfrac{d\Phi}{dt}$

$$= \dfrac{0 \cdot 002}{\dfrac{\pi}{4} \times 2^2 \times 10^{-4}} = 6 \cdot 36 \ \text{Wb/m}^2/\text{sec}$$

(c) It is easier to calculate the mutual inductance between the two windings as the flux linkages with the concentrated coil per ampere in the uniform coil, than as the flux linkages with the uniform coil per ampere in the concentrated coil. The latter being difficult if not impossible, the former method is used.

Average field strength in the core per ampere in the uniform coil

$$= \dfrac{1 \times N_1}{2\pi r_m}$$

Therefore average flux density in the core per ampere in the uniform coil

$$= \dfrac{\mu_0 N_1}{2\pi r_m} \ \text{Wb/m}^2$$

Total flux in the core per ampere in the uniform coil $= \dfrac{\mu_0 N_1 A}{2\pi r_m} \ \text{Wb}$

Therefore mutual inductance between the windings $= \dfrac{\mu_0 A N_1 N_2}{2\pi r_m} \ \text{H}$

$$= \dfrac{4\pi \times 10^{-7} \times \pi \times 2^2 \times 10^{-4} \times 500 \times 50}{4 \times 2\pi \times 0 \cdot 15} = 10 \cdot 48 \times 10^{-6} \ \text{H}$$

Example 2.11

A single-layer long solenoid has an effective diameter of 10 cm and is wound with 20 T/cm length. A small concentrated coil has its plane lying in the

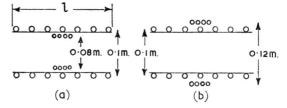

(a) (b)

Fig. 2.31. Arrangement for the Mutual Inductance
of Example 2.11

centre cross-sectional plane of the long solenoid. Calculate the mutual inductance between the two coils in each case, if the concentrated coil has 100 turns on an effective diameter of (a) 8 cm (b) 12 cm (Fig. 2.31).

Suppose a current i_1 flows in the solenoid.

Flux density in solenoid $= B = \mu_0 H = \dfrac{\mu_0 i_1 N}{l} = \mu_0 i_1 \times 20 \times 100 \ \text{Wb/m}^2$

(a) Effective area of search coil $= A_1 = \dfrac{\pi}{4} \times 8^2 \times 10^{-4} = 16\pi \times 10^{-4} \ \text{m}^2$

Flux linked with search coil $= \Phi_{12} = BA_1 = 2{,}000 \ \mu_0 i_1 \times 16\pi \times 10^{-4}$

$$= 12 \cdot 62 i_1 \times 10^{-6} \ \text{Wb}$$

Mutual inductance $M = \dfrac{\Phi_{12}N_2}{i_1}$ . . . . . . (2.19)

$$= 12\cdot62i_1 \times 10^{-6} \times \frac{100}{i_1} = \underline{\underline{1\cdot262 \times 10^{-3} \text{ H}}}$$

(b) The effective area of the concentrated coil through which the flux passes equals the area of the long solenoid since the field strength outside the long solenoid is assumed negligible.

Therefore effective area of solenoid $= A_2 = \dfrac{\pi}{4} \times 10^2 \times 10^{-4} = \dfrac{\pi}{4} \times 10^{-2} \text{ m}^2$

Flux linked with search coil $= \Phi_{12} = BA_2 = 2{,}000\ \mu_0 i_1 \times \dfrac{\pi}{4} \times 10^{-2}$

$$= 19\cdot73i_1 \times 10^{-6} \text{ Wb}$$

Mutual inductance $M = \dfrac{\Phi_{12}N_2}{i_1}$ . . . . . . (2.19)

$$= 19\cdot73i_1 \times 10^{-6} \times \frac{100}{i_1} = \underline{\underline{1\cdot973 \times 10^{-3} \text{ H}}}$$

It may be noted that the effective area of a concentrated coil is extremely difficult to estimate since the inside turns, in a multi-layer winding, loop a smaller area than the outer turns. In case (b) in the above example the mutual inductance did not depend on this effective area so that it may be taken as more accurately known than the mutual inductance in case (a).

2.17. Mutual Inductance in a Circuit: The Dot Notation

For two circuits with mutual inductance coupling, the relative directions of the e.m.f.s in each winding depend on the relative direction of the turns and the relative position of the windings. One of the best systems for quickly indicating relative directions is given by the *dot notation*—a dot is placed at one end of the first coil and the current is regarded as entering at this end at a given instant. A second dot is placed at the end of the second coil at which the current should enter at the same instant to give an additive flux.

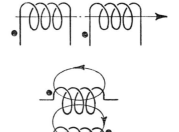

FIG. 2.32. THE DOT NOTATION

The dots may be painted on the coils in an actual circuit or may be placed beside the symbols representing a coil in a circuit diagram (Fig. 2.32).

Once the relative current directions which give additive fluxes are known, the relative e.m.f. directions are also known as follows. Suppose a potential is applied to the first coil so that the dotted end is made positive with respect to the undotted end, the current then enters at the dotted end and increases. E.m.f.s will be set up in coil 1 due to the self-flux linkages increasing and in coil 2 due to the mutual-flux linkages increasing. The e.m.f. in coil 1 will make the dotted end positive with respect to the undotted end to oppose the flux change; also the e.m.f. induced in coil 2 will make the dotted end positive with respect to the undotted end, to tend to make current leave at the dotted end of this coil, i.e. both dotted ends will simultaneously be driven positive with respect to the undotted ends.

2.18. Coupling Coefficient

For two coils with self inductances of L_1 and L_2 henrys placed together so that the mutual inductance between them is M henrys. The coupling coefficient is defined as—

$$k = \frac{M}{\sqrt{L_1 L_2}} \qquad . \qquad . \qquad . \qquad . \qquad (2.21)$$

The coupling coefficient has a maximum value of unity when the entire self flux of each coil links the other. For all other conditions, where less than the entire self flux is mutual, the coupling coefficient is less than unity. Iron cored coils represent the nearest approach to perfect or unity coupling.

2.19. Series Connexion of Mutually-coupled Coils

It is possible to connect two coils (Fig. 2.33) in series in two ways

(a) so that the common current enters or leaves both coils at the dotted end, i.e. both produce flux in the same direction, and

(b) so that, while the current enters at the dotted end of one, it leaves at the dotted end of the other.

Suppose that in case (a) the current is increasing at a rate di/dt A/sec. The applied voltage must overcome the self-induced e.m.f. of each coil and also the mutually-induced e.m.f. in each coil. In this case the e.m.f.s are all driving the dotted ends of the coils positive with respect to the undotted ends.

Therefore applied voltage $= L_1 \dfrac{di}{dt} + M \dfrac{di}{dt} + L_2 \dfrac{di}{dt} + M \dfrac{di}{dt}$

$$= (L_1 + L_2 + 2M) \frac{di}{dt} \quad \text{V}$$

Therefore effective inductance of two coils in series aiding is

$$L = (L_1 + L_2 + 2M) \text{ H} \qquad . \qquad . \quad (2.22)$$

In case (b), while the current is increasing the self induced e.m.f. in each coil will drive the "current entry" terminal positive with respect to the current exit terminal. With regard to the mutually-

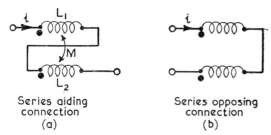

Series aiding connection
(a)

Series opposing connection
(b)

FIG. 2.33. SERIES CONNEXION OF MUTUALLY-COUPLED COILS

induced e.m.f.s: the current still enters the first coil at the dotted end and increases so that the mutual e.m.f. in the second coil tends to make its dotted terminal positive. This is in opposition to the e.m.f. of self inductance in the second coil.

Therefore total e.m.f. in second coil $= (L_2 - M) \dfrac{\mathrm{d}i}{\mathrm{d}t}$

The current now leaves the second coil at the dotted terminal and increases so the mutual e.m.f. in the first coil must tend to make its dotted terminal negative with respect to the undotted terminal. This is in opposition to the e.m.f. of self inductance in the first coil.

Thus   total e.m.f. in first coil $= (L_1 - M) \dfrac{\mathrm{d}i}{\mathrm{d}t}$

and   total e.m.f. for two coils $= (L_1 + L_2 - 2M) \dfrac{\mathrm{d}i}{\mathrm{d}t}$

Therefore, effective inductance for two coils in series opposing is

$$L = L_1 + L_2 - 2M \quad . \qquad . \qquad . \quad (2.23)$$

2.20. Energy Storage in an Inductor

When the switch (Fig. 2.34) closes the current will increase towards a final value of V/R ampere. During the period while the current is increasing an e.m.f., set up by the changing flux linkages, will oppose the current. At an instant t sec after closure of the switch let the current be i A and the rate of change of current be $\mathrm{d}i/\mathrm{d}t$ A/sec.

From equation (2.12), e.m.f. induced in the coil $= e = L\,\mathrm{d}i/\mathrm{d}t$ V. This e.m.f. opposes the current, so the current, i A, is flowing against an e.m.f. of e V. The coil is then absorbing energy from the battery.

Rate of energy absorption by the coil

$$= \text{power entering the coil}$$

$$= ei \ \text{W}$$

$$= L\frac{\mathrm{d}i}{\mathrm{d}t} \times i \ \text{J/sec}$$

Over a very short interval, Δt, let the energy absorbed $= \Delta W$ J.

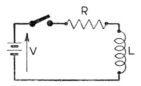

FIG. 2.34. ENERGY STORAGE

Therefore

$$\Delta W = ei \,.\, \Delta t \ \text{J}$$

$$= i \times L\frac{\Delta i}{\Delta t} \times \Delta t \ \text{J}$$

$$= i \times L\Delta i \ \text{J}$$

where Δi is the small current increment which occurs in the time Δt.

Therefore $\qquad\qquad \dfrac{\Delta W}{\Delta i} = Li$

Therefore in the limit, as $\quad \Delta t \to 0,\ \dfrac{\mathrm{d}W}{\mathrm{d}i} = Li$

Therefore total energy stored $= W = \displaystyle\int_0^i Li\,.\,\mathrm{d}i = \tfrac{1}{2}Li^2 \quad \text{J} \quad (2.24)$

(This last step will be clear to those familiar with integration. Others may verify the last step by differentiating the result.)

The energy is said to be stored in the magnetic field of the coil and is called magnetic energy.

When the current in the coil decreases the e.m.f. induced is in such a direction as to attempt to maintain the current. The current and e.m.f. are then in the same direction so that the coil is acting as an instantaneous source and is delivering energy to the circuit. Thus the magnetic energy, which is stored in a coil during instants when the current is increasing, will be returned to the circuit at instants when the current is decreasing. This theory assumes that the inductor does not have an iron core so that L is constant and there is no "magnetic iron loss" (see-hysteresis loss later). The returning magnetic energy is manifest by the spark which would occur when the switch of Fig. 2.34 is opened.

Example 2.12

For the circuit illustrated in Fig. 2.35 calculate

(a) the current taken from the supply at the instant of switch closure;

(b) the rate of increase of current in the inductor at the instant of switch closure;

(c) the supply and inductor currents after the switch has been closed for a long time;

(d) the maximum energy stored in the inductor;

(e) the e.m.f. induced in the inductor at an instant when the switch is opened after being closed for a long time.

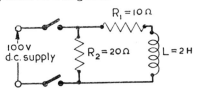

Fig. 2.35. Dissipation of Stored Energy

(a) When the switch is closed the supply potential of 100 V is applied to both arms of the circuit. The current through the non-inductive arm will immediately become 5 A (V/R); but instantaneously there will be no current in the inductance arm since even a small current, Δi, arising in zero time in the inductance L would result in an infinite e.m.f., $\dfrac{(L \cdot \Delta i)}{O}$, opposing current in the inductor. Therefore current taken from the supply at the instant of switch closure = 5 A.

(b) At the instant of switch closure there is no current in the inductor arm and, hence, no potential drop across the resistor R_1. The entire supply potential is then applied to the inductor so that the current through the inductor will increase at a rate, di/dt, giving an e.m.f. equal to the applied potential.

$$\text{i.e. } V = L \frac{di}{dt}$$

Therefore $\qquad \dfrac{di}{dt} = \dfrac{V}{L} = \dfrac{100}{2} = \underline{\underline{50 \text{ A/sec}}}$

(c) As the current in the inductor arm increases a potential drop appears across R_1 and there is less potential applied to the inductor so that the rate of increase of current diminishes. When the potential drop across the resistor equals the applied potential there will be no further current increase since $L \dfrac{di}{dt} = 0$.

Therefore final value of inductor current is given by

$$V = I_{\text{final}} \times R$$

$$I_{\text{final}} = V/R = \frac{100}{10} = 10 \text{ A}$$

Therefore current drawn from the supply after the switch has been closed for a long time$\Big\} = 10 + 5 = \underline{\underline{15 \text{ A}}}$

By "long time" is meant a time sufficiently long to enable the current to effectively equal its final value. Theoretically, the current never quite attains its final value.

(*d*) by equation (2.24) maximum energy stored $= \frac{1}{2}LI^2_{\text{final}}$ J

$$= \frac{1}{2} \times 2 \times 10^2 = \underline{100 \text{ J}}$$

(*e*) When the switch is opened the current through the inductive arm cannot immediately change since any immediate change would again give an infinite e.m.f. Thus immediately after the opening of the switch the inductor current is still 10 A. The current through the non-inductive branch can immediately change so that the path for the inductor current will be through R_2 and R_1

Potential drop across R_1 and $R_2 = 10 \times (10 + 20) = \underline{\underline{300 \text{ V}}}$
i.e. e.m.f. in the inductor $= 300$ V.

2.21. Energy Storage in a Magnetic Field

The magnetic field associated with a large diameter toroid of length l m, cross-sectional area A m² and uniformly wound with N turns may be taken as uniform with a magnetizing force H AT/m at each point and a flux density B Wb/m² at each point. For any value of current i A

$$H = \frac{iN}{l} \text{ AT/m}$$

and

$$i = \frac{Hl}{N}$$

Let a change of current Δi in a time Δt sec produce a change of flux density ΔB Wb/m².

During the change the e.m.f. induced in the coil $= AN \cdot \dfrac{\Delta B}{\Delta t}$ V

Therefore power supply during the change $= ei$ W

$$= AN \cdot \frac{\Delta B}{\Delta t} \cdot \frac{Hl}{N} \text{ W}$$

Therefore energy supplied over the interval Δt is

$$\Delta W = AlH \cdot \frac{\Delta B}{\Delta t} \cdot \Delta t \text{ J}$$

$$= \text{volume of field} \times H \cdot \Delta B \text{ J}$$

If $H = \dfrac{B}{\mu}$ where μ is constant,

total energy supplied for a flux density $B = \text{volume} \times \displaystyle\int_0^B \frac{B}{\mu} \cdot dB$

$$= \text{volume} \times \frac{1}{2}\frac{B^2}{\mu} \text{ J}$$

Making the assumption that, since the field is everywhere uniform, the energy will be distributed uniformly throughout the volume, then energy stored at any point in the field $= \frac{1}{2}\frac{B^2}{\mu}$ J/m³. Generalizing it may be said that in a magnetic field where the permeability is constant the energy stored at any point is given by

$$
\left.
\begin{array}{l}
\dfrac{1}{2} \cdot \dfrac{B^2}{\mu} \ \ \text{J/m}^3 \\[2mm]
\tfrac{1}{2}\mu H^2 \ \ \text{J/m}^3 \\[2mm]
\tfrac{1}{2}HB \ \ \text{J/m}^3
\end{array}
\right\} \qquad . \qquad . \qquad . \qquad . \qquad (2.25)
$$

or

or

where B and H are the flux density and magnetizing force respectively at the point considered.

2.22. Tractive Force

In general two abutting pieces of iron will always have, at least, a molecular thickness of air between them. In the arrangement of

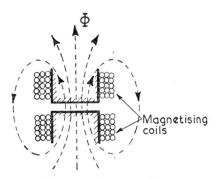

FIG. 2.36. TRACTIVE FORCE

Fig. 2.36 two pole pieces of cross-sectional area A m² have a flux density of B Wb/m² in the space between their poles.

Let F newtons be the mechanical force between the poles. Suppose the poles are moved apart by a distance Δx so small that neither F nor B are altered appreciably. Work done by an external agency in producing the movement is

$$\Delta W = F \cdot \Delta x \ \ \text{J}$$

also   increase in air gap volume $= A \cdot \Delta x \ \ \text{m}^3$

Therefore increase in stored energy in the air gap

$$= \frac{1}{2}\frac{B^2}{\mu} \times \text{increase in volume}$$

$$= \frac{1}{2}\frac{B^2 A \, \Delta x}{\mu} \quad \text{J}$$

Since the flux density has not changed there could be no e.m.f. in the magnetizing circuit and thus no energy supplied by the circuit. Therefore increase in stored energy = mechanical work done

therefore

$$\frac{1}{2}\frac{B^2 A \, . \, \Delta x}{\mu} = F \, . \, \Delta x$$

hence   force between poles $= F = \dfrac{B^2 A}{2\mu}$ Nw .   . (2.26)

2.23. Relationship between B and H in a Ferro-magnetic Material

The simplest system from which to calculate H and B is the toroid with a large ratio of diameter to cross-section. This system is usually

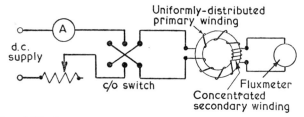

FIG. 2.37. ARRANGEMENT FOR TESTING MAGNETIC PROPERTIES OF A SPECIMEN OF MAGNETIC MATERIAL

used since others involve corners where the field strengths may not be estimated with satisfactory accuracy. To carry out the necessary tests a ballistic galvanometer or a fluxmeter is necessary. The latter, being the simpler instrument to use, will be assumed to be in use here (Fig. 2.37).

A primary winding of N_1 turns is uniformly distributed around a core of the magnetic material, and the primary current of I_1 A may be varied by the rheostat. The secondary winding is usually a smaller number of turns, say N_2, wound on the core underneath the primary so that the only flux which links this winding is the flux actually in the material. The secondary winding need not be uniformly distributed. The effective cross-sectional area of the core and the mean length should be measured, A m² and l m respectively, say.

The usual type of fluxmeter (i.e. Grassot Fluxmeter) measures the change of flux linkages through the coil to which it is connected, not the actual flux at any instant. The ideal procedure is to vary the current in small steps over the required range and at each step to note the change of linkages which are recorded on the fluxmeter scale. Suppose the ring is initially unmagnetized and the current

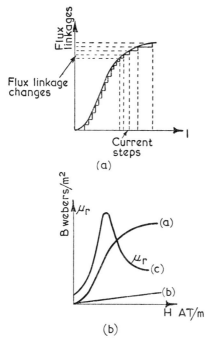

FIG. 2.38. MAGNETIZATION CURVES

through the ring is increased in steps over a prescribed range. Fig. 2.38(a) shows the resulting curve for a particular ferro-magnetic material. The total flux linkage changes which have occurred may be found by the addition of the previous changes.

The flux density B may be calculated from the change in flux linkages knowing the cross-sectional area of the ring and the number of turns on the search coil. The value of H may be found from the current knowing the number of turns on the primary winding and the length of the magnetic circuit.

The results illustrated in Fig. 2.38(a) may be replotted as shown in Fig. 2.38(b), giving a B-H curve (a) representative of the material.

Curve (b), in Fig. 2.38(b) is the B-H curve for a non-magnetic material to approximately the same scale, i.e.

$$B = \mu_0 H$$
$$= 4\pi \times 10^{-7} \times H$$

The striking features of curve (a) are its height and its non-linearities. It is evident that for a given magnetizing force in a ferro-magnetic material there is a much greater flux density than would be produced by the same magnetizing force in air. The permeability of a ferro-magnetic material is much higher than that of air. The permeability, μ, of the material is usually stated as relative to the permeability of air.

i.e. $$\mu = \frac{B}{H} = \mu_r \times \mu_0 \qquad . \qquad . \qquad . \quad (2.27)$$

where $\qquad \mu_0$ = permeability of air

and $\qquad \mu_r = \dfrac{\mu}{\mu_0}$ = relative permeability $= \dfrac{B}{\mu_0 H} \qquad . \quad (2.28)$

μ and μ_0 are measured in henrys/metre. μ_r is a pure number.

The variation of μ_r with H is shown in curve (c) of Fig. 2.38(b). At small flux densities μ_r has usually a low value, called the initial relative permeability, though in some materials developed particularly for low flux density operation the initial permeability is high. The permeability has a maximum value corresponding approximately to the steepest part of the B-H curve. There is a more or less sudden transition from the rising portion of the curve to a relatively constant portion where it is said that the material has reached *"magnetic saturation"*.

2.24. Magnetic Circuits

Consider the magnetic circuit of Fig. (2.39). Let a current of I A flow through N uniformly distributed turns. If the length of the mean magnetic path or circuit is l m, its constant cross-sectional area is A m², the relative permeability of the magnetic material is μ_r, and Φ is the total flux traversing the magnetic circuit, then

flux density in magnetic material, $B = \dfrac{\Phi}{A}$ Wb/m²

magnetizing force in magnetic material, $H = \dfrac{B}{\mu_0 \mu_r} = \dfrac{\Phi}{\mu_0 \mu_r A}$ AT/m

work done in moving unit pole once round the magnetic circuit $\Big\}$ = ampere-turns linked

Therefore $$H \times l = IN$$

$$\frac{\Phi}{\mu_0 \mu_r A} \times l = IN$$

$$\Phi = \frac{IN}{l / \mu_0 \mu_r A} \text{ Wb} \qquad . \qquad (2.29)$$

It is of interest to compare the terms of this important equation with that of a simple series electrical circuit comprising a cell of

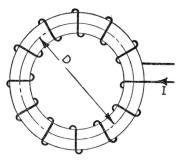

FIG. 2.39. BASIC MAGNETIC CIRCUIT

e.m.f. E V and negligible internal resistance supplying current I A to a resistance of R Ω.

$$\text{The current } I = \frac{E}{R} = \frac{E}{(l/gA)} \text{ A}$$

where l is the length of the conductor and g is the conductivity of the conductor material, and A its cross-sectional area.

Because of the similarity in the structure of the above two equations it is possible to develop an analogy between magnetic and electric circuits. Thus the magnetic flux Φ is analogous to current, though it would be mistaken to think of flux as a continuous flow.

The ampere turns, IN, producing the magnetization in the magnetic circuit is called the *magnetomotive force* (m.m.f.) which is defined as the work done in moving unit magnetic pole once round the magnetic circuit. Magnetomotive force is analogous to e.m.f. and it can be seen that there is considerable similarity in the definition of the two quantities.

The expression $\dfrac{l}{\mu_0 \mu_r A}$ is called the reluctance of the magnetic circuit and is analogous to the resistance of an electric circuit.

$$\text{magnetic flux} = \frac{\text{m.m.f.}}{\text{reluctance}}, \text{ and electric current} = \frac{\text{e.m.f.}}{\text{resistance}}$$

A comparison between a parallel or series-parallel magnetic circuit and its electrical equivalent is particularly helpful when determining the ampere-turns required to establish a given flux in such a circuit. Fig. 2.40(a) shows a series magnetic circuit and Fig. 2.40(b) a series-parallel magnetic circuit.

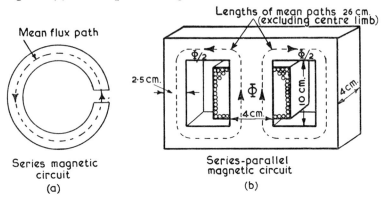

FIG. 2.40. MAGNETIC CIRCUITS

It must be noted that in the case of a magnetic circuit μ_r is not constant so that the reluctance must be re-calculated for each value of flux density whereas the conductivity of an electric circuit is usually constant. As a result the reluctance conception does not lead to an elegant calculation in many practical problems. Nevertheless it is a most useful conception and the analogy between magnetic and electric circuits is an aid to clear thinking about magnetic circuits.

Example 2.13

A steel ring of mean diameter 30 cm having a circular cross-section of 5 cm² is uniformly wound with 500 turns. Determine the magnetizing current required to establish a flux of 5×10^{-4} Wb (a) with no air gap (b) with a radial air gap of 1 mm.

The *B H* curve for the material is given in Fig. 2.42(b).

(a) In this case the magnetic circuit is a simple series circuit having only one part.

Total flux required, $\Phi = 5 \times 10^{-4}$ Wb

Flux density, $B = \dfrac{\Phi}{A} = \dfrac{5 \times 10^{-4}}{5 \times 10^{-4}} = 1$ Wb/m²

Magnetizing force required $H = 450$ AT/m (from *B-H* curve for material)

Mean length of magnetic circuit $= \pi \times D = \pi \times 30 \times 10^{-2}$

m.m.f. = ampere-turns $= H \times l = 450 \times \pi \times 30 \times 10^{-2} = 424$

Magnetizing current required $= \dfrac{IN}{N} = \dfrac{424}{500} = \underline{0.848 \text{ A}}$

(b) In this case the magnetic circuit is a series circuit similar to that of Fig. 2.40(a) comprising two reluctances in series, that of the ring, and that of the air gap. The total ampere-turns required is the sum of the ampere-turns required to establish the flux in the ring and the ampere-turns required to establish the flux in the gap.

Neglecting the small decrease in the length of the steel caused by cutting the gap the ampere-turns required for the ring are as calculated in (a) i.e. 424

Flux density in gap, $B_g = \dfrac{\Phi}{A} = \dfrac{5 \times 10^{-4}}{5 \times 10^{-4}} = 1 \text{ Wb/m}^2$

Magnetizing force required in air gap $H = \dfrac{B}{\mu_0 \mu_r} = \dfrac{1}{4\pi \times 10^{-7} \times 1}$

$$= 7 \cdot 96 \times 10^5 \text{ AT/m}$$

Ampere-turns required for air gap $= H \times \quad = 7 \cdot 96 \times 10^5 \times 10^{-3} = 796$

Total ampere-turns required $= 424 + 796 = 1{,}220$

Magnetizing current $= \dfrac{IN}{N} = \dfrac{1{,}220}{500} = \underline{\underline{2 \cdot 44 \text{ A}}}$

Example 2.14

For the magnetic circuit shown in Fig. 2.40(b), calculate the ampere-turns necessary to establish a magnetic flux of 16×10^{-4} Wb in the centre-limb. The *B-H* curve for the material is given in Fig. 2.42(b).

Since the two outer limbs are symmetrical, their reluctances are equal and the centre-limb flux divides equally between them. The two outer limbs are in parallel, hence the same ampere-turns or m.m.f. serve to establish the outer-limb flux in each outer limb, just as two resistors in parallel have a common potential difference across them. A tabular method is illustrated in obtaining the solution.

Part	Φ Wb	A m²	$B = \dfrac{\Phi}{A}$ Wb/m²	*$H = IN/l$ AT/m	l m	IN
Centre limb	16×10^{-4}	16×10^{-4}	1	450	10×10^{-2}	45
Outer limb	8×10^{-4}	10×10^{-4}	0·8	280	26×10^{-2}	72·8

Total ampere-turns required $\quad \underline{\underline{117 \cdot 8}}$

* Obtained from the *B-H* curve (Fig. 2.42(b)) for the material.

In this example the parallel branches of the magnetic circuit are symmetrical. Where the parallel branches are not symmetrical the calculation is more difficult since it is not so easy to determine the division of the flux between the branches. This is so because for each different flux density the branches have differing permeabilities and hence differing reluctances. In most practical cases involving parallel magnetic circuits the parallel branches are symmetrical.

2.25. Leakage and Fringing Flux

The permeability of iron in a magnetic circuit is of the order of 10^3 times that of air whereas the conductivity of a copper conductor in an electric circuit is at least 10^{20} times that of air. Leakage of flux from iron to air is therefore of greater magnitude than leakage of electric current from a conductor and in most practical magnetic circuits magnetic leakage must be taken into account.

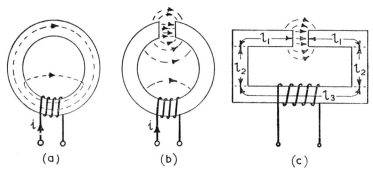

FIG. 2.41. VARIOUS COMPOSITE MAGNETIC CIRCUITS OF UNIFORM THICKNESS

Fig. 2.41 shows a number of magnetic circuits. In (a) the flux leakage across the air may reasonably be neglected; in (b) the greater part of the flux through the coil may be assumed to pass across the gap. However a portion of the flux crossing the gap "fringes" the gap (i.e. fringing flux). The effect of fringing is to make the effective gap area larger than that of the ring and the average flux density less. Furthermore some of the flux by-passes the gap altogether (i.e. leakage flux).

If Φ_a = the flux across the gap

Φ_i = the flux in the ring

leakage coefficient $= \dfrac{\Phi_i}{\Phi_a} = k.$

The flux in the ring, Φ_i, is not constant all round the core, but this variation in Φ_i is usually disregarded and a mean value taken.

Example 2.15

The cross-section of a simple relay is shown in Fig. 2.42 together with the characteristic of the yoke and armature material. Calculate the ampere-turns required on the coil for a flux density of 0·1 Wb/m² in the air gaps. Assume a leakage coefficient of 1·3 and an air gap area of 6·5 cm².

Total flux in the air gap $= \Phi_a = 6\cdot5 \times 10^{-4} \times 0\cdot1 = 6\cdot5 \times 10^{-5}$ Wb

$=$ total flux in the armature also.

Total flux in the yoke $= \Phi_i = k\Phi_a = 1\cdot3 \times 6\cdot5 \times 10^{-5}$ Wb

$= 8\cdot45 \times 10^{-5}$ Wb

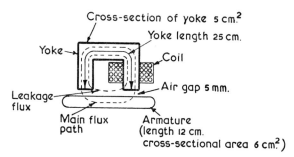

Cross-section of yoke 5 cm.²

Yoke length 25 cm.

Yoke

Coil

Air gap 5 mm.

Leakage flux

Main flux path

Armature
(length 12 cm.
cross-sectional area 6 cm.²)

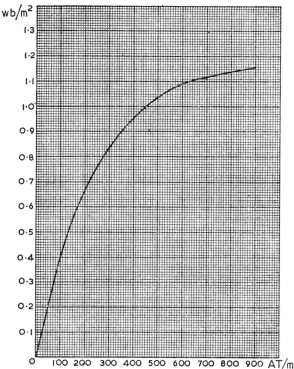

FIG. 2.42. CROSS-SECTION OF A SIMPLE RELAY AND
CHARACTERISTIC OF THE YOKE AND ARMATURE MATERIAL

Flux density in the armature $= \dfrac{6 \cdot 5 \times 10^{-5}}{6 \times 10^{-4}} = 0 \cdot 108$ Wb/m^2

Flux density in the yoke $= \dfrac{8 \cdot 45 \times 10^{-5}}{5 \times 10^{-4}} = 0 \cdot 169$ Wb/m^2

Field strength in the air gaps $= H_a = \dfrac{B_a}{\mu_0} = \dfrac{0 \cdot 1}{4\pi \times 10^{-7}}$

$$= 7 \cdot 97 \times 10^4 \text{ AT/m}$$

Field strength in the armature $= H_1 = 30$ AT/m

(from given characteristic corresponding to $B = 0 \cdot 108$ Wb/m^2.)

Similarly field strength in the yoke $= H_2 = 45$ AT/m

Therefore

m.m.f. $= H_a\{(l)_{a_1} + (l)_{a_2}\} + H_1 l_1 + H_2 l_2$

$\qquad = 7 \cdot 97 \times 10^4 (5 + 5) 10^{-3} + 30 \times 0 \cdot 12 + 45 \times 0 \cdot 25$

$\qquad = 797 + 3 \cdot 6 + 11 \cdot 3$

$\qquad = \underline{\underline{812}} = \text{AT required on the coil}$

Example 2.16

An iron-cored choke is to be made for a current of 100 mA. A proposed design is sketched in Fig. 2.43(a) and the B-H curve is given in Fig. 2.43(b). Calculate the flux density when the current has the above value. What does the flux density become if (a) the current is halved, (b) the air gap length is halved? Leakage and fringing may be neglected.

It should be recognized that this problem is the inverse of the previous two examples where the flux density was known initially. This problem requires graphical solution. The basis of the solution is still the work law.

$$H_i l_i + H_a l_a = \text{total AT} = IN$$

Therefore $\qquad\qquad H_a l_a = IN - H_i l_i$

and $\qquad\qquad\qquad H_a = \dfrac{IN - H_i l_i}{l_a}$

$$B_a = \mu_0 \left\{\dfrac{IN - H_i l_i}{l_a}\right\}$$

$$\Phi_a = \mu_0 A_a \left\{\dfrac{IN - H_i l_i}{l_a}\right\}$$

But $\qquad \Phi_a = \Phi_i$, therefore $\Phi_i = \mu_0 A_a \left\{\dfrac{IN - H_i l_i}{l_a}\right\}$

and $\qquad\qquad\qquad B_i = \mu_0 \dfrac{A_a}{A_i} \left\{\dfrac{IN - H_i l_i}{l_a}\right\}$

This gives a linear relationship between B_i and H_i. There is also the graphical relationship depending on the material. Both must be satisfied simultaneously so that the intersection of the two graphs gives the operating flux density.

Two points are sufficient to give the straight line relationship,

say when $H_i = 0$, $\qquad B_i = \dfrac{\mu_0 A_a}{A_i} \times \dfrac{IN}{l_a}$ Wb/m²

when $B_i = 0$, $\qquad H_i = \dfrac{IN}{l_i}$ AT/m

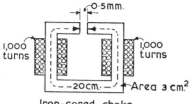

Iron-cored choke
(coils are joined in
series aiding)
(a)

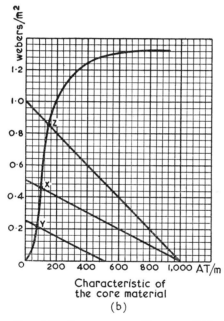

Characteristic of
the core material
(b)

FIG. 2.43. ILLUSTRATING EXAMPLE 2.16

Inserting values,

when $H_i = 0$, $B_i = \dfrac{4\pi \times 10^{-7} \times 3 \times 10^{-4} \times 200}{3 \times 10^{-4} \times 0.5 \times 10^{-3}} = 0.503$ Wb/m²

when $B_i = 0$, $\qquad H_i = \dfrac{200}{0.2} = 1,000$ AT/m

The intersection X of the straight line and the B-H curve gives the working flux density, (0·45 Wb/m²). If the current is halved then the total ampere-turns are halved.

Therefore   when $H_i = 0$, $B_i = 0·25$ Wb/m²

and   when $B_i = 0$, $H_i = 500$ AT/m

The intersection is Y and the working flux density is 0·215 Wb/m².
If the air gap length (l_a) is halved while the current remains at its original 100 mA,

when $H_i = 0$, $B_i = 1·006$ Wb/m²

when $B_i = 0$, $H = 1,000$ AT/m

Intersection Z gives the working flux density 0·86 Wb/m².

2.26. Hysteresis Loop

In § 2.23 the saturation or magnetization curve for a magnetic material was determined by a fluxmeter method, i.e. the curve

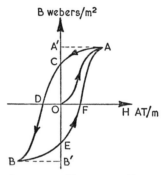

Fig. 2.44. Hysteresis Loop

corresponding to the increase in flux from zero to a positive value. A similar curve could have been found with a reversed current for an increase from zero magnetization towards a negative value.

If, after a specimen is magnetized, the current in the winding is reduced to zero, it is found that the flux density does not fall to zero, but to a value such as OC in Fig. 2.44. Reversing the current, and increasing it to its previous maximum value, brings the flux density to its previous value, but in the opposite direction ($OA' = OB'$). The curve traced out is $ACDB$. A subsequent reduction of the current to zero and increase to its original positive value causes the curve $BEFA$ to be traced out, forming a closed loop. This is called the hysteresis loop (from the Greek word meaning "lagging behind").

The magnetism remaining when the current is switched off, i.e. OC, is termed the *remanent magnetism* or *remanence*. The field strength, OD, necessary to reduce the magnetism to zero is termed the *coercive force*. The values of these quantities if magnetic saturation is reached at the tips of the hysteresis loop are known as the *retentivity* and *coercivity* of the material.

The hysteresis loop drawn in Fig. 2.44 is one of many possible loops. The shape and size of the loop depends on the maximum value of flux density, and also on the initial magnetic state of the specimen. In order to make comparisons between different materials the loops are normally shown for a cyclic state (i.e. equal areas above and below the H axis), and with a peak flux density sufficient to saturate the material.

It should be noted that for a given maximum flux density the area of the loop is not altered by introducing a small air gap into the specimen, but the value of the magnetizing force required is increased by a large amount.

2.27. Hysteresis Energy Loss in a Magnetization Cycle

Consider a large diameter toroid with a uniform winding of N turns on an iron core. The core has length l m and cross-sectional area A m². Let the current at a given instant $= i$ A, then the magnetizing force at this instant $= H = \dfrac{iN}{l}$ AT/m.

Therefore
$$i = \frac{Hl}{N}$$

Suppose that a small increase in current, Δi, in a time Δt sec, causes a small increase in flux density, ΔB Wb/m².

Then
$$\text{e.m.f. in winding} = AN \frac{\Delta B}{\Delta t} \text{ V}$$

This e.m.f. opposes the current i so that energy, ΔW, is delivered to the toroid,

$$\Delta W = \text{e.m.f.} \times i \times \Delta t \text{ J}$$

$$= AN \cdot \frac{\Delta B}{\Delta t} \times i \times \Delta t$$

$$= AN \cdot \Delta B \times \frac{Hl}{N}$$

$$= H \cdot \Delta B \times Al$$

$$= (H \cdot \Delta B \times \text{volume of iron}) \text{ J}$$

Since the magnetizing force and flux density are uniform for all points in the toroid, the energy absorbed by unit volume of iron is $H.\Delta B$ J. If ΔB represented a decrease of flux density, $H.\Delta B$ would be the energy given to the electric circuit by unit volume of the iron. For other shapes of magnetic circuit where H and B vary from point to point $H.\Delta B$ J/m³ may be taken as the energy absorbed or given out for a particular region where the field strength is H and the flux density change is ΔB.

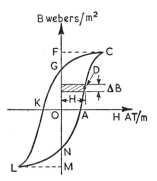

FIG. 2.45.　HYSTERESIS LOOP

Consider a region in a magnetic material which is subject to a cyclical magnetization as represented by the loop of Fig. 2.45. Starting at the point A, the increase in magnetization to the point C may be divided into a number of small steps, ΔB, such as the step shown at D. During this step an energy of $H.\Delta B$ J/m³ will be absorbed by the iron so that the energy absorbed is represented by the shaded element at D. Hence for the complete increase from A to C the energy absorbed is represented by the area $OACFO$.

Similarly for the demagnetization from C to G the energy given back to the circuit is represented by the area $FCGF$ since this area is compounded of a number of ΔB steps where the flux density decreases at each step. For the magnetic state change $A \rightarrow C \rightarrow G$ the net energy absorbed is then represented by the area $OACGO$. For the demagnetization G to K and the subsequent negative magnetization to L, energy proportional to the area $GKLMG$, is absorbed since H has reversed. In completing the cycle to A energy proportional to $LMNL$ is returned to the circuit but energy proportional to $NAON$ is absorbed.

Over the complete cycle the net energy absorbed is represented by the area of the loop.

For the elemental area at D

energy absorbed/$m^3 = H.\Delta B$ J

$$= \text{(area of element) joules}$$

where the area is expressed in AT/m $\times$ Wb/m^2 units. Therefore when the iron is taken through one cycle of magnetization

energy absorbed /m^3 = area of loop

when the area is expressed in AT/m $\times$ Wb/m^2 units.

The external energy absorbed by the iron in a magnetization cycle is converted to thermal energy within the iron with a consequent rise of temperature of the iron.

The relationship between the hysteresis energy loss per cycle and the maximum flux density, B_m, attained, is found to depend on the manner in which the magnetization is produced and the processes used in the manufacture of the iron. The law is of the form

energy loss per cycle $\propto B_m{}^n$

where n lies in the range 1·6 to 2.

The suitability of a given iron specimen for use in a particular application is largely dependent on the area and shape of the hysteresis loop of the material. The following points should be noted—

(*a*) High flux density with a small magnetizing force is desirable to decrease the iron volume required for a given total flux and to decrease the magnetizing current required to produce the flux.

(*b*) For an electrical machine or an alternating current choke, the area of the hysteresis loop should be small to give the minimum power loss.

(*c*) For a permanent magnet a large hysteresis loop is required to give both a high remanence and a high coercive force.

Example 2.17

A transformer is made of 200 kg of steel plate with a specific gravity of 7·5. It may be assumed that the maximum operating flux density is 1·1 Wb/m^2 for all parts of the steel. When a specimen of the steel was tested it was found to have a hysteresis loop of area 100 in.^{2} for a maximum flux density of 1·1 Wb/m^2. If the scales of the hysteresis loop graph were 50 AT/m per inch and 0·1 Wb/m^2 per inch calculate the hysteresis energy loss per cycle and the hysteresis power loss when the transformer is operated on 50-c/s (cycles per second) mains.

Energy loss per cycle per cubic metre = area of loop in Wb/m^2 $\times$ AT/m units

$$= 100 \times 50 \times 0.1$$

$$= 500 \text{ J}$$

Total volume of iron $= \dfrac{200}{7 \cdot 5} \times 1,000 \text{ cm}^3$

$$= 0 \cdot 0267 \text{ m}^3$$

Therefore total energy loss/cycle $= 500 \times 0 \cdot 0267$

$$= 13 \cdot 3 \text{ J}$$

and power loss at 50 c/s $= 13 \cdot 3 \times 50 \text{ J/sec}$

$$= \underline{\underline{667 \text{ W}}}$$

2.28. Eddy-current Loss

If a loop of material, Fig. 2.46(*a*), or a block of material, Fig. 2.46(*b*), is linked by a changing flux, Φ, then an e.m.f. will be induced

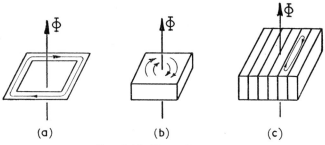

(a)   (b)   (c)

Fig. 2.46. Eddy Currents

in the loop or block. If the loop or block happens to be a conducting material then the e.m.f. will give rise to currents circulating round the loop or block: such currents are called "eddy currents". The eddy currents will give rise to a power loss in the resistance of the conducting material: this loss is called the "eddy-current loss".

The eddy currents will always be in such a direction as to oppose the flux changes occurring and it is found that at high frequencies the eddy currents may greatly alter the magnitude and distribution of the flux over the cross-section of the loop or block. For thin sheets at low frequencies (50 c/s) it is possible to assume that the flux magnitude and distribution are undisturbed by the eddy currents produced.

Suppose that a sinusoidally varying flux is given by

$$\Phi = A B_m \sin \omega t$$

where A is the cross-sectional area of the magnetic field (assumed uniform)

B_m is the maximum flux density per cycle

and ω is the pulsatance (314 rad/sec, for 50 c/s).

Therefore e.m.f. in loop or block $\propto$ rate of change of flux through block

$$\propto \frac{d}{dt} (A B_m \sin \omega t)$$

$$\propto A B_m \, \omega \cos \omega t$$

r.m.s. value of e.m.f. $\propto A B_m \omega$

r.m.s. eddy current $\propto \dfrac{A B_m \omega}{r}$

where r is the effective resistance to eddy currents.

Therefore   eddy-current power loss $(I^2 r) \propto \dfrac{A^2 B_m^2 \omega^2}{r}$

i.e. the eddy-current power loss is proportional to the maximum flux density squared, B_m^2, and to the frequency squared, f^2. It is also inversely proportional to the resistivity of the material.

In many pieces of apparatus it is necessary to have a magnetic material carrying a varying flux. Since magnetic materials are conductors there will be eddy currents in these materials and in general there would be a quite excessive eddy-current power loss if a solid block of the material were used. To reduce the power loss to a reasonable value the apparatus is usually constructed of a number of sheets, called laminations, which are "lightly" insulated from one another by an oxide or a varnish layer. Dividing the block in this manner reduces the flux linking any given eddy-current path and greatly increases the resistance of such a path, Fig. 2.46(c). It is also useful to have an iron with as high a resistivity as possible provided its magnetic properties are satisfactory.

Example 2.18

When a particular laminated iron core carries an alternating flux at a frequency of 50 c/s the hysteresis and eddy-current power losses are found to be equal. If the core is operated at 25 c/s with the same maximum flux density find the relative hysteresis and eddy-current power losses.

Since the maximum flux density is constant the eddy-current losses are proportional to the frequency^2.

Eddy current loss at 25 c/s $= \frac{1}{4}$ eddy-current loss at 50 c/s

and hysteresis loss at 25 c/s $= \frac{1}{2}$ hysteresis loss at 50 c/s

$$= 2 \times \text{eddy-current loss at 25 c/s}$$

EXAMPLES 2

1. Define one weber.
A square coil of 10-cm side and with 100 turns is rotated at a uniform speed of 1,000 r.p.m. about an axis at right angles to a uniform field of 0·5 Wb/m². Calculate the instantaneous value of the induced e.m.f. when the plane of the coil is (a) at right angles to the plane of the field, (b) at 30° to the plane of the field, (c) in the plane of the field. (*O.N.C.*)
Ans. 0 V; 45·2 V; 52·3 V.

2. Define one ampere.
A long conductor lying perpendicular to a magnetic field of flux density 0·12 Wb/m² carries a current of 50 A. Calculate the force exerted on the conductor in lb/ft run.
Ans. 0·408 lb(wt)/ft run.

3. Calculate the torque on a rectangular coil of length 80 cm and breadth 30 cm in a uniform magnetic field of 0·5 Wb/m². The coil axis is central and perpendicular to the magnetic field direction. The coil current is 10 A and it has 10 turns. Perform the calculation using (1) the flux linking rule, (2) the *Bli* rule. (*O.N.C.*)
Ans. 12 Nw-m.

4. The coil of a permanent magnet moving coil instrument has a length of 4 cm, a width of 3 cm and 50 turns. The flux density in the air gap is 0·1 Wb/m² and the controlling torque is 0·5 dyne-cm/deg. What current will be required to give a deflexion of 60°? (*O.N.C.*)
Note: 1 dyne = 0·00001 newtons.
Ans. 500 μA.

5. Deduce an expression for the force, in lb/ft run, between two long parallel current-carrying conductors.
Two such conductors carry load currents of 12,000 A each. Calculate the minimum permissible spacing of the conductors if the force per foot run is not to exceed 11·15 lb.
Show also, the field distribution for the two possible current directions relative to each other. (*O.N.C.*)
Ans. 0·58 ft.

6. The force between two long, parallel conductors is 10 lb/ft run. The conductor spacing is 10 cm. If one conductor carries twice the current of the other, calculate the current in each conductor. (*O.N.C.*)
Ans. 6,050 A; 12,100 A.

7. Define the unit of current in the rationalized M.K.S. system of units.
Three parallel conductors, *a*, *b*, and *c*, lie in the same plane, with *b* in the centre. The distances from *b* to *a* and *c* are 6 and 8 cm respectively. The currents in *a* and *b* are 1,000 and 700 A respectively, flowing in opposite directions. The resultant force on *b* is 2 Nw/m run acting towards *c*. Determine the magnitude and direction of the current in *c*. (*O.N.C.*)
Ans. 190·5 A.

8. Define (a) self inductance, (b) one henry. (c) Calculate the AT/m to produce a flux density of 0·001 Wb/m² at the centre of a long straight solenoid. (d) A non-magnetic ring has a mean diameter of 44·5 cm and a cross-sectional

Elements of Electromagnetism 87

area of 12 cm². It is uniformly wound with 500 turns. Calculate the field strength and the total flux produced in the ring by a current of 1 A. *(O N.C.*
Ans. 796 AT/m; 358 AT/m, 0·539 μ-Wb.

9. Calculate the approximate resistance and inductance of a solenoid, 1 cm in diameter and 1 m long with 1,000 turns of wire 0·5 mm in diameter. What p.d. exists at the terminals of the solenoid at the instant of switching on when the current is 1 A and increasing at the rate of 10,000 A/sec?
Specific resistance of copper is (1/58) Ω per m per mm². *(O.N.C.)*
Ans. 2·77 Ω; 0·0985 mH; 3·76 V.

10. Define mutual inductance.
Show that the mutual inductance in henrys is equal to the mutual flux linkages per ampere.
A coil of 50 turns having a mean diameter of 3 cm is placed co-axially at the centre of a solenoid 60 cm long, wound with 2,500 turns and carrying a current of 2 A. Determine the mutual inductance of the arrangement. *(O.N.C.)*
Ans. 0·185 mH.

11. Give a brief explanation of the term self inductance and define the unit in which it is measured.
A long air-cored solenoid is wound with 50 turns/in. on a former 2 ft long and 2 in² in cross-sectional area. Determine the self inductance of the coil.
A second coil of 3,000 turns is wound over the first and is connected to a fluxmeter which has a constant of 10⁻⁴ Wb-T per division. When a current in the first coil is reversed a deflexion of 1·8 divisions is noted on the fluxmeter. Find the magnitude of the current in the first coil. *(O.N.C.)*
Ans. 3·84 mH; 9·4 mA.

12. Two identical 750-turn coils *A* and *B* lie in parallel planes. A current changing at the rate of 1,500 A/sec in *A* induces an e.m.f. of 11·25 V in *B*. Calculate the mutual inductance of the arrangement. If the self inductance of each coil is 15 mH calculate the flux produced in coil *A* per ampere, and the percentage of this flux which links the turns of *B*. *(O.N.C.)*
Ans. 7·5 mH; 2 × 10⁻⁵ Wb/A; 50 per cent.

13. A coil consists of 1,000 turns of wire uniformly wound on a non-magnetic ring of mean diameter 40 cm and cross-sectional area 20 cm². Calculate (*a*) the inductance of the coil, (*b*) the energy stored in the magnetic field when the coil is carrying a current of 15 A, (*c*) the e.m.f. induced in the coil if this current is completely interrupted in 0·01 sec. *(O.N.C.)*
Ans. 2 mH; 0·225 J; 3 V.

14. A non-magnetic ring having a mean diameter of 30 cm and a cross-sectional area of 4 cm² is uniformly wound with two coils *A* and *B*, one over the other. *A* has 90 turns and *B* has 240 turns. Calculate from first principles the mutual inductance between the two coils. Neglect the space occupied by the winding. Also, calculate the e.m.f. induced in *B* when a current of 6 A in *A* is reversed in 0·02 seconds. With the aid of a diagram indicate clearly the direction of this e.m.f. relative to the initial direction of the current, giving the reason. *(L.U., 1943)*
Ans. 11·5 μH; 6·9 mV.

15. A toroidal coil of 1,000 turns of copper wire of diameter 0·0108 in. is wound uniformly in a single layer on a circular ring of rectangular cross-section with an inside diameter of 7·5 in., an outside diameter of 10 in., and an axial depth of 2·5 in.

If the ring is of non-magnetic material, if the radial thickness of insulation on the wire is 0·005 in. and 1 m of copper of 1 mm² cross-sectional area has a resistance $\frac{1}{58}$ Ω, determine the resistance and inductance of the coil and the energy stored in the magnetic field when a steady current of 0·5 A flows through the coil.   (*L.U.*, 1949)

Ans. 56·2 Ω; 3·63 mH; 0·453 × 10⁻³ J.

16. Define the unit of mutual inductance. A cylinder, 5 cm in diameter and 100 cm long, is uniformly wound with 3,000 turns of wire in a single layer. A second layer of 100 turns of much finer wire is wound over the first one, near its centre. Calculate the mutual inductance between the two coils. Derive any formula used.   (*L.U.*, 1951)

Ans. 0·72 mH.

17. An iron ring 300 cm mean circumference and of circular cross-section 5 cm² has a saw cut 2 mm wide in it. It is wound with 400 turns of wire. Find the current required to produce a flux of 0·1 mWb across the gap, given that the leakage factor is 1·2 and the relative permeability of the iron is 500. (*O.N.C.*)

Ans. 3·66 A.

18. A ring of iron has a mean diameter of 15 cm, a cross-section of 1·5 cm² and has a radial air gap of 0·5 mm cut in it. It is uniformly wound with 1,500 turns of insulated wire and a current of 1·2 A produces a flux of 1 × 10⁻⁴ Wb across the gap. Calculate the relative permeability of iron, on the assumption that there is no magnetic leakage.   (*O.N.C.*)

Ans. 163.

19. A circular crane magnet has an iron cross-section of 200 cm² and a mean magnetic path of 80 cm. Assuming the total length of each air gap to be 1·5 mm calculate (*a*) the ampere-turns to produce a gap flux of 0·025 Wb (*b*) the force in tons to separate the contact surfaces assuming no leakage or fringing.

Points on the magnetization curve are given as follows—

B Wb/m²	1·0	1·2	1·4
H AT/m	900	1,230	2,100

(*O.N.C.*)

Ans. 4,080 AT; 2·5 tons.

20. A cast iron ring having a mean circumference of 40 cm and a cross-sectional area of 3 cm² has two radial saw cuts at diametrically opposite points. A brass plate is inserted in each gap (thickness 0·5 mm). If the ring is wound with 800 turns, calculate the magnetizing current to exert a total pull of 3 kg, between the two halves. Neglect any magnetic leakage and fringing and assume the magnetic data for the cast iron to be—

Flux density (lines/cm²)	2,000	3,000	4,000	5,000
AT/cm	8·5	11·5	15	20

Prove the formula used for the relationship between the magnetic pull and the flux density.   (*L.U.*, 1945)

(N.B. 1 Wb/m² = 10⁴ lines/cm²)

Ans. 1·04 A.

21. A cast iron ring has a mean circumference of 40 cm and a cross-sectional area of 3 cm². The ring has a radial air gap of 1 mm and is uniformly wound with 1,000 turns. If the ring is excited by a current of 1·0 A calculate the flux density and total flux in the ring.

Magnetization curve for cast iron is given as—

Flux density (Wb/m²)	0·2	0·3	0·4	0·5
AT/m	850	1150	1500	2000

Ans. 0·43 Wb/m²; 1·29 × 10⁻⁴ Wb.

CHAPTER 3

Elementary Instruments and Measurements

BEFORE THE operation of any electrical apparatus can be studied it is necessary to have instruments which will indicate the electrical quantities present. To be satisfactory the instruments must be reliable and easily read, as well as having little effect on the circuit to which they are connected. It is important to appreciate the properties of each type of instrument and to know the most suitable instrument for a given measurement or the likely accuracy of a given instrument when used for a particular measurement.

3.1. D.C. Galvanometers

A galvanometer is an instrument which is required to register a small current by the deflexion of a pointer or a mirror. D.c. galvanometers are usually of the moving coil type construction, i.e. a small coil on a metal or insulating former is suspended in a permanent magnetic field so that when a current passes through the coil a torque is set up, displacing the coil against the restraining torque of a pair of hair springs or a fine suspension.

Usually the coil former is rectangular and the coil is suspended in a radial uniform magnetic field as shown in Fig. 3.1. If a plane uniform magnetic field were used the torque/unit current would vary with the coil deflexion (see Example 2.7) and the deflexion would not be proportional to the current.

The hair springs are spirals of phosphor-bronze alloy at either end of the coil and act as current conductors feeding the coil. The two springs are wound in opposition and so positioned that their torques balance when the pointer is at the zero position. When the movement is deflected the springs set up a torque opposing and proportional to the deflexion.

Let θ be the deflexion produced by a current of I A

Then   spring restraining torque $= K\theta$ Nw-m

where K is the spring factor; K is expressed as newton-metres/unit deflexion and is a constant for the spring assembly.

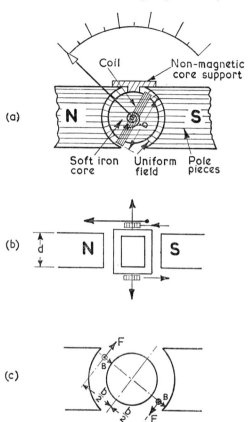

FIG. 3.1. MOVING COIL GALVANOMETER

When the instrument attains a steady deflexion

torque set up by the coil current = spring restoring torque

$$= K\theta$$

For the movement of Fig. 3.1,

radial flux density in the gap = B Wb/m^2

depth of coil side in the magnetic field = d m

Therefore   force on each coil side = BdI Nw

Each coil side is a distance $\dfrac{b}{2}$ m from the axis

Therefore torque exerted by each coil side $= BdI \times \dfrac{b}{2}$ Nw-m.

Each side of each turn exerts a torque of this magnitude in the same direction.

Therefore

for N turns total torque exerted by the coil $= 2N \times BdI \times \dfrac{b}{2}$

Therefore $\qquad\qquad\qquad K\theta = BdbIN$ Nw-m

Therefore $\qquad\qquad\qquad \theta = \dfrac{BdbN}{K} I$

Thus $\dfrac{BdbN}{K}$ represents the sensitivity of the galvanometer.

In a sensitive galvanometer the spring and jewel suspension arrangement is replaced by a fine fibre suspension with light annealed silver spirals as the leads to the coil. The pointer is replaced by a small mirror which deflects a beam of light.

If the coil former is made of an insulating material then it is unaffected by its movement through the magnetic field of the instrument. If, however, the coil former is a conductor (e.g. aluminium) currents will be generated in the coil former as it moves through the magnetic field of the instrument. It may be shown that these currents reacting with the magnetic field produce a torque which always opposes the coil's motion (Lenz's law).

Referring to the previous symbols and Fig. 3.1(c), suppose the coil is swinging clockwise with angular velocity ω rad/sec at a given instant.

Then the velocity of each former side through the magnetic field is,

$$v = \dfrac{b}{2}\,\omega \quad \text{m/sec}$$

Therefore e.m.f. induced in each side $= Bd\dfrac{b}{2}\,\omega$

By the right-hand rule, the e.m.f.s round the former are additive.

Therefore $\qquad$ total e.m.f. in former $= Bdb\omega$

Suppose $\qquad R =$ resistance of the former (Ω)

then $\qquad$ current in former $= \dfrac{Bdb\omega}{R}$

A force will be set up due to the current-carrying former side lying in the instrument's magnetic field.

Force on each former side

$$= Bd \times \text{former current}$$

$$= Bd \times \frac{Bdb\omega}{R} \quad \text{Nw}$$

Therefore torque on the former due to the current in the former

$$= 2 \times \frac{b}{2} \times Bd \times \frac{Bdb\omega}{R} \quad \text{Nw-m}$$

$$= \frac{B^2 d^2 b^2 \omega}{R} \quad \text{Nw-m}$$

The current direction is the same as the e.m.f. direction. The torque on the former is in opposition to the coil's angular velocity and is proportional to the angular velocity of the coil.

The currents which flow in the metallic former when it moves through the magnetic field are called "eddy currents" and will give rise to a loss of energy as heat in the coil former. When a sensitive galvanometer is required for a measuring circuit it is built without a metallic former but when the galvanometer is required to operate as an indicating instrument with a calibrated scale it usually has a metallic former.

In an indicating instrument the pointer is required to follow the variations of current as quickly as possible. If a non-metallic former is used the pointer will always overshoot the correct position on its first movement and continue to oscillate about this position for some time. The oscillating period wastes time and also severely limits the speed of current variation which may be watched with the instrument. The size and resistance of the former may be adjusted until there are just no overshoots and then the instrument is said to be *critically damped*. It is best to have one small overshoot to indicate that the instrument is not sticking.

Example **3.1**

A moving-coil, permanent magnetic instrument is to give a full-scale deflexion of 60° when the coil current is 15 mA. The uniform radial flux density in the air gaps is 0·2 Wb/m²; the rectangular coil has an effective depth of 2·2 cm and an effective breadth of 2 cm. For control springs giving a spring constant of 0·9 × 10⁻⁶ Nw-m per degree deflexion, calculate the number of turns required on the coil.

The arrangement is illustrated in Fig. 3.1 and the symbols are defined in § 3.1.

Restoring torque of spring at full scale deflexion $= 0.9 \times 10^{-6} \times 60$
$$= 54 \times 10^{-6} \text{ Nw-m}$$
Coil torque with 15 mA current $= BdbNI = 54 \times 10^{-6}$ Nw-m

Therefore $N = \dfrac{54 \times 10^{-6}}{0.2 \times 2 \times 10^{-2} \times 2.2 \times 10^{-2} \times 15 \times 10^{-3}} = \underline{\underline{40.8 \text{ turns}}}$

say 40·5 turns are used to give current entry at one end and current exit at the other.

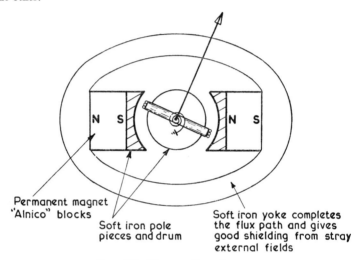

Permanent magnet "Alnico" blocks

Soft iron pole pieces and drum

Soft iron yoke completes the flux path and gives good shielding from stray external fields

FIG. 3.2. MOVING COIL AMMETER

3.2. Moving Coil Ammeters

The moving coil d.c. ammeter (Fig. 3.2) is very similar to the moving coil galvanometer and operates on the same principle. While the galvanometer is used for the detection of small currents the ammeter is used to measure all ranges of current from micro-amperes to kilo-amperes. For micro-ampere measurements the moving coil has a large number of turns to obtain the desired sensitivity and the instrument is rather delicate. An ammeter or milliammeter, giving full scale deflexion (f.s.d.) with a current of around 1 mA to 15 mA is a much more robust instrument and an instrument of this range, with a parallel resistor called a "shunt", is used for the measurement of higher currents (see circuit of Fig. 3.3).

Example 3.2

A milliammeter, which has a resistance of 5 Ω and which gives full scale deflexion when the coil current is 15 mA, is to be used with a shunting resistance to indicate half full scale deflexion on a current of 5 A. Calculate the required shunt resistance.

Fig. 3.3 shows the circuit adopted.

When the total current $I_T = 5$ A,

milliammeter current $I_A = 0.0075$ A (for half f.s.d.)

Therefore shunt current $I_s = (5 - 0.0075)$ A $= 5(1 - 0.0015)$ A

Since the shunt and the milliammeter are in parallel, volt drop across shunt = volt drop across milliammeter.

Therefore $I_S R_S = I_A R_A$

Therefore shunt resistance $= R_s = \dfrac{I_A}{I_s} R_A$

$$= \frac{0.0075}{5(1 - 0.0015)} \times 5 \ \Omega$$

$$= \frac{0.0075}{5} \times (1 + 0.0015) \times 5 \ \Omega$$

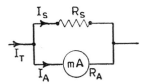

FIG. 3.3. SHUNT CIRCUIT FOR AN AMMETER

$\left(\text{since } 0.0015 \ll 1, \text{ by the binomial theorem } \dfrac{1}{1 - 0.0015} \doteqdot \dfrac{1 + 0.0015}{1}\right)$

Therefore shunt resistance $= \underline{\underline{0.007511 \ \Omega}}$

Several important points may be concluded from this fairly typical example—

1. The shunt resistance is usually very low so that care must be taken to minimize the effect of contact resistances at the junctions— a contact resistance may easily be $0.01 \ \Omega$ i.e. greater than the above shunt resistance. The use of four-terminal resistors is the best method of minimizing contact resistance; Fig. 3.4(a) shows a four terminal shunt and Fig. 3.4(b) gives an appropriate circuit diagram with R_c representing contact resistance. It is evident that if the milliammeter leads were bonded to the main conductors, or joined the shunt at the same terminals as the main conductors, the contact resistances $(R)_{c_1}$ and $(R)_{c_2}$ would be in series with the shunt and would greatly affect the effective shunt resistance. When, however, the milliammeter is joined to the inner pair of terminals the resistances $(R)_{c_1}$ and $(R)_{c_2}$ do not affect the division of current between shunt and instrument and thus do not affect the accuracy. $(R)_{c_3}$ and $(R)_{c_4}$ do affect division of current but since these are in series with a relatively high resistance $(5 \ \Omega)$ the effect is not great. Nevertheless the terminals should be cleaned regularly.

2. The accuracy depends directly on the relative resistances of the shunt and the instrument circuit, which includes the leads from the shunt. The instrument should be calibrated with the leads in use and the same leads must always be used.

3. Changes in resistance of either shunt or instrument circuit will greatly affect the accuracy: thus temperature changes create difficulty. It is usual to make the shunt of a zero temperature coefficient

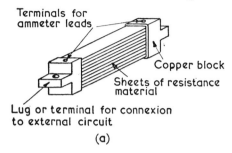

(a)

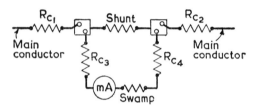

Contact resistances at a shunt

(b)

Fig. 3.4. Ammeter Shunt

material, e.g. manganin, and to put a zero temperature coefficient resistor in series with the copper coil of the instrument to swamp any temperature resistance changes of the coil.

Example 3.3

A moving coil instrument has a coil resistance of $1.5 \ \Omega$ at 20°C and gives full scale deflexion for a current of 10 mA; the coil material has a zero temperature coefficient of $4 \times 10^{-3}/°C$. The instrument is to be used with a shunt to give full scale deflexion for a total current of 10 A. If the resistance of the shunt may be taken as constant at all temperatures, calculate (*a*) the shunt resistance to give correct readings at 20°C; (*b*) the percentage error at 30°C; (*c*) the shunt resistance to give correct readings at 20°C when a swamping resistance of $4.5 \ \Omega$ is connected in series with the instrument coil, and (*d*) the percentage error at 30°C when the instrument is used with the swamping resistor. It may be assumed that the resistance of the swamping resistor is unaffected by temperature changes.

(*a*) at 20°C

Total current = 10 A

Instrument current = $I_t = 0.01$ A

Therefore shunt current $= I_s = (10 - 0.01) = 10(1 - 0.001)$ A

Since the instrument and the shunt are in parallel,

$$I_s R_s = I_i R_i$$

where $\quad R_i =$ the instrument resistance $= 1.5\ \Omega$

and $\quad R_s =$ the shunt resistance

$$= \frac{I_i R_i}{I_s} = \frac{0.01 \times 1.5}{10(1 - 0.001)}$$

$$\fallingdotseq \frac{0.01 \times 1.5 \times (1 + 0.001)}{10} = \underline{\underline{0.0015015\ \Omega}}$$

(b) at 30°C

Instrument resistance $= R_{30} = R_i \times \dfrac{1 + \alpha_0 30}{1 + \alpha_0 20}$

by equation (1.9), where α_0 is the zero temperature coefficient.

Therefore $R_{30} = \dfrac{1.5(1 + 4 \times 10^{-3} \times 30)}{(1 + 4 \times 10^{-3} \times 20)} = 1.56\ \Omega$

When the instrument reads full scale deflexion the current through the coil is 10 mA.

p.d. across instrument for full scale deflexion $= I_i \times R_{30} = 0.01 \times 1.56$ V

Therefore shunt current at full scale deflexion $= \dfrac{0.01 \times 1.56}{0.0015015} \fallingdotseq 10.4$ A

and total current at f.s.d. $= 10.4 + 0.01 \fallingdotseq 10.4$ A

Therefore percentage error $= \dfrac{0.4}{10} \times 100 = \underline{\underline{4\text{ per cent}}}$

This is taken as a negative percentage error since the instrument reads low.

(c) at 20°C with the 4.5-Ω swamping resistance in series with the coil. The instrument and shunt currents will be the same as in section (a).

Total instrument resistance $= R_i' = 1.5 + 4.5 = 6\ \Omega$

Therefore shunt resistance $= R_s' = \dfrac{I_i R_i'}{I_s} = \dfrac{0.01 \times 6}{10 \times (1 - 0.001)} \fallingdotseq \underline{\underline{0.006006\ \Omega}}$

(d) at 30°C with swamping resistance.

Instrument resistance $= 1.56 + 4.5 = 6.06\ \Omega$

p.d. across instrument at f.s.d. $= I_i R_{30}' = 0.01 \times 6.06$ V

Therefore shunt current at f.s.d. $= \dfrac{0.01 \times 6.06}{0.006006} \fallingdotseq 10.1$ A

Therefore percentage error $= \underline{\underline{1\text{ per cent}}}$

3.3. Moving Coil Voltmeters

Since the current through a metallic conductor is exactly proportional to the potential difference across its terminals, a potential

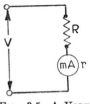

FIG. 3.5. A VOLT-
METER CIRCUIT

difference may be measured by the current it produces through a resistor. Thus the combination of a resistor and an ammeter forms a potential meter or voltmeter. In practice it is most convenient to have a voltmeter operating on the smallest possible current, thus a milliammeter in series with a high resistance is generally used.

Fig. 3.5 shows the arrangement of a voltmeter.
Let V volts be the required full-scale range of the instrument.

Then if I A is the instrument current to give f.s.d. and r Ω is the instrument resistance

$$V = I(r + R)$$

where R Ω is the multiplier resistance.

The total resistance of the instrument is $(R + r)$ Ω and it is advantageous that for any given voltage range this total resistance should be as high as possible. When describing voltmeters a "figure of merit" is often quoted and this is the Ω/V for the instrument.

$$\text{Figure of merit} = \frac{R + r}{V}$$

$$= \frac{1}{I} \ \Omega/V$$

e.g. moving coil instruments frequently use 10 mA f.s.d. movements.

This would correspond to $\dfrac{1}{10 \times 10^{-3}} = 100 \ \Omega/V$. A 1-mA movement

would be better, giving 1000 Ω/V.

3.4. Dynamometer Instruments

The moving coil instruments previously described will not respond to alternating currents since, owing to the use of the permanent magnet, the direction of the torque will alternate with each half cycle and with a rapidity which prevents the relatively heavy movement from following the variations in torque. The instrument would record the mean value of the alternating torque but unless the positive and negative half waves are unsymmetrical the mean value is zero. The permanent magnet is said to polarize the instrument. To overcome the reversals of torque, the magnetic field in which the rotating coil lies must reverse with each alternation; this is the principle of dynamometer instruments.

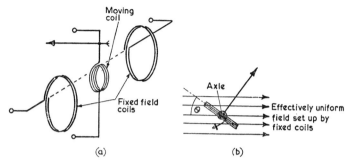

FIG. 3.6. DYNAMOMETER MOVEMENT

A typical dynamometer movement is illustrated in Fig. 3.6—the current passing through the fixed coils sets up a magnetic field which is effectively uniform in the region around the moving coil. Since no magnetic materials are present the flux density B at the moving coil may be taken as exactly proportional to the current, i_f, in the fixed coils.

$$B \propto i_f$$

i.e. $\quad\quad B = K_1 i_f$ where K_1 is a constant.

Let A m² be the loop area of the moving coil with, say, N turns. Flux linkages with the moving coil (Fig. 3.6(b)) $= BAN \sin \theta$ Wb-T. Therefore, if i_m is the current in the moving coil, by equation (2.8)

$$\text{torque on the moving coil} = T = i_m \cdot \frac{\mathrm{d}(\Phi N)}{\mathrm{d}\theta} \text{ Nw-m}$$

$$= i_m BAN \cos \theta \ \text{Nw-m}$$

$$= i_m i_f K_1 AN \cos \theta \ \text{Nw-m}$$

$$= K_2 i_m i_f \cos \theta \ \text{Nw-m}$$

where K_2 is a constant for the instrument.

When a dynamometer instrument is used as a wattmeter the currents in the fixed and moving coils are different. In ammeters and voltmeters the same current is passed through both fixed and moving coils, so the torque direction remains constant since a reversal in current is accompanied by a simultaneous flux reversal.

Dynamometer ammeters can be made for current measurements from about 20 mA up to very high currents, but each instrument has usually only two ranges, one with the two fixed coils in series and the second with the two fixed coils in parallel. In the latter case the field strengths will be halved since there is only half current in each coil so that the current must be doubled to give full scale deflexion. It is not advisable to use shunts with alternating currents as the shunting ratio may change with frequency. Instrument transformers should be used. For voltmeter operation the moving and fixed coils are connected in series with a multiplying resistance. Many ranges may be obtained by using a corresponding number of multiplying resistances.

When used as an ammeter or voltmeter the fixed coil and moving coil currents are the same or proportional to one another

Therefore $\qquad i_m = K_3 i_f$ where K_3 is a constant.

Let $\qquad\qquad i_f = i$ and $i_m = K_3 i$

thus $\qquad\qquad$ torque $= K_2 K_3 i^2 \cos \theta$ Nw-m

$$= K_4 i^2 \cos \theta \ \text{Nw-m}$$

When the instrument is used on direct current, $i = I_{d.c.}$, say.

$$\text{Torque} = K_4 I_{d.c.}^2 \ \cos \theta$$

If the deflexion, θ, is equal to $K_5 \times$ torque

then $\qquad\qquad \theta = K_6 I_{d.c.}^2 \ \cos \theta$

where $\qquad\qquad K_6 = K_5 \times K_4$

According to the $I_{d.c.}^2$ term the instrument should have a "square law" scale, e.g. the angular deflexion corresponding to 2 A should be four times that corresponding to 1 A. However, the $\cos \theta$ term upsets this relationship and the instrument scale is usually crowded at both top and bottom ends. Accurate readings are usually only obtainable above about 20 per cent of the full scale reading. The initial or zero deflexion value of θ, the angle between the fixed and moving coils, may be adjusted to give a more or less uniform spacing of the scale divisions in a particular range.

On alternating current operation

$$\text{instantaneous torque} = K_4 i^2 \cos \theta$$

where i is the instantaneous current. Due to its inertia the pointer remains stationary at a given deflexion and does not alter during a cycle of the alternating current.

Therefore

actuating torque = cyclical mean of instantaneous torque

$$= \text{cyclical mean of } i^2 \times K_4 \cos \theta$$

$$= I^2_{\text{r.m.s.}} \times K_4 \cos \theta$$

since $K_4 \cos \theta$ is constant throughout any one cycle and the cyclical mean of $i^2 = I^2_{\text{r.m.s.}}$ (see § 1.12).

Thus the instrument will have the same scale law on alternating current as on direct current and, indeed, if calibrated on direct current and then used on alternating current the instrument will directly read the true r.m.s. value of the alternating current irrespective of waveform and frequency, provided the latter is not too high.

Dynamometer instruments are common as wattmeters but are seldom used as general purpose voltmeters or ammeters. Since the operating current as a voltmeter is relatively high there is a large power to be dissipated in the instrument and the current taken may be sufficiently great to upset the operation of the circuit which is being examined. As an ammeter the instrument has a relatively high resistance which leads also to a high power dissipation and the possibility of upsetting the circuit in which the measurement is being made. The principal use of dynamometer ammeters and voltmeters is as transfer instruments, i.e. since the instruments have a good accuracy on both low frequency alternating and direct currents, they may be calibrated against a d.c. potentiometer and a standard cell (see § 3.9) then used as comparison standards for other alternating current instruments.

3.5. Moving Iron Instruments

This type of instrument is principally used for alternating current and voltage measurements. The instruments will also operate with direct currents but are then liable to small errors due to remanent magnetism in the iron.

The simplest manner in which the operation may be understood is to consider that when a piece of iron is placed in a magnetic field it becomes magnetized in the direction of the magnetic field, i.e. it assumes a N-polarity at the end where the lines of force emerge and a S-polarity at the opposite end. If, as arranged in the system of Fig. 3.7, one pole lies in a more intense field than the other then that pole will be acted on by the greater mechanical force so that there is a resultant force on the iron piece or armature. If the field reverses, but maintains the same shape, then the polarity induced in the iron armature will reverse, but the resultant force directions will not reverse since both the field and the polarity have reversed. If the iron lay in a uniform field there would be no resultant force since though the same poles would exist the force on each would be the same; hence the type of construction of Fig. 3.7(a) is adopted.

Instantaneous torque $\propto$ field strength $\times$ pole strength
$$\propto \text{(field strength)}^2$$
$$\propto \text{(coil current)}^2 \propto i^2$$

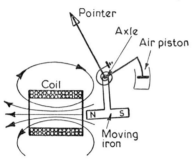

Attracted-armature
moving-iron instrument
(a)

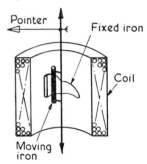

Repulsion type moving-iron
instrument
(b)

Fig. 3.7

where i is the instantaneous current through the coil.

Deflexion $\propto$ mean torque
$$\propto \text{mean of } i^2$$
$$\propto \text{(r.m.s. value of the coil current)}^2$$

The instrument thus indicates r.m.s. values. It may be used directly as an ammeter, or with a series multiplier resistor it may also operate as a voltmeter. The instruments have wide use in power engineering though the resistance of a moving iron ammeter is much greater than that of the corresponding moving coil unit with shunt and as a voltmeter the moving iron instrument takes a large current (0·1 A). The instruments are cheap and robust.

The most difficult design problem is the realization of a fairly uniform scale. In the attracted-armature type the soft-iron armature is shaped to give the most uniform scale possible. In the repulsion type, Fig. 3.7(b), similar shaping of the soft iron pieces takes place for the same reason. In this type there are two soft iron pieces lying in the magnetic field; one is attached to the spindle and one is fixed. Both lie in the almost uniform field within the coil so that the field induces the same polarity directions in each but does not give rise to a resultant force on either due to the uniformity of the field. Since, however, these are together two magnetized pieces of iron with their like poles adjacent there will be a repulsive force between them. This force is utilized to operate the movement.

Deflexion $\propto$ mean repulsive force

$\propto$ mean of product of pole strengths

$\propto$ mean of (magnetic field strength)^2

$\propto$ mean of (coil current)^2

$\propto$ (r.m.s. coil current)^2

Thus this instrument gives r.m.s. indications; as does the attracted-armature type.

Damping in moving iron and dynamometer instruments is usually provided by the air damping of a piston movement in a closed box.

Moving iron instruments are robust and suitable for measurements in low-frequency, high-power circuits.

3.6. Thermal Instruments

Since the heating effect of a current is independent of the direction of current flow, measurement of the heat produced forms an obvious

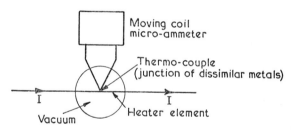

FIG. 3.8. THERMO-COUPLE AMMETER

method of measuring the value of an alternating current. Originally instruments were constructed in which the extension of a wire, when current passed through it and heated it, caused the movement of a pointer. These instruments were delicate and unsatisfactory. In the modern thermal instrument the current is passed through a fine wire whose temperature is measured by a thermo-couple and d.c. galvanometer. The principle of thermo-couples will be found in an elementary physics text-book.

The modern instrument (Fig. 3.8) is very satisfactory up to very high frequencies (radio frequencies of 1 Mc/s.) and has the advantage of reading true r.m.s. values no matter what waveform is used, since the heating effect of a current is always proportional to the (r.m.s. value)^2. Disadvantages include—a non-linear scale, a low overload capacity (i.e. the fine wire is easily fused), and a somewhat sluggish response since the wire temperature follows changes of current slowly.

3.7. Electrostatic Voltmeter

This instrument utilizes the very small force which is found to exist between charged objects. In the usual instrument (Fig. 3.9) there are two sets of plates, one fixed and the other attached to

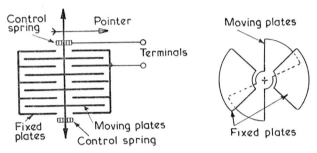

FIG. 3.9. ELECTROSTATIC VOLTMETER

the spindle. One terminal is joined to the fixed plates and the other to the moving plates so that when the instrument is used as a voltmeter the p.d. is connected between the plates and the resulting electrostatic force gives rise to the deflexion.

The instrument is a "square law" (r.m.s.) reading instrument with the particular and valuable feature that it draws negligible current when connected in circuit. It can always be used on any waveforms up to fairly high frequencies and always gives an r.m.s. indication. Usually the lowest voltage range obtainable is 50–300 V.

3.8. Rectifier Instruments

An ideal rectifier is a unit having zero resistance to current flow in one direction and infinite resistance to current flowing in the opposite direction. The main types of rectifier are arc rectifiers, valve rectifiers and solid rectifiers. Solid rectifiers are used in conjunction with moving coil galvanometers to give simple a.c. voltmeters and sometimes a.c. milliammeters.

The essential feature of a solid rectifier is the boundary region between a good conductor and a semi-conductor.

There are two common types, selenium and copper oxide. Fig. 3.10(*a*) shows a cross-section of each type; it will be seen that in each case there is a very thin insulating layer with a semi-conductor on one side and a good conductor on the other.

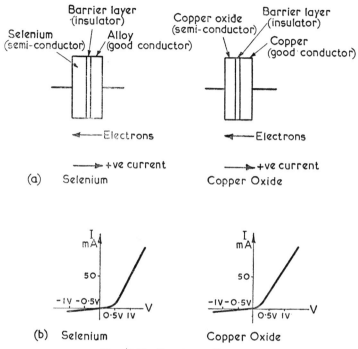

FIG. 3.10. RECTIFIER ELEMENTS

This arrangement is found to give a low resistance to current flow from the semi-conductor to the good conductor and a high resistance to current flow in the opposite direction.

Typical characteristics for the rectifier elements are shown in Fig. 3.10(*b*). It is seen that in both cases there is only a small current in the reverse or good conductor to semi-conductor directions. In the forward direction the characteristics are curved showing a non-constant resistance so that the scale of a rectifier instrument cannot be linear unless a large swamping resistor is connected in series with the rectifier element. This means that the instrument may only be used as a voltmeter.

Copper oxide rectifiers are preferred for instruments due to the lower position of the bend in the characteristic. Selenium rectifiers are used on higher power circuits.

If a rectifier voltmeter were constructed using only one rectifier element (or a few elements in series) the circuit would be as shown in Fig. 3.11(a). This connexion is not actually used as there are several

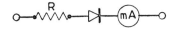

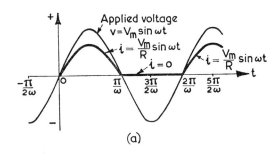

(a)

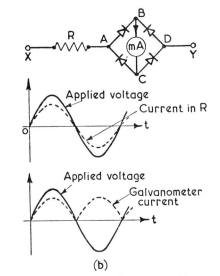

(b)

FIG. 3.11. RECTIFIER VOLTMETER CIRCUITS

serious disadvantages which may be easily eliminated by bridge connexion.

Suppose that the reverse current through the rectifier is zero (i.e. infinite resistance in the reverse direction) and suppose that the forward resistance of the rectifier is much less than the series resistance $R\ \Omega$. (This condition is necessary if the scale is to be uniformly divided.)

Therefore instrument current $= \dfrac{v}{R}$ A

for all positive values of the applied voltage v. The instrument current is zero for all negative values of v.

Suppose the applied voltage is sinusoidal and is given by

$$v = V_m \sin \omega t \text{ volts.}$$

Then $$i = \frac{V_m}{R} \sin \omega t \text{ for } 0 < t < \frac{\pi}{\omega}$$

and all similar positive half-cycles

and $$i = 0 \text{ for } \frac{\pi}{\omega} < t < \frac{2\pi}{\omega}$$

and all similar negative half-cycles.

The wave-forms of voltage and current are shown in Fig. 3.11(a).

The quantity of electricity passed through the milliammeter per cycle $= Q$.

$$Q = \int_0^{\pi/\omega} i\ \mathrm{d}t = \frac{V_m}{R} \int_0^{\pi/\omega} \sin \omega t\ \mathrm{d}t = \frac{2V_m}{R\omega} \text{ A-sec}$$

Therefore

average current $= \dfrac{Q}{\text{period}} = \dfrac{2V_m}{R\omega} \times \dfrac{1}{2\pi/\omega} = \dfrac{1}{\pi}\dfrac{V_m}{R}$ A

Therefore milliammeter deflexion $\propto \dfrac{V_m}{\pi R}$

i.e. $\propto$ mean voltage per positive half-cycle.

It will be observed that the instrument reading depends on the mean value of the positive half of the impressed voltage. If the wave shape were to change from sinusoidal to another shape with the same mean value then the instrument reading would remain constant. This means that the instrument scale could be marked off in mean voltage values. However, all other instruments operating on alternating quantities are scaled for r.m.s. values and it has become universal practice to scale rectifier instruments for r.m.s. values also, assuming that the voltage waveform is always sinusoidal. The procedure is satisfactory so long as the voltages are sinusoidal but errors, called *waveform errors*, are introduced if the voltage does not vary sinusoidally.

One very obvious defect of the single rectifier circuit is that it actually measures only the positive half-cycle and takes no recognition of the negative half-cycle; thus the negative half-cycle might include much variation without affecting the instrument readings. It will only be on rare occasions that this defect is of any importance but another defect is much more important. It will be realized that during negative half-cycles the entire applied potential will appear across the rectifier unit since, there being no current, there will be no p.d. across R or the galvanometer. Now the allowable "back voltage" across a solid rectifier element is of the order of only 15 V to give a suitable safety margin and prevent breakdown of the rectifier, thus many rectifier elements would be required in series for even a 100-V range. This would increase the non-linear forward resistance and upset the scale divisions. Bridge connexion overcomes this and the first difficulty as well as giving "smoother" input and galvanometer currents.

The circuit shown in Fig. 3.11(b) is that of a bridge-connected rectifier voltmeter. By the use of this connexion the alternating current always flows through the galvanometer in the same direction, though the direction reverses in the alternating current circuit. The operation may be realized as follows—

(a) When X is positive with respect to Y current flows from X to Y—then AB conducts, the current flows through the galvanometer from B to C, and element CD conducts also. Elements AC and BD remain non-conducting.

(b) When Y is positive with respect to X current flows from Y to X—elements AC and BD conduct and the current still flows through the galvanometer from B to C. Elements AB and CD remain non-conducting.

It is seen that—

1. The current in R flows in each half-cycle so giving rise to a volt-drop in both half-cycles.

2. The galvanometer current has twice the value which it had in the previous case for the same voltage and the same series resistance.

With bridge connexion it is sufficient to use four single elements so the forward resistance is never greater than that of two elements in series and for voltage ranges over about 50 V the scale is substantially linear. The back voltage across each non-conducting rectifier can never be greater than the forward voltage across a conducting element plus the milliammeter volt-drop, both of which are small.

For an applied voltage of $V_m \sin \omega t$

milliammeter deflexion $\propto \dfrac{2V_m}{\pi R}$ (i.e. twice previous value)

$\propto$ mean voltage over both half-cycles

It is assumed that the instrument deflexion is to be proportional to r.m.s. values,

i.e. it is assumed that

$$\text{milliammeter deflexion} \propto \frac{V_m}{\sqrt{2} \cdot R}$$

and the scale is marked accordingly

There is then waveform error if the voltage waveform is not sinusoidal.

Rectifier instruments have the advantages of

1. An almost uniform scale.

2. Operation on small currents e.g. 1 mA (the figure of merit may be 1000 Ω/V or higher while moving iron instruments have values seldom in excess of 100 Ω/V),

3. Being more suitable at high frequencies than moving iron or dynamometer instruments (most rectifier instruments may be used up to 10,000 c/s without appreciable error: the corresponding upper frequency for a moving iron instrument might be 150–500 c/s).

3.9. D.C. Potentiometer Measurements

The "null" method of measurement utilizes the principle of balancing two potentials against one another so that the measurement may be made without drawing energy from the terminals at which the test unit is connected. The instruments previously described are all indicating instruments which draw their operating energy from the terminals at which they are connected; care must always be taken to ensure that the energy so drawn does not upset the test.

A potentiometer is a unit which employs the null method, and measures e.m.f. or p.d. without taking any energy from the measured circuit. It requires a separate source of energy. It may be easily adapted to measure current in terms of p.d. and a standard resistance, and to compare two resistors. The principle of the d.c. potentiometer is illustrated in Fig. 3.12. A long uniform wire AB is supplied with a steady current from a battery. There will be a uniform volt drop along AB, proportional to the length of wire considered. The unknown voltage is connected in series with a sensitive galvanometer from one end, A, of the wire to a movable tapping point, P, on the wire, with the polarity shown.

When there is no indication on the galvanometer (balanced condition) then the volt drop down the tapped portion of the wire must be equal to the voltage measured. When this occurs, there is obviously no current in the galvanometer circuit, and hence no energy is then taken from the measured circuit.

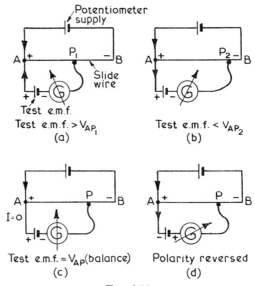

FIG. 3.12
(arrows indicate resultant current direction)

The d.c. potentiometer is used as follows—

1. To COMPARE E.M.F.s

A large 4-V cell (Fig. 3.13) supplies a constant current to a uniform resistance wire, AB, 200 cm long, through a variable resistance R.

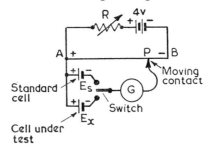

FIG. 3.13. D.C. POTENTIOMETER FOR MEASURING E.M.F.

The p.d. between A and any point P on the wire is proportional to the length of wire between A and P (l_{AP}). The potentiometer is standardized by connecting a Weston Standard Cadmium Cell in the galvanometer circuit with the polarity shown. This cell has a constant e.m.f. of 1·0186 V which is only slightly affected by small temperature changes. The point P is set at 101·86 cm from A, and the resistor R is adjusted until no deflexion is observed on the galvanometer G. At this point no current is taken from the standard cell, and hence the volt drop down the wire from A to P must be exactly equal to the e.m.f. of the standard cell. The volt drop per cm of wire is thus $\dfrac{1 \cdot 0186}{101 \cdot 86} = 0 \cdot 01$ V per cm, and the potentiometer can therefore measure voltages up to $200 \times 0 \cdot 01 = 2$ V, provided that the slide-wire current remains unaltered. If the polarity of the standard cell is reversed it is impossible to obtain balance.

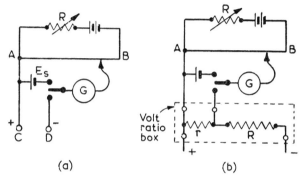

FIG. 3.14. POTENTIOMETER COMPARISON OF P.D.s

The cell under test, E_x, is now connected in circuit in place of the standard cell, E_s, and the sliding contact P is moved until the galvanometer again shows no deflexion. The new length of slide-wire between A and P, multiplied by the volt drop per cm gives the e.m.f. of the cell under test.

2. To Compare P.D.s

For the measurement of p.d. the same standardizing and test procedure as for the measurement of e.m.f. are used, but in this case the test cell, E_x, is replaced by leads connected to the two points (C and D) across which the p.d. has to be found. Since at balance no current flows through the galvanometer circuit, the resistance of the leads is unimportant. The wire is calibrated against a standard cell as before, and then balance is obtained for the unknown voltage. If the voltage exceeds 2 V, a volt ratio box may be connected as shown in Fig. 3.14(b). This consists of a resistor tapped at a known point, such that the voltage applied to the potentiometer is a fixed fraction of the total voltage applied to the box. Since the potentiometer will draw no current from the volt ratio box at balance, the arrangement of the box is simple.

Let n be the desired voltage ratio and let I be the current through the volt ratio box, i.e. through R and r. Since the potentiometer circuit takes no current,

$$n = \frac{(r + R)I}{rI} = \frac{r + R}{r}$$

3. To Compare Resistances

Basically the potentiometer compares voltages. To compare resistances the same current should be passed through the resistors in series so that the voltages across the resistors will be in proportion to their resistances.

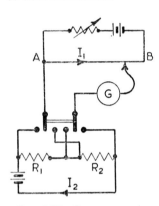

FIG. 3.15. COMPARISON OF
RESISTORS

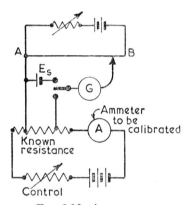

FIG. 3.16. AMMETER
CALIBRATION

The arrangement is shown in the circuit of Fig. 3.15 where R_1 and R_2 are the resistors to be compared. A standard cell is not necessary for the method, but both sources of current should be reliably constant so that there will be negligible change of current over a period long enough to balance the potentiometer with the selector switch first set at R_1 and then set at R_2.

Potential across $R_1 = I_2 R_1 \propto I_1 l_1$

where l_1 is the balance length when R_1 is selected.

Potential across $R_2 = I_2 R_2 \propto I_1 l_2$

where l_2 is the balance length when R_2 is selected.

Therefore
$$\frac{R_1}{R_2} = \frac{l_1}{l_2}$$

4. To Calibrate Ammeter

The reading on a voltmeter may easily be checked if the voltmeter is connected across the terminals of the volt ratio box in the circuit of Fig. 3.14(*b*) and a suitable supply voltage is applied.

Since the potentiometer actually compares an unknown p.d. with the e.m.f. of a standard cell, the ammeter current must be passed through a known resistance so that the p.d. across the known resistance may be compared by the potentiometer. This arrangement is shown in Fig. 3.16. The control resistance is varied until the ammeter pointer is at a principal division on the scale (or at some suitable reading). The potentiometer then compares the p.d. across the known resistor with the e.m.f. of the standard cell, so that the p.d. across the resistor is known and the true current in the ammeter may be calculated. It should be noted that the known resistor has four terminals to eliminate contact resistance troubles as in the case of ammeter shunts. The standard resistance is usually called a standard shunt.

3.10. Measurement of Resistance

1. Potentiometer Method

This has already been referred to in the previous section.

2. Voltmeter-Ammeter Method

The ammeter resistance, R_a, (Fig. 3.17) is normally very small, while the voltmeter resistance R_v is very high. There are two methods of connecting the ammeter and voltmeter to measure the resistance R.

Let voltmeter read V volts, and ammeter read I amperes, then for connexion A

$$V = IR_a + IR$$

$$R = \frac{V}{I} - R_a$$

If R_a is much smaller than R,

then
$$R \fallingdotseq \frac{V}{I}$$

For connexion B, the ammeter current equals the sum of current through voltmeter and current through R.

Therefore
$$I = \frac{V}{R} + \frac{V}{R_v}$$

and
$$R = \frac{V}{\left(I - \dfrac{V}{R_v}\right)}$$

If the voltmeter current is small compared with the total current I,

then
$$R \fallingdotseq \frac{V}{I}$$

These methods are suitable for rough measurement of resistance and for non-linear resistances where the resistance depends on the voltage used, e.g. the resistance of a lamp.

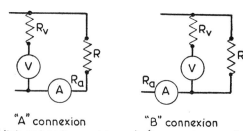

"A" connexion
(High and medium resistances)

"B" connexion
(Low resistances)

FIG. 3.17. VOLTMETER-AMMETER MEASUREMENT OF RESISTANCE

3. WHEATSTONE BRIDGE METHOD

The potentiometer method of comparing resistances suffers from the disadvantage that the accuracy is limited by the constancy of the current through the two resistors compared—however it is a good method for resistors less than about 1 Ω .

The ammeter-voltmeter method has an accuracy which is limited by the accuracy of calibration of the instruments and the accuracy

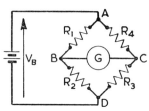

FIG. 3.18. WHEATSTONE BRIDGE CIRCUIT

with which their resistances are known, and though the simplicity of the method is appealing it is generally difficult to find simultaneously a suitable ammeter, a suitable voltmeter and a suitable supply.

The Wheatstone bridge method—a null method independent of the constancy of a supply or the calibration of an indicating instrument—is generally the most popular method for measurements over the range 0·1 Ω to 10 M Ω.

Consider the circuit arrangement shown in Fig. 3.18. The rhombus of four resistors is typical of a bridge circuit with a supply potential across one pair of diagonals, and a galvanometer or detector across the other pair. With a battery applied across AD, a condition can exist for which no current flows through the galvanometer connected across BC. This condition is realized when the potentials of B and C are the same with respect to some given reference potential.

Suppose the potential of D is taken as the reference potential.

Then the potential of B with respect to D is

$$R_2 I_2 = R_2 \cdot \frac{V}{R_1 + R_2}$$

since the same current I_2 flows through R_1 and R_2 when no current flows in the galvanometer.

Similarly the potential of C with respect to D is

$$R_3 \cdot \frac{V}{R_3 + R_4}$$

Therefore with no deflexion of the galvanometer, i.e. with no galvanometer current,

$$R_2 \cdot \frac{V}{R_1 + R_2} = R_3 \cdot \frac{V}{R_3 + R_4}$$

whence
$$R_2 R_4 = R_1 R_3$$

To use the circuit for resistance measurements—R_2, say, is replaced by an unknown resistor; R_1, R_3 and R_4 are known variable resistors for which it is usually sufficient if R_1 and R_4, known as the ratio arms, have each possible values of 1, 10, 100 and 1000 Ω and R_3 may be varied in 1 Ω steps from 0 to 10,000 Ω.

3.11. The Ballistic Galvanometer

This instrument is basically the same as the galvanometers described previously, with the particular features of

1. Minimum damping.
2. Relatively large inertia mass.

Damping is made small by the use of a long fibre suspension, and a mirror reflecting system is generally used. The coil former must, of course, be insulating.

The coil and magnetic system of the usual galvanometer are present, thus

deflecting torque $\propto$ coil current at all instants for which the current flows.

The galvanometer movement must be initially at rest. Suppose that, with the movement at rest, a current is passed through the coil for a short interval of time. This interval must be so short that effectively the coil does not move from its initial rest position during the interval for which the current passes. Then it may be assumed that the coil receives an impulsive torque which effectively accelerates the coil from rest to an angular velocity ω in a very short time while the coil does not effectively move. The coil then starts from its rest position with an angular velocity ω, but with no longer a driving torque, for the current ceases after the first short interval. The coil deflects against the restoring torque of the suspension and will continue to swing backwards and forwards until the stray losses bring it to its original zero position. If the damping is small the magnitude of the first swing may be taken as exactly proportional to the total impulsive torque exerted by the short current pulse through the coil.

Deflexion $\propto$ impulsive torque $\times$ time

i.e.   Deflexion $\propto$ current through coil and the time
for which it passes

i.e. $\propto$ quantity of electricity passed.

Thus the ballistic galvanometer is an instrument which shows a deflexion proportional to the quantity of electricity which passes through it provided that quantity completely passes in a very short time (say $\frac{1}{1000}$ of the periodic time of the galvanometer).

3.12. Delineation of the *B-H* Curve of a Magnetic Material using a Ballistic Galvanometer

Three important pieces of apparatus are required.

1. The specimen of the material. This should be in a ring form with at least one uniformly wound magnetizing winding to prevent flux leakage and to give a uniform magnetic field strength everywhere inside the core. A search winding is also required.

2. A standard mutual inductance. This may be constructed in the form of a single layer long solenoid with a short concentrated coil at the central cross-section (see Example 2.11 for the calculation of mutual inductance M).

3. Ballistic galvanometer as previously described.

The complete circuit for the method is illustrated in Fig. 3.19. There are two distinct parts—the specimen circuit and the standardizing circuit. These operate independently but both output coils are connected in series to the galvanometer throughout so that the resistance of the galvanometer circuit is constant throughout.

Before commencing measurements it is important to eliminate any residual magnetism which might remain from a previous test; this is performed by increasing the specimen current to a maximum and then decreasing it slowly while the current direction is continually reversed. If there is any interruption or mistake during the experimental procedure demagnetization should be carried out before the experiment is resumed.

The short-circuiting key across the galvanometer is an additional feature of great value—as well as protecting the galvanometer from large impulses during demagnetization, it may be used to stop the galvanometer swing quickly after the magnitude of the swing has been observed.

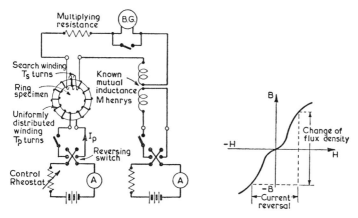

FIG. 3.19. DELINEATION OF A *B-H* CURVE

The multiplying resistor should be as large as possible consistent with reasonably large deflexions. To vary the sensitivity the number of turns on the search winding may be varied, so long as their resistance is insignificant compared with that of the multiplying resistance.

To delineate the *B-H* curve the current through the uniform winding on the specimen should be increased in stages. At each stage the current direction should be reversed and the deflexion of the ballistic galvanometer noted. It is important (*a*) that the current reversal should be accomplished in as short a time as possible to ensure the correct operation of the ballistic galvanometer and (*b*) that the current is always increased so the stray hysteresis effects do not upset the *B-H* curve obtained, i.e. always increase the current at each stage, never decrease it.

To evaluate the constant of the galvanometer, the deflexion when the primary current of the mutual inductance is reversed should also be noted.

Let I_s amperes be the primary current reversed in the mutual inductance,

M henrys be the known mutual inductance,

D_s be the galvanometer deflexion corresponding to the current reversal in the mutual inductance,

Δt sec be the time taken for the reversal,

and R Ω be the total galvanometer circuit resistance.

In the mutual inductance a current change from $+I_s$ to $-I_s$ takes place in Δt sec.

Thus   e.m.f. induced in secondary of M $= \dfrac{2MI_s}{\Delta t}$

and   current through the galvanometer $= \dfrac{2MI_s}{R \cdot \Delta t}$

Therefore charge passed through the galvanometer $= \dfrac{2MI_s}{R \cdot \Delta t} \times \Delta t$

$$= \frac{2MI_s}{R} \text{ C}$$

corresponding to deflexion D_s divisions

Therefore the sensitivity of the galvanometer

$$= \frac{D_s R}{2MI_s} \text{ divisions/coulomb}$$

Considering a representative stage in the magnetization of the specimen

Let B Wb/m² be the flux density at the particular stage

H AT/m be the corresponding field strength

D divisions be the galvanometer deflexion.

I A be the corresponding current

N_p be the number of turns on the uniform winding

N_s be the number of turns on the test winding

A m² be the area of cross-section of the specimen

and l m be the mean circumferential length of the specimen.

Then for any current value I A the field strength is directly calculable from

$$H = \frac{IN_p}{l} \text{ AT/m}$$

as shown in § 2.15. The value of the field strength is then known and the corresponding value of flux density may be calculated from the galvanometer deflexion when the current I is reversed. Suppose the reversal takes place in Δt sec.

Deflexion of galvanometer $= D$ divisions

quantity passed through the galvanometer $= \dfrac{D \times 2MI_s}{D_s R}$ C

average current through the galvanometer $= \dfrac{D \times 2MI_s}{D_s R \Delta t}$ A

and average e.m.f. in secondary $=$ current average $\times R$

$$= \frac{D \times 2MI_s}{D_s \times \Delta t}$$

(thus R need not be known so long as it is constant).

Therefore average rate of change of flux through the search coil

$$= \frac{\text{e.m.f.}}{N_s} \text{ Wb/sec}$$

$$= \frac{D \cdot 2M \cdot I_s}{D_s \cdot \Delta t \cdot N_s} \text{ Wb/sec}$$

But this flux change continued for Δt sec

Therefore total flux change $= \dfrac{D \cdot 2M \cdot I_s}{D_s \cdot \Delta t \cdot N_s} \times \Delta t$ Wb

$$= \frac{D \cdot 2M \cdot I_s}{D_s N_s} \text{ Wb}$$

Therefore total flux density change $= \dfrac{D \cdot 2M \cdot I_s}{D_s \cdot A \cdot N_s}$ Wb/m²

and this change is from $-B$ to $+B$ Wb/m²

therefore $2B = \dfrac{D \cdot 2M \cdot I_s}{D_s A T_s}$

$$B = D \times \frac{D_s A T_s}{MI_s} \text{ Wb/m}^2$$

Thus the flux density at each stage may be calculated from the galvanometer deflexion and the standardizing test.

3.13. Delineation of a Hysteresis Loop, using a Ballistic Galvanometer

A typical major hysteresis loop is illustrated by $ACDEA$ in Fig. 3.20. There are an infinite number of such loops depending on the maximum flux density which is obtained, e.g. another major hystersis loop for a smaller maximum flux density is illustrated

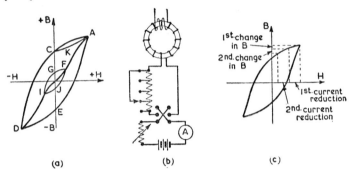

(a)   (b)   (c)

FIG. 3.20. DELINEATION OF HYSTERESIS LOOP

by $FGIJF$. Many other hysteresis loops are possible, e.g. when the maximum current value is not the same in both directions— $ACKA$ is a hysteresis loop for a case where the positive current is reduced to zero then increased again. The first type of loop is by far the most important and only this type will be examined. The same apparatus as was used for the saturation curve determination may again be used with the addition of the stepped resistor in the excitation circuit of the specimen.

In delineating the hysteresis loop the current is not put through a number of reversals as in the previous method but a series of ordered steps are made round the loop. The experiment is commenced by demagnetizing the specimen and setting the current to full value in one direction so that the specimen is magnetized to the state represented by the point A. The current is then reduced in steps to zero and increased in steps to a negative maximum. The galvanometer swing at each step should be noted so that the changes in B may be calculated in the same manner as previously. The loop may then be plotted (Fig. 3.20(c)), the side DEA being added by further observations or by symmetry.

3.14. The Grassot-type Fluxmeter

Though this instrument is called a fluxmeter, it, in fact, measures change of flux linkages—i.e. weber-turns (Wb-T). It is a moving-coil, permanent-magnet instrument with practically no control spring effect or air damping, i.e. there is usually an ordinary pivoted coil (on an insulated former) in a uniform radial magnetic field but no control springs, the current being led to the coil by soft annealed silver spirals, exerting a minimum torque. When operating, the instrument must be accurately levelled so that there is as far as possible no resultant gravitational force acting on the movement.

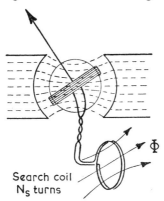

FIG. 3.21. GRASSOT FLUXMETER

When the flux Φ (Fig. 3.21) linking the search coil changes, an e.m.f., e, is induced in the search coil where

$$e = N_s \frac{d\Phi}{dt}$$

This e.m.f. will drive a current through the instrument coil so that the instrument coil deflects. When the instrument coil moves an opposing e.m.f. will be set up due to the coil moving in the instrument's magnetic field.

Then

e.m.f. developed in search coil

= volt drop in resistance + back e.m.f. in instrument coil

i.e.

$$N_s \frac{d\Phi}{dt} = iR + N_c Bbl \frac{d\theta}{dt}$$

where $R\ \Omega$ is the total resistance of the search and instrument coils.
B Wb/m² is the flux density in the instrument gap
  l m is the coil length in the gap
  b m is the coil breadth
  $\dfrac{d\theta}{dt}$ is the coil's angular velocity at a given instant

and N_c is the number of turns on the instrument coil.

9—(T.824)

If R is made small the equation becomes

$$N_s \frac{d\Phi}{dt} = N_c B.bl \frac{d\theta}{dt}$$

This type of fluxmeter is used to measure the change in flux linkages with its search coil, e.g. the changes with magnetizing current of the flux in a toroidal specimen (see § 2.14 and § 2.23).

Suppose Φ_1 Wb is the initial flux linking the search coil and Φ_2 Wb is the final flux linking the coil, and that the flux change ($\Phi_2 - \Phi_1$) Wb takes place in Δt sec. Before the change of flux there will be no current in the search or instrument coils ($i = 0$) and the instrument pointer will have some random deflexion θ_1, say. (The instrument pointer may not be at zero deflexion since there is no hair spring controlling torque to return it to zero). After the flux change there will again be no current in the search and instrument coils and the instrument pointer will have some new position θ_2, say.

The above equation may then be approximately written as

$$N_s \frac{(\Phi_2 - \Phi_1)}{\Delta t} = N_c Blb \frac{(\theta_2 - \theta_1)}{\Delta t}$$

or

$$N_s(\Phi_2 - \Phi_1) = K(\theta_2 - \theta_1)$$

where K is a constant of the instrument. Thus the instrument may be calibrated so that the change in flux linkages with the search coil is directly indicated by the change of pointer position on the scale.

Theoretically it may be proved that neither the coil resistance nor the time taken for the change of flux affect the operation of the instrument but this is based on the assumption of zero damping within the instrument. Zero damping is impossible to achieve, so that inaccurate readings are obtained if the search coil resistance is not kept low and if the change of flux is not produced smartly by the sudden operation of a switch or the swift manual movement of the search coil through the magnetic field.

EXAMPLES 3

1. A moving coil instrument has a resistance of 10 Ω and gives a full scale deflexion when carrying 50 mA. Show how the instrument can be adapted to measure voltages up to 750 V and currents up to 100 A.   (*O.N.C.*)

Ans. 14,990 Ω in series; 0·005003 Ω in parallel.

2. A moving coil instrument has a resistance of 5 Ω and gives full scale deflexion for 100 mV. Show how the instrument may be used to measure (a) voltages up to 50 V and (b) currents up to 10 A.   (*O.N.C.*)

Ans. 2,495 Ω in series; 0·01002 Ω in parallel.

3. A permanent-magnet moving-coil instrument has an air gap flux density of 0·08 Wb/m². There are 60 turns of wire on the moving coil which has an effective length in the gap of 4 cm, a width of 2·5 cm and negligible resistance. The control springs exert a torque of 0·00004905 Nw-m at full scale deflexion. Find the resistance to be connected in series wih the coil to enable the instrument to be used as a voltmeter reading up to 500 V.   (*O.N.C*)

Ans. 49,000 Ω.

4. A moving-coil instrument, giving full-scale deflexion with a current of 15 mA, is fitted with a remote shunt to give full-scale deflexion at 15 A. The coil of the instrument and the shunt leads are of copper having a total resistance of 1·2 Ω at 15°C with a resistance-temperature coefficient of 0·004/°C at 0°C.

A manganin temperature-compensating resistance of negligible resistance temperature coefficient and resistance 3·8 Ω is connected in series with the coil. If the shunt is 10 cm long and is cut from manganin sheet 1 mm thick, having a specific resistance of 42 μΩ-cm, find the breadth of the shunt to give correct indication at 15°C.

Find also the percentage error of the combination at 25°C.   (*O.N.C.*)

Ans. 0·84 cm, 0·9 per cent.

5. Explain the use of a "long solenoid" for checking the calibration of a fluxmeter.

The primary winding of a long solenoid has 10 turns per cm. A secondary winding of 500 turns, which has an effective area of 5 cm², is placed at its centre and connected to a fluxmeter. When a current of 3·82 A is reversed in the primary winding a deflexion of 20 is obtained on the fluxmeter.

Calculate the fluxmeter constant.   (*L.U.*, 1949)

Ans. 1·2 × 10⁻⁴ Wb-T/division.

6. Sketch and explain the shape of a typical *B-H* curve for an iron specimen.

An iron ring of mean diameter 16 cm and cross-section 5 cm² is uniformly wound with a primary winding of 600 turns carrying a current of 1·5 A. A secondary winding of 500 turns is connected to a ballistic galvanometer. If the galvanometer indicates the passage of 3,000 μC when the current in the primary winding is reversed, calculate the permeability of the iron. The combined secondary circuit resistance is 250 Ω.   (*O.N.C.*)

Ans. 667.

CHAPTER 4

Capacitance and Electrostatics

THE FUNDAMENTAL electrical unit is the ampere (A); from this unit of current the unit of charge may be defined. Unit charge is *one coulomb* (C) and is the charge passing across a conductor cross-section in one second when the conductor current is one ampere.

Current is reckoned as a flow of positive charge; thus if current can be arranged to flow into a body for a finite time then that body is said to "accumulate an excess positive charge" and so to become "positively charged". On the other hand if current can be made to flow out of a body for a finite time then that body must "attain a deficiency in positive charges" leaving an "excess of negative charges" and becoming "negatively charged". In the normal, or uncharged, state, a body contains equal positive and negative charges.

Experimentally it is found that a force exists between two charged bodies and that the direction of the force accords with the simple rule: like charges repel, unlike charges attract.

4.1. Capacitance

Consider the circuit shown in Fig. 4.1. When K is closed the ballistic galvanometer deflects, showing that a charge has passed through it; there is no permanent deflexion showing that there is

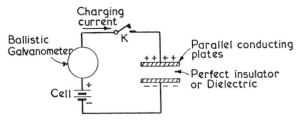

FIG. 4.1. MEASUREMENT OF THE CHARGE ON A CAPACITOR

no permanent current through the galvanometer. The e.m.f. of the cell will be seen to direct positive current (through the conducting circuit) from the lower towards the upper plate. However,

124

since the plates are separated by an insulator (called the dielectric) the circuit is incomplete, and any charges passing round the circuit must accumulate on the upper plate, giving an excess positive charge to this plate and leaving an equal excess negative charge on the lower plate. The current (i.e. charge movement) cannot continue indefinitely, as both the accumulated positive charge on the upper plate and the negative charge on the lower plate will set up electrostatic forces repelling further charge movements round the circuit. Thus any charge, after the first, which arrives at the positive plate must do so against the repelling effect of all previously accumulated charges. In other words, a potential difference arises across the plates. The magnitude of the potential difference at any instant will depend on the accumulated charge at the instant, and may be stated as the work done in moving a unit charge from one plate to the other.

The e.m.f. of the cell must then act against the potential of the accumulated charges; so long as the former exceeds the latter, charge continues to move round the circuit, but the longer the movement continues the greater becomes the repellant force until no further charge movement takes place. Except when the circuit resistance is high, the period between switch closure and zero charge movement is extremely short. When there is no further charge motion there will be no current or resistance volt drops in the circuit. Then, by Kirchhoff's second law, the p.d. across the plates must equal that across the terminals of the cell. The plates are charged to the potential V volts where, in this case, V volts is the cell potential.

Let Q coulombs be the total charge which has moved round the circuit from the instant of closure of K to an instant after the current has ceased. Associated with the transference of the charge of Q coulombs from one plate to the other plate a potential of V volts arises across the plates.

If the plate separation of Fig. 4.1. is not altered but the cell potential is varied the corresponding galvanometer deflexions will be observed to be proportional to the potential applied, i.e. the total accumulated charge will be proportional to the potential.

Therefore $\qquad\qquad V \propto Q$

or $\qquad\qquad\qquad Q = CV \qquad\qquad \ldots \quad (4.1)$

The constant C is called the *capacitance* of the parallel plate arrangement; it is found to depend on the geometry of the plates, their separation and also on the materials between, and surrounding, the plates. The arrangement, which need not be of parallel plate form, is called a *capacitor* or, an older term, a *condenser*.

The *capacitance* of a capacitor may be defined as the property of a capacitor by which it accumulates charge when a potential is applied.

Unit capacitance is that capacitance in which one coulomb is accumulated when a potential of one volt is applied.

Unit capacitance is called *one farad* (F).

where   1 farad = 1 coulomb/volt

One farad is actually an enormous capacitance. The usual units are microfarads (μF) or even micro-microfarads ($\mu\mu$F) which are often called pico-farads (pF).

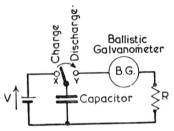

Fig. 4.2. Discharge of a Capacitor through a Resistor

After a capacitor has been charged, to a potential V say, it may be discharged through a resistor R, or other circuit, by an arrangement such as that illustrated in Fig. 4.2. The excess positive charge accumulated on the upper plate will move round the circuit to neutralize the excess negative charge on the lower plate. The ballistic galvanometer will indicate the quantity discharged.

It must not be thought that a capacitor will retain a charged state indefinitely. Since no insulator is perfect there will always be a "leakage" path from one plate to the other. However, good capacitors may retain their charge for a considerable period.

4.2. Capacitance Charging Current

If Δq is the small charge which accumulates on a capacitor plate in the small time interval Δt, then,

$$\text{rate of arrival of charge} = \frac{\Delta q}{\Delta t} \quad \text{C/sec}$$

$$= \text{average current during interval } \Delta t$$

Thus, when $\Delta t \to 0$ the current at an instant is given by

$$i = \frac{dq}{dt} \qquad \qquad . \quad . \quad . \quad . \quad (4.2a)$$

$$= \frac{d}{dt}(Cv) \qquad \text{from equation (4.1)}$$

where C is the capacitance of the arrangement being charged and v is the instantaneous potential between its plates. C is a constant independent of time,

therefore $\qquad \qquad i = C\frac{dv}{dt} \ \text{A} \qquad \qquad . \quad . \quad . \quad . \quad (4.2b)$

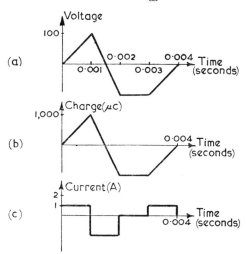

FIG. 4.3. PERTAINING TO EXAMPLE 4.1

Example 4.1

A capacitor of 10 μF is connected across a supply whose voltage rises linearly from 0 to 100 V in 0·001 sec, then falls linearly to -100 V in 0·001 sec, remains at this value for a further 0·001 sec and returns to zero linearly in a final period of 0·001 sec. Plot curves of the capacitor charge and charging current throughout the voltage cycle.

Fig. 4.3(a) shows the supply voltage cycle; since there is assumed to be no resistance in the circuit the capacitor will, at all instants, be charged to the supply potential at that instant. Therefore the supply potential, Fig. 4.3(a), is also the capacitor potential, v, at each instant throughout the cycle.

By equation (4.1)

$$q = Cv$$

where q is the instantaneous capacitor charge

Therefore $\qquad q = 10 \times 10^{-6} \times v$ coulombs $= 10v$ μ-coulombs

Hence Fig. 4.3(*b*), showing the capacitor charge, has the same shape as the potential curve of Fig. 4.3(*a*).

By equations (4.2(*a*)) and (4.2(*b*))

Charging current, $i = \dfrac{\mathrm{d}q}{\mathrm{d}t} = C\,\dfrac{\mathrm{d}v}{\mathrm{d}t}$

Therefore

charging current during first stage $= 10 \times 10^{-6} \times \dfrac{100}{0 \cdot 001} = 1\ \mathrm{A}$

charging current during second stage $= 10 \times 10^{-6} \times \left\{\dfrac{-100 - 100}{0 \cdot 001}\right\}$
$$= -2\ \mathrm{A}$$

charging current during third stage $= 10 \times 10^{-6} \times \dfrac{0}{0 \cdot 001} = 0\ \mathrm{A}$

charging current during fourth stage $= 10 \times 10^{-6} \times \left\{\dfrac{0 - (-100)}{0 \cdot 001}\right\} = 1\ \mathrm{A}$

The charging current, or capacitor current, waveform is shown in Fig. 4.3(*c*).

Example 4.2

(*a*) What is the initial current drawn by an uncharged capacitor of any size from a supply of 100 V when the connecting leads have a resistance of $0 \cdot 01\ \Omega$?

(*b*) What is the initial discharge current when a capacitor of any size charged to a potential of 100 V is discharged through a resistance of $0 \cdot 01\ \Omega$?

(*a*) Since the capacitor is initially uncharged it will not limit the initial current.

Therefore initial current $= \dfrac{V}{R} = \dfrac{100}{0 \cdot 01} = \underline{\underline{10{,}000\ \mathrm{A}}}$

(*b*) Initially the full capacitor potential will be applied to the resistance.

Therefore initial current $= \dfrac{V}{R} = \dfrac{100}{0 \cdot 01} = \underline{\underline{10{,}000\ \mathrm{A}}}$

In the above instances the current will rapidly fall towards zero as the capacitor becomes fully charged or fully discharged.

4.3. Energy Storage in a Capacitor

Consider a capacitor, C, during the interval when it is being charged from a source of potential, V.

$$\text{Final charge} = Q = CV \text{ coulombs}$$

At an intermediate interval let the accumulated charge be q.

Hence the instantaneous potential difference $= v = \dfrac{1}{C} \cdot q$

Suppose a small charge Δq coulombs moves round the circuit at this instant, then

work done on the elemental charge, Δq,
in its movement against the potential $\left.\right\} = \Delta q \times v$
of the previously accumulated charge

$$= \frac{1}{C} \cdot q \Delta q \quad \text{J}$$

This work will appear as energy stored in the capacitor. Therefore

energy stored during movement of Δq coulombs $= \frac{1}{C} \cdot q \cdot \Delta q$

Therefore

energy stored for full charging to potential $V = \sum_{q=0}^{q=Q} \frac{1}{C} \cdot q \cdot \Delta q$

$$= \int_0^Q \frac{1}{C} \cdot q \cdot \mathrm{d}q$$

$$= \frac{1}{2} \frac{Q^2}{C} \quad \text{J} \qquad . \qquad . \qquad . \qquad . \qquad (4.3a)$$

$$= \tfrac{1}{2} Q V \quad \text{J} \qquad . \qquad . \qquad . \qquad . \qquad (4.3b)$$

$$= \tfrac{1}{2} C V^2 \quad \text{J} \qquad . \qquad . \qquad . \qquad . \qquad (4.3c)$$

The circuit of Fig. 4.2 demonstrates that energy must be stored in a charged capacitor, for when the discharge current passes through the resistor R it will give rise to thermal energy in the resistor R. This energy must have been stored in the capacitor, C, during the interval when the switch was moved from contact X to contact Y.

Example 4.3

In the circuit of Fig. 4.2 suppose that the supply voltage is 100 volts and that the capacitor has a capacitance of $0.5 \ \mu\text{F}$. Calculate (*a*) the average current through the galvanometer, and (*b*) the average power dissipation in R_1 when the switch makes 100 operations per sec, and when, during each operation, the switch remains sufficiently long at X and at Y to completely charge and to completely discharge the capacitor.

(*a*) Total charge accumulated when at $X = Q = CV = 0.5 \times 10^{-6} \times 100$
$$= 5 \times 10^{-5} \ \text{C}$$

This quantity is passed through the galvanometer at each operation assuming no leakage within the capacitor.

Hence, quantity passed through galvanometer per 100 operations (i.e. per second)
$$= 5 \times 10^{-5} \times 100 = 5 \times 10^{-3} \ \text{C}$$

i.e. average current through galvanometer $= \underline{\underline{5 \ \text{mA}}}$

(b) Total energy stored when at $X = \frac{1}{2} CV^2$

$$= \frac{1}{2} \times 0.5 \times 10^{-6} \times 10^4$$

$$= 0.25 \times 10^{-2} \text{ J}$$

This energy is dissipated in R each complete operation.

Therefore energy dissipated in R per 100 operations $= 0.25 \times 10^{-2} \times 100 \text{ J} = 0.25 \text{ J}$

Therefore average energy dissipation in $R = 0.25$ J/sec

$$= \underline{0.25 \text{ W}}$$

When a capacitor is discharged it does not give up all the energy which it received during the corresponding charge period.

Apart from unavoidable leakage between the plates there are several other energy losses the most important of which is termed "dielectric loss". This loss has some resemblance to hysteresis loss in iron, as both give rise to heating when cyclical variations of charging or magnetization occur. In good quality capacitors, e.g. those with the plates separated by an air, mica, or impregnated paper dielectric, the dielectric loss is extremely small and may usually be neglected.

Example 4.4

A mica capacitor, of capacitance $0.4 \, \mu\text{F}$, is connected across a supply whose voltage varies linearly as shown in Fig. 4.4(a). Draw the corresponding waveforms of capacitor current and stored energy. What is the average energy drawn from the supply, assuming the mica capacitor to be lossless?

(Since the capacitor is lossless, it stands to reason that it cannot on average draw energy from an alternating supply. However, this result is still worthy of detailed deduction.)

At any instant the current $= \dfrac{\mathrm{d}q}{\mathrm{d}t} = C \dfrac{\mathrm{d}v}{\mathrm{d}t}$ A   .   .   . (4.2)

During the half cycles when the voltage is increasing,

$$\frac{\mathrm{d}v}{\mathrm{d}t} = \frac{100}{0.01} = 10^4 \text{ V/sec}$$

Therefore current during these half cycles $= 0.4 \times 10^{-6} \times 10^4 = 0.004$ A

Similarly current during other half cycles $= -0.004$ A

The current waveform is given in Fig. 4.4(b).

At any instant the energy stored $= \frac{1}{2}Cv^2$.   .   .   .   . (4.3)

Thus maximum energy stored $= \frac{1}{2} \times 0.4 \times 10^{-6} \times 10^4 = \underline{\underline{2 \times 10^{-3} \text{ J}}}$

It is immaterial from the point of view of stored energy whether the voltage is positive or negative.

The energy waveform is shown in Fig. 4.4(c). When the stored energy is decreasing then energy must be returned to the supply, since the mica capacitor is to be regarded as lossless, and there are no resistances in which the energy might be dissipated.

Thus the average energy drawn from the supply must be zero.

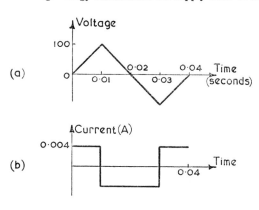

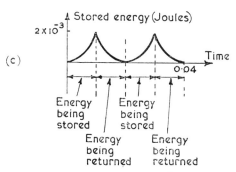

FIG. 4.4. WAVEFORMS FOR EXAMPLE 4.4

4.4. Capacitors in Parallel

Closure of K in Fig. 4.5 will result in both C_1 and C_2 being charged to a potential V volts.

Let Q be the total charge moving round the circuit. Effective

combined capacitance $= C = \dfrac{Q}{V}$ F

Let $\qquad Q_1 = C_1 V$ be the charge accumulated on C_1

and $\qquad Q_2 = C_2 V$ be the charge accumulated on C_2

Now $Q = Q_1 + Q_2$ by Kirchhoff's first law

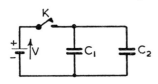

Therefore $CV = C_1 V + C_2 V$

and $C = C_1 + C_2$

For n capacitors in parallel

FIG. 4.5. CONNEXION OF
CAPACITORS IN PARALLEL

$$C = C_1 + C_2 + C_3 \dots C_n \quad . \quad (4.4)$$

Example 4.5

If capacitors, C_1 and C_2 of 1 μF and 2 μF respectively are connected in parallel and, at a particular instant when the applied potential is increasing positively, together take a current of 4 A. Find the current taken by each, and the instantaneous rate of increase of potential across them.

Let i = instantaneous total current = 4 A

i_1 = instantaneous current taken by capacitor C_1

i_2 = instantaneous current taken by capacitor C_2

and v = instantaneous applied potential.

Then, $i = \text{(combined capacitance)} \times \dfrac{dv}{dt} = (C_1 + C_2)\dfrac{dv}{dt}$

and $i_1 = C_1 \dfrac{dv}{dt}$

Therefore $i_1 = i \times \dfrac{C_1}{C_1 + C_2} = 4 \times \dfrac{1}{1 + 2} = 1{\cdot}33$ A

similarly $i_2 = i \times \dfrac{C_2}{C_1 + C_2} = 4 \times \dfrac{2}{1 + 2} = 2{\cdot}67$ A

Instantaneous rate of $\Big\}$ $= \dfrac{dv}{dt} = \dfrac{i}{C_1 + C_2} = \dfrac{4}{(1 + 2) \times 10^{-6}} = \underline{\underline{1{\cdot}33 \,.\, 10^6 \text{ V/sec}}}$
increase of potential

Example 4.6

A 10-μF capacitor is charged to 100 V. It is then connected across a 5-μF capacitor which is initially uncharged. Determine (a) the original energy stored in the 10-μF capacitor (b) the voltage across the combination and (c) the total energy stored in the combination.

(a) original stored energy, (from equation (4.3))

$$= \tfrac{1}{2} \times 10 \times 10^{-6} \times 100^2 = \underline{\underline{0{\cdot}05 \text{ J}}}$$

(b) From equation (4.1), original charge on 10-μF capacitor

$$= Q = 10 \times 10^{-6} \times 100 = 0{\cdot}001 \text{ C}$$

This charge must be distributed between the two capacitors after they have been connected together.

From equation (4.4) total capacitance after connexion

$$= 10 \times 10^{-6} + 5 \times 10^{-6} = 15 \times 10^{-6} \text{ F}$$

Therefore voltage across capacitors $= \dfrac{Q}{C} = \dfrac{0{\cdot}001}{15 \times 10^{-6}} = \underline{\underline{66{\cdot}7 \text{ V}}}$

(c) From equation (4.3c), the total energy stored after connexion is,

$$\text{energy} = \tfrac{1}{2}CV^2 = \tfrac{1}{2} \times 15 \times 10^{-6} \times 66 \cdot 7^2 = \underline{\underline{0 \cdot 0333 \ \text{J}}}$$

The difference between this figure and the original stored energy must represent the energy which is dissipated by the currents flowing when the switch makes contact.

The energy may be dissipated in the resistances of the conductors or in the switch contact resistance. In certain cases the excess energy may be radiated from the circuit as an electromagnetic wave.

4.5. Electrostatically Induced Charges

An uncharged conductor consists of equal numbers of positive and negative charges which neutralize one another. If a charged body is brought towards one end of a conductor then some of the unlike charges in the conductor will be attracted towards that end, while an equal number of the like charges will be repelled towards the other end (Fig. 4.6).

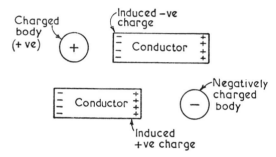

FIG. 4.6. INDUCED CHARGES

The number of charges which move is, in fact, only a very small fraction of the total number of charges in the conductor since with the accumulation of the first negative charges at one end (and corresponding positive charges at the other), the force per unit charge tending to cause movement within the conductor will be decreased.

Consider a conductor introduced between the parallel plates of a charged capacitor and assume that the area of the conductor is at least equal to the area of the parallel plates (see Fig. 4.7(a)). Positive charges within the conductor will be attracted towards the negatively charged plate and negative charges within the conductor will be attracted towards the positively charged plate. The charge movement will continue until the force per unit charge within the conductor is zero, i.e. in this arrangement, until the induced charge on each surface of the conductor is equal to the charge on the corresponding plate, in other words until there are equal (and therefore neutralizing) positive and negative charges both above and below any point within the conductor.

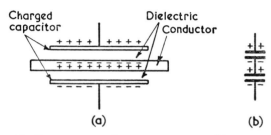

FIG. 4.7. EFFECT OF A CONDUCTOR IN THE DIELECTRIC OF A CAPACITOR

Now the conductor could equally well be in two parts, joined by a conducting wire, and the same induced charges would arise. This is shown in Fig. 4.7(b) from which it will be realized that the condition is that of two capacitors connected in series. Therefore when two or more capacitors are connected in series and charged, then the same charge must accumulate on corresponding plates of each capacitor, i.e. $+Q$ on all upper plates and $-Q$ on all lower plates.

4.6. Capacitors in Series

In Fig. 4.8 when key K is closed the combined capacitor will charge to a potential V volts. Assume that the charge which correspondingly moves round the circuit is Q coulombs.

Effective combined capacitance $= C = \dfrac{Q}{V}$ farads.

All capacitors in series connexion carry the same charge Q coulombs, as explained in the previous section.

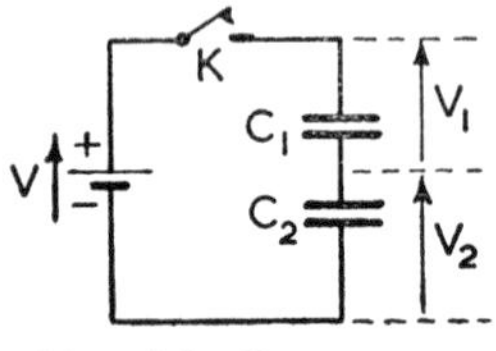

Therefore

$$V_1 = \frac{1}{C_1} \cdot Q \quad . \qquad . \qquad . \qquad . \quad (4.1)$$

and

$$V_2 = \frac{1}{C_2} \cdot Q \quad . \qquad . \qquad . \qquad . \quad (4.1)$$

FIG. 4.8. CAPACITORS IN SERIES

Now
$$V = V_1 + V_2, \text{ by Kirchhoff's second law}$$

$$\frac{Q}{C} = \frac{Q}{C_1} + \frac{Q}{C_2}$$

$$\frac{1}{C} = \frac{1}{C_1} + \frac{1}{C_2}$$

For n capacitances

$$\frac{1}{C} = \frac{1}{C_1} + \frac{1}{C_2} + \frac{1}{C_3} \cdots \frac{1}{C_n} \quad . \quad . \quad . \quad (4.5)$$

Example 4.7

If two perfect capacitors (no leakage) of 1 μF and 10 μF respectively are connected in series across a 100-V, d.c. supply, find the potential to which each will charge.

Combined capacitance = C

where
$$\frac{1}{C} = \frac{1}{C_1} + \frac{1}{C_2} \quad . \quad . \quad . \quad (4.5)$$

Therefore
$$C = \frac{C_1 C_2}{C_1 + C_2}$$

Charge accumulated = $Q = VC = \frac{VC_1 C_2}{C_1 + C_2}$

Therefore potential across 1-μF capacitor = $V_1 = \dfrac{Q}{C_1} = \dfrac{VC_2}{C_1 + C_2}$

$$= \frac{100 \times 10 \times 10^{-6}}{1 \times 10^{-6} + 10 \times 10^{-6}} = 90 \cdot 9 \text{ V}$$

and potential across 10-μF capacitor $V_2 = \dfrac{Q}{C_2} = \dfrac{VC_1}{C_1 + C_2}$

$$= \frac{100 \times 1 \times 10^{-6}}{1 \times 10^{-6} + 10 \times 10^{-6}} = \underline{\underline{9 \cdot 1 \text{ V}}}$$

4.7. Lines of Electrostatic Force

A visual image of an electrostatic field can be obtained by considering the forces which would act on an imaginary unit positive charge as it is moved about in the field. The motion, if free, will always be in the general direction from a positively charged plate to a negatively charged plate. Though singly charged particles may be obtained, direct experimental verification of the force directions is extremely difficult and indirect methods are used.

If a unit positive charge is released from the positive plate, and is allowed to move towards the negative plate under the influence of the electrostatic field and unhindered by mechanical resistance or inertia effects, the charge will always move in the direction of the electrostatic force at each point, and the trace of the path is called *a line of force.* It is assumed that the presence of the unit charge does not affect the field distribution; (actually, since 1 coulomb is a very large charge, there would be considerable disturbance of the field). In charged parallel plate, concentric conductor and single sphere cases the electrostatic lines of force are found to be as illustrated in Fig. 4.9.

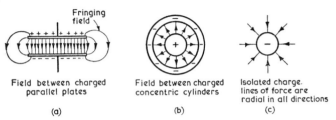

Field between charged
parallel plates

(a)

Field between charged
concentric cylinders

(b)

Isolated charge.
lines of force are
radial in all directions

(c)

Fig. 4.9. Simple Electrostatic Field Patterns

A unit charge at any point in an electrostatic field will experience a force in the direction of the "line of force" through the point.

The symbol $\mathscr{E}$ (newtons per unit charge) is taken to represent the force magnitude at the point considered. This is called the *electrostatic field strength* at the point. It is also termed the *electric stress* at the point.

4.8. Relationship between Electrostatic Field Strength and Potential

When the capacitor of Fig. 4.1. was charged to a potential of V volts it was implied that the work done in moving a unit charge through the circuit from one terminal to the other was V joules. No matter which path the charge takes in moving from one plate to the other the work done against or by the electrostatic forces is still V joules per unit charge transferred. The unit charge may be moved directly across the intervening material between the plates and the work done (neglecting mechanical resistances) is V joules per unit charge.

If $\mathscr{E}$ newtons per unit charge is the electrostatic field strength at a point, and the charge is moved a distance Δl metre from the point, then, work done per unit charge in movement $= -\mathscr{E}\,\Delta l \cos\theta$ joules per unit charge where θ is the angle between the field direction and the direction of Δl at the point (Fig. 4.10). A negative sign must be included with the above equation since if the charge movement occurs from the negative plate towards the positive plate then the potential will increase positively, but the movement is against the electrostatic field strength at each point and hence $\mathscr{E}$ has a negative direction with respect to the movement.

If the unit charge is moved along a line of force, then $\theta = 0$ and $\cos \theta = 1$ (Fig. 4.11).

Therefore   work done in movement $= -\Delta l \cdot \mathscr{E}$ J

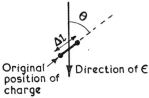

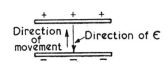

FIG. 4.10. ILLUSTRATING WORK DONE IN MOVING A CHARGE IN AN ELECTROSTATIC FIELD

FIG. 4.11. WORK DONE IN MOVING A UNIT CHARGE ALONG A LINE OF FORCE

Since it is most common to consider charge movements parallel to the lines of force, this will be assumed to be the case unless otherwise stated.

Let ΔV be the increase in potential corresponding to the charge movement Δl

then
$$\Delta V = -\Delta l \times \mathscr{E}$$

$$\frac{\Delta V}{\Delta l} = -\mathscr{E}$$

as
$$\Delta l \to 0, \qquad \frac{\Delta V}{\Delta l} \to \frac{dV}{dl}$$

Therefore
$$\frac{dV}{dl} = -\mathscr{E} \qquad\qquad . \quad . \quad (4.6)$$

i.e. the electrostatic field strength or electric stress, measured in the "$-l$" direction at a point, is the rate of change of potential measured in the "$+l$" direction at the point.

The electric stress, $\mathscr{E}$, is fundamentally given in "newtons per unit charge" units, but by equation (4.6) the units of $\mathscr{E}$ may also be "volts per metre" (V/m). The latter (or its derivative "volts per centimetre" (V/cm)) is more generally used.

It may be seen that

1 volt per metre $=$ (1 joule per unit charge) per metre

                $=$ (1 newton-metre per unit charge) per metre

                $=$ 1 newton per unit charge.

Note that the electric stress, $\mathscr{E}$, at any point is a vector whose direction is the direction of the force on a unit charge at the point. This is also the direction of the greatest rate of change of voltage. The voltage or potential at the point is not itself a vector.

4.9. Electric Flux and Flux Density

When a capacitor is charged the plates will carry equal and opposite charges, and an electric field will exist between them. The electric field is considered to be filled with electric flux, (just as a magnetic field is filled with magnetic flux), and each unit of charge is assumed to give rise to one unit of electric flux. The symbol for electric flux is the Greek letter Ψ (psi). It is measured in coulombs (C). Thus if the charge on each plate of a capacitor is Q coulombs, the electric flux between the plates will be $\Psi = Q$ coulombs. The flux is assumed to have the same direction as the lines of force.

The electric flux density, D, is the flux passing through unit area at right angles to the direction of the field. In the uniform field of a parallel plate capacitor, with plate area A m², and total flux Ψ C, the electric flux density is

$$D = \frac{\Psi}{A} = \frac{Q}{A} \quad \text{C/m}^2 \quad . \qquad . \qquad . \qquad . \quad (4.7)$$

D is a vector and applies to a point in the field. Its direction is taken as the direction of the line of force at the point in the electric field which is considered.

4.10. Permittivity or Dielectric Constant

Considering the simple case of a parallel plate capacitor of large area and small spacing; the fringing field at the edge may be neglected in comparison with the large uniform field remote from the edges.

Let Q = the total charge (coulombs) on each plate.

Then the total electric flux between the plates = $\Psi = Q$ coulombs.

If A is the area of each plate (metre²), then, from equation (4.7),

electric flux density at any point between the plates = $D = \dfrac{Q}{A}$ C/m²

In this expression it is assumed that the field between the plates is uniform, since the effect of the ends is to be neglected.

Let V volts be the potential difference between the plates corresponding to the charged condition of Q coulombs on each plate. Since the field is to be considered uniform the electric stress, $\mathscr{E}$, at all points between the plates must be the same.

Therefore

$$\left.\begin{array}{l}\text{work done in moving a unit charge} \\ \text{from one plate to the other}\end{array}\right\} = \mathscr{E} \times t$$

$$= V \text{ volts}$$

$$\mathscr{E} = \frac{V}{t} \quad \text{V/m}$$

where t (metres) is the distance between the parallel plates, i.e. at all points between the plates there is

(a) an electric flux density $= D = \dfrac{Q}{A}$ C/m²

(b) an electric stress $\quad = \mathscr{E} = \dfrac{V}{t}$ V/m

Also

$$\text{the capacitance} = C = \frac{Q}{V} = \frac{DA}{\mathscr{E}t}$$

$$= \left(\frac{D}{\mathscr{E}}\right) \cdot \frac{A}{t} \quad \text{F}$$

Experimentally it may be verified that the capacitance of a parallel plate arrangement of constant area, A, and constant spacing, t, is independent of applied voltage, but is dependent on the material between the plates.

$\dfrac{D}{\mathscr{E}} = $ a constant, dependent on the material between the plates only.

$\quad = \varepsilon$ (pronounced epsilon)

where ε is termed the permittivity or dielectric constant of the material between the plates. Hence, for the parallel plate capacitor,

$$C = \frac{\varepsilon A}{t} \qquad . \qquad . \qquad . \qquad . \quad (4.8)$$

Also $\qquad\qquad\qquad D = \varepsilon\mathscr{E} \qquad . \qquad . \qquad . \qquad . \quad (4.9)$

ε is usually expressed by the equation

$$\varepsilon = \varepsilon_r \times \varepsilon_0 \qquad . \qquad . \qquad . \quad (4.10)$$

where

$\varepsilon_0 = $ the permittivity in vacuum

$$= \frac{1}{36\pi \times 10^9} \quad . \qquad . \qquad . \qquad . \qquad . \qquad . \quad (4.11)$$

and

$\varepsilon_r = $ the experimentally determined permittivity in the particular material relative to the permittivity in vacuum (relative permittivity).

Formerly the symbol κ (kappa) was also used for permittivity.

More advanced theory shows that the permittivity in vacuum is related to the permeability, μ_0, in vacuum, and the velocity of electromagnetic waves $(c_0 = 3 \times 10^8 \text{ m/sec})$, in vacuum, by the equation

$$\frac{1}{\mu_0\varepsilon_0} = c_0^2 \qquad . \qquad . \qquad . \qquad . \quad (4.12)$$

Hence ε_0 must have the value given by equation (4.11) when, as in the M.K.S. rationalized system, μ_0 has the value $4\pi \times 10^{-7}$ (see § 2.11).

Values of ε_r vary from unity for air to two to six for paper, five for porcelain, six for mica, and much higher values for other special materials. In general there is no analogy with the very large values of μ_r obtained with ferro-magnetic materials in the case of magnetic fields.

From equation (4.8),

$$\varepsilon = \frac{Ct}{A} \text{ farad metres per metre}^2$$

so that the units for ε must be farad per metre.

The force F newtons between two charges Q_1 and Q_2 coulombs separated by a distance d metres in a medium of relative permitivity ε_r is

$$F = \frac{Q_1 Q_2}{4\pi\varepsilon_0\varepsilon_r d^2} \text{ Nw}$$

The field strength at a point d metres from a charge Q is the force exerted on a unit charge placed at that particular point in the field and is therefore given by

$$\mathscr{E} = \frac{4\pi\varepsilon_0\varepsilon_r d^2}{Q} \text{ newtons per unit charge}$$

In cases where the field under consideration is non-uniform, this method of determining the field may be used.

Example 4.8

Calculate the capacitance of the capacitor formed when two parallel plates of 1 m² area are placed 1 mm apart in air. Find the total charge on each plate when the electric stress in the air is 1,000 V/cm.

Capacitance $= \dfrac{\varepsilon A}{t} = \dfrac{10^6}{36\pi \times 10^9 \times 10^{-3}} = \underline{0\cdot00884 \ \mu\text{F}}$

Electric flux density $= D = \varepsilon\mathscr{E} = \dfrac{1,000 \times 100 \times 10^6}{36\pi \times 10^9} = 0\cdot884 \ \mu\text{C/m}^2$

Therefore total electric flux $\Psi = DA = 0\cdot884 \times 1 = 0\cdot884 \ \mu\text{C}$

Alternatively, $\mathscr{E} = \dfrac{V}{t}$ for the parallel plate capacitor

Therefore applied voltage $= V = \mathscr{E}t = 1,000 \times 10^{-1} = 100 \text{ V}$

Therefore charge on each plate $= Q = CV = 0\cdot00884 \times 10^{-6} \times 100 \times 10^6$

$$= \underline{0\cdot884 \ \mu\text{C}}$$

Example 4.9

A parallel plate capacitor has plates of area 20,000 cm² spaced by three layers of different dielectric materials. The relative permittivities are 2, 4, 6 and the the thicknesses are 0·5, 1·5, and 0·3 mm respectively. Calculate the combined capacitance and the electric stress in each material, when the applied voltage is 1,000 V. It may be assumed that the plate area is sufficiently great compared with the plate separation to ignore end effects.

Let $\mathscr{E}_1$, $\mathscr{E}_2$, $\mathscr{E}_3$ V/m be the electric stress in each dielectric material respectively, where the thicknesses of these materials are t_1, t_2, t_3, metres (Fig. 4.12).

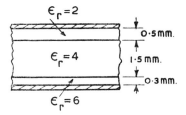

FIG. 4.12. SECTION OF COMPOSITE DIELECTRIC CAPACITOR
OF EXAMPLE 4.9

Since the capacitor is of the parallel plate form the electric stress will be everywhere directed from one plate straight across to the other.

Therefore total voltage across plates $= V = \mathscr{E}_1 t_1 + \mathscr{E}_2 t_2 + \mathscr{E}_3 t_3$.

Let Q be total charge on each plate, then Q coulomb is also the total electric flux through each material.

Therefore electric flux density in each material $= D = \dfrac{Q}{A}$ C/m²

where A is the area of each plate (m²)

Let $\varepsilon_1, \varepsilon_2, \varepsilon_3$ be the permittivities of the materials, i.e.

$$\varepsilon_1 = \varepsilon_{r1}\varepsilon_0; \quad \varepsilon_2 = \varepsilon_{r2}\varepsilon_0; \quad \varepsilon_3 = \varepsilon_{r3}\varepsilon_0.$$

$$V = \mathscr{E}_1 t_1 + \mathscr{E}_2 t_2 + \mathscr{E}_3 t_3$$

$$= \frac{D}{\varepsilon_1} t_1 + \frac{D}{\varepsilon_2} t_2 + \frac{D}{\varepsilon_3} t_3$$

$$= \frac{Q}{A\varepsilon_0} \left\{ \frac{t_1}{\varepsilon_{r1}} + \frac{t_2}{\varepsilon_{r2}} + \frac{t_3}{\varepsilon_{r3}} \right\}$$

Therefore capacitance $= C = \dfrac{Q}{V}$

$$= \frac{Q}{\dfrac{Q}{A\varepsilon_0} \left\{ \dfrac{t_1}{\varepsilon_{r1}} + \dfrac{t_2}{\varepsilon_{r2}} + \dfrac{t_3}{\varepsilon_{r3}} \right\}}$$

$$= \frac{A\varepsilon_0}{\dfrac{t_1}{\varepsilon_{r1}} + \dfrac{t_2}{\varepsilon_{r2}} + \dfrac{t_3}{\varepsilon_{r3}}} \quad \text{F}$$

Therefore

$$C = \frac{1}{36\pi \times 10^9} \cdot \frac{2}{\dfrac{0\cdot5 \times 10^{-3}}{2} + \dfrac{1\cdot5 \times 10^{-3}}{4} + \dfrac{0\cdot3 \times 10^{-3}}{6}} \times 10^6 = \underline{\underline{0\cdot0262 \ \mu F}}$$

Plate charge $= VC = 1{,}000 \times 0\cdot0262 = 26\cdot2 \ \mu C$

$$\left. \begin{array}{l} \text{Electric flux density} \\ \text{at any point} \end{array} \right\} = D = \frac{Q}{A} = \frac{26\cdot2}{2} = 13\cdot1 \ \mu C/m^2$$

$$\left. \begin{array}{l} \text{Electric stress in} \\ \text{first dielectric} \end{array} \right\} = \mathscr{E}_1 = \frac{D}{\varepsilon_1} = \frac{13\cdot1 \times 10^{-6}}{(1/36\pi) \times 10^{-9} \times 2} \times 10^{-2} = \underline{\underline{7{,}400 \ V/cm}}$$

Similarly, stress in second dielectric $= \underline{\underline{3{,}700 \ V/cm}}$

and stress in third dielectric $= \underline{\underline{2{,}460 \ V/cm}}$

It will be seen that the stress is greatest in the material of least permittivity. This leads to an important precaution in the manufacture of capacitors and high voltage equipment, namely, air has a low permittivity ($\varepsilon_r = 1$), and since air at normal pressure has also a low breakdown voltage any small air pockets or voids which occur in a dielectric will tend to have a high electric stress in them and this may cause breakdown in the void. Often the breakdown does not cause the immediate breakdown of the whole unit, but the burning occurring in the void will enlarge the void and give complete breakdown after a short time.

4.11. Force between Charged Plates

Consider two parallel plates carrying constant charges of $+Q$ and $-Q$ coulombs respectively.

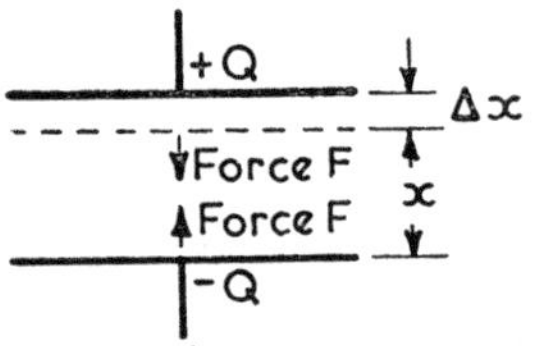

FIG. 4.13. FORCE BETWEEN CHARGED PARALLEL PLATES

Let the force between the plates be F newtons (Fig. 4.13). Suppose the plates are moved apart through a small distance Δx metre.

Mechanical work done in small movement $= F \Delta x$ newton-metre. Since the plate charge is constant, no electrical energy can move into the system during the period of the movement Δx.

Therefore

work done $=$ change in energy stored.

If C is the capacitance of the system before the movement, then

$$\text{initial stored energy} = \frac{1}{2} \cdot \frac{Q^2}{C} \ \text{J} \qquad . \qquad . \quad (4.3)$$

If the capacitance changes to $(C + \Delta C)$ with the movement Δx, then

$$\text{final energy stored} = \frac{1}{2} \cdot \frac{Q^2}{(C + \Delta C)}$$

$$= \frac{1}{2} \cdot \frac{Q^2}{C} \cdot \frac{1}{\left(1 + \dfrac{\Delta C}{C}\right)}$$

$$= \frac{1}{2} \cdot \frac{Q^2}{C} \cdot \left(1 - \frac{\Delta C}{C}\right) \text{ if } \Delta C \ll C$$

Therefore

$$\text{change of stored energy} = \frac{1}{2}\frac{Q^2}{C} - \frac{1}{2}\frac{Q^2}{C} \cdot \left(1 - \frac{\Delta C}{C}\right)$$

$$= \frac{1}{2}\frac{Q^2}{C} \cdot \frac{\Delta C}{C} \quad \text{J}$$

Therefore $\quad F\Delta x = \frac{1}{2}\frac{Q^2}{C^2} \cdot \Delta C \quad$ Nw-m

$$F = \frac{1}{2}\frac{Q^2}{C^2} \cdot \frac{\Delta C}{\Delta x} \quad \text{Nw}$$

as $\quad \Delta x \to 0, \quad \dfrac{\Delta C}{\Delta x} \to \dfrac{dC}{dx}$

Therefore $\qquad F = \frac{1}{2}\frac{Q^2}{C^2} \cdot \frac{dC}{dx}$

$$= \tfrac{1}{2}V^2 \cdot \frac{dC}{dx} \quad \text{Nw} \qquad . \qquad . \qquad . \qquad . \quad (4.13)$$

where V is the potential between the plates of the capacitor. In the case of the parallel plate capacitor of plate area A m², and plate separation x m

$$C = \frac{\varepsilon A}{x} \qquad . \qquad . \qquad . \qquad . \quad (4.8)$$

Therefore $\qquad \dfrac{dC}{dx} = -\dfrac{\varepsilon A}{x^2}$

Hence, for a parallel plate capacitor charged to a potential V volts,

$$\text{force between plates} = -\tfrac{1}{2}V^2 \frac{\varepsilon A}{x^2} \quad \text{Nw} \quad . \quad (4.14)$$

The negative sign indicates that the force is in the opposite direction to that in which x is measured, i.e. the force is one of attraction for a capacitor.

Equation (4.14) is the basic equation describing the operation of an electrostatic voltmeter. It should be noted that the force, and hence the deflexion, depends on the square of the applied voltage so that the indicated voltage will always be the true r.m.s. voltage.

Example 4.10

A parallel-plate air capacitor is charged to 100 V. Its plate separation is 2 mm and the effective area of each of its two plates is 120 cm².

Calculate, and account for, the increase or decrease of stored energy when the plate separation is reduced to 1 mm—

(*a*) at constant voltage

(*b*) at constant charge.   (*L.U. Part* 1, 1954)

Original capacitance $= C_1 = \dfrac{\varepsilon A}{x_1}$ from equation (4.8)

$$= \frac{1}{36\pi \times 10^9} \cdot \frac{120 \times 10^{-4}}{2 \times 10^{-3}}$$

$$= 53 \cdot 1 \times 10^{-12} \quad \text{F}$$

Final capacitance $= C_2 = \dfrac{\varepsilon A}{x_2}$

$$= 106 \cdot 2 \times 10^{-12} \quad \text{F (since separation is halved capaci-}$$
$$\text{tance is doubled)}$$

(*a*) constant voltage

Change of stored energy $= \frac{1}{2} C_2 V^2 - \frac{1}{2} C_1 V^2$

$$= \frac{1}{2} \cdot 100^2 \cdot (106 \cdot 2 - 53 \cdot 1) \cdot 10^{-12}$$

$$= \underline{\underline{26 \cdot 55 \times 10^{-8} \quad \text{J}}}$$

This is an increase, since energy must be supplied from an external electrical supply to increase the charge on the plates when the capacitance increases at constant voltage, and hence the stored energy ($\frac{1}{2} Q V$) must increase.

(*b*) constant charge

From equation (4.3) initial energy stored $= \frac{1}{2} \cdot \dfrac{Q^2}{C_1}$

Final energy stored $= \frac{1}{2} \dfrac{Q^2}{C_2}$

Change in stored energy $= \frac{1}{2} \cdot Q^2 \left\{ \dfrac{1}{53 \cdot 1} - \dfrac{1}{106 \cdot 2} \right\} \times 10^{12}$

$$= \frac{1}{2} (C_1 V_1)^2 \{0 \cdot 0188 - 0 \cdot 0094\} \times 10^{12}$$

$$= \frac{1}{2} \cdot 53 \cdot 1^2 \times 10^{-24} \times 10^4 \times 0 \cdot 0094 \times 10^{12}$$

$$= \underline{\underline{13 \cdot 3 \times 10^{-8} \quad \text{J}}}$$

This is a decrease, since if the charge remains constant when the capacitance increases, the voltage must fall, and hence the stored energy ($\frac{1}{2} Q V$) must fall. In this case the change in stored energy must be the mechanical work done on whatever arrangement resisted the attraction of the two plates, since, when the charge is constant no current will flow in the capacitor circuit, and no energy may be transferred to or from the capacitor by the electric circuit. In the constant voltage case the charge changes, and a current flows in the capacitor circuit, so that energy will be transferred to or from the electrical source. When the plates are brought closer at constant voltage there is both a mechanical work output and an increase in stored energy. Both of these energies must be drawn from the supply.

Analysing the constant voltage condition,

$$\text{force between plates} = \frac{1}{2} \cdot V^2 \frac{dC}{dx} \quad \text{Nw} \quad \dots \quad (4.13)$$

For a movement Δx metre,

$$\text{work done} = F \cdot \Delta x$$

$$= \frac{1}{2} V^2 \frac{dC}{dx} \cdot \Delta x \text{ Nw-m}$$

Change of stored energy = (rate of change of stored energy with x) $\times \Delta x$

$$= \frac{d}{dx} (\tfrac{1}{2} C V^2) \times \Delta x$$

$$= \tfrac{1}{2} V^2 \frac{dC}{dx} \times \Delta x \text{ Nw-m,}$$

since, in this case V is constant.

When the capacitance is C farad,

charge on capacitor plates $= CV$ coulomb

and change of charge with movement Δx

$$= \text{(rate of change of charge with } x) \times \Delta x$$

$$= \frac{d}{dx} (CV) \times \Delta x$$

$$= V \cdot \frac{dC}{dx} \cdot \Delta x$$

since this change of charge occurs at voltage V volts.

Energy transferred to capacitor $= V \times$ (change of charge)

$$= V^2 \cdot \frac{dC}{dx} \cdot \Delta x$$

i.e. as predicted.

Electrical energy input $= V^2 \dfrac{dC}{dx} \cdot \Delta x$

$$= \tfrac{1}{2} V^2 \frac{dC}{dx} \cdot \Delta x + \tfrac{1}{2} \cdot V^2 \frac{dC}{dx} \cdot \Delta x$$

= mechanical work + increase in stored energy

It is noteworthy that the increase in stored energy is equal to the mechanical work done.

EXAMPLES 4

1. Prove the formula for calculating the capacitance of a number of capacitors (a) in parallel, (b) in series. Calculate the number of sheets of tin foil and mica for a capacitor of $0 \cdot 33$-μF capacitance if the area of each sheet of tin foil is 82 cm^2, the mica sheets are $0 \cdot 2$ mm thick, and have a permittivity of 5. Find the energy stored in this capacitor when the p.d. between its terminals is 500 volts.

Ans. 182 sheets of mica; 183 sheets of tin foil; $0 \cdot 041$ J.

2. A parallel-plate capacitor, plate area 400 cm², plate separation 1 mm, relative permittivity 1, is joined in series with a second capacitor, plate area 100 cm², plate separation 0·5 mm, relative permittivity of dielectric 8. The dielectric stress in the first capacitor is 10^7 V/m. Calculate the total voltage across both capacitors.

Ans. 12,500 V.

3. A capacitor is composed of two plates separated by 3 mm of dielectric of permittivity 4. An additional piece of insulation 5 mm thick is now inserted between the plates. If the capacitor has now ½ of its original capacitance, find the relative permittivity of the additional dielectric.

Ans. 3·33.

4. Explain how the area and spacing of the plates of a parallel-plate capacitor for a specified capacitance and given maximum voltage are affected by the permissible electric stress and the permittivity of the dielectric.

A capacitor, formed by two parallel plates of large area, spaced 2 cm apart in air, is connected to a 10,000-V d.c. supply. Calculate the electric stress in the air when a flat sheet of glass of thickness 1·5 cm and permittivity 7 is introduced between the plates.   (*L.U.*, 1950)

Ans. 1·4 × 10⁶ V/m.

5. A flat plate capacitor has a plate area of 20 cm² and the plates are separated by three dielectric layers each 1 mm thick and of permittivity 2, 4, and 5, respectively relative to air.

Find the capacitance of the composite capacitor, and the electric stress in each dielectric if the applied voltage is 1,000 V.

Ans. 18·6 μμF; 5·26 × 10⁵ V/m; 2·63 × 10⁵ V/m; 2·11 × 10⁵ V/m.

6. Find an expression for the electrical energy stored in a capacitor of capacitance C farads charged to a p.d. of V volts.

A capacitor having a capacitance of 3 μF is charged to a p.d. of 200 V and then connected in parallel with another capacitor having a capacitance of 2 μF. Calculate the p.d. across the parallel capacitors and the energy stored in each capacitor before and after being connected in parallel. Account for the difference.   (*L.U.*, 1941)

Ans. 120 V; 6 × 10⁻² J; 0; 2·16 × 10⁻² J; 1·44 × 10⁻² J.

CHAPTER 5

Single-phase Alternating Current Circuits

ALTERNATING CURRENTS of various wave shapes have already been introduced in Chapter 1; these currents will now be considered in circuits containing inductance and capacitance. Attention will be confined to cases where the wave shape is in fact sinusoidal. To a first approximation this applies to a majority of a.c. circuits.

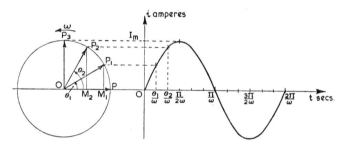

FIG. 5.1. VECTORIAL REPRESENTATION OF SINUSOIDAL ALTERNATING QUANTITIES

5.1. Vectorial Representation of Alternating Quantities

Consider a vector OP (Fig. 5.1), rotating with a constant angular velocity of ω rad/sec. Let OP_1, OP_2, OP_3, (making angles θ_1, θ_2 and $\pi/2$ radians with the horizontal), be different positions of OP with respect to the initial position. Then, from the figure,

$$\frac{P_1 M_1}{OP_1} = \frac{P_1 M_1}{OP} = \sin \theta_1$$

$$\frac{P_2 M_2}{OP_2} = \frac{P_2 M_2}{OP} = \sin \theta_2$$

$$\frac{OP_3}{OP} = \sin \frac{\pi}{2} = 1$$

where M_1 and M_2 are the projections of P_1 and P_2 on the horizontal.

147

If the heights P_1M_1, P_2M_2 etc., are plotted to a base of the angle of rotation (in radians) of the rotating vector OP, the resulting graph will be a sine wave. If the base in radians is divided by the angular velocity (ω rad/sec) the units of the base will be converted into seconds.

The angle, θ, swept out by the rotating vector OP, is given by

$$\theta = \omega t \text{ radians}$$

One cycle of the alternating quantity is equivalent to one complete revolution of OP (2π radians). The period, T, of the wave is the time occupied by one complete cycle, and the frequency, f, is the number of cycles occurring per second,

Therefore
$$T = \frac{2\pi}{\omega} \text{ sec} \qquad , \quad . \quad . \quad . \quad (5.1)$$

and
$$f = \frac{1}{T} = \frac{\omega}{2\pi} \text{ c/s} \qquad . \quad . \quad . \quad . \quad (5.2)$$

Thus a rotating vector OP may be made to represent a sinusoidal alternating quantity of maximum value I_m and frequency f c/s by making $OP = I_m$ (to a chosen scale) and $\omega = 2\pi f$ rad/sec. Thus, a sinusoidal alternating current may be written as

$$i = I_m \sin \theta \qquad . \qquad . \qquad . \qquad (5.3(\text{i}))$$

An alternative form is—

$$i = I_m \sin \omega t, \quad \text{since } \theta = \omega t \text{ .} \qquad . \qquad (5.3(\text{ii}))$$

Another alternative form is—

$$i = I_m \sin 2\pi f t, \quad \text{since } \omega = 2\pi f \text{ .} \qquad . \qquad (5.3(\text{iii}))$$

E.m.f.s, voltages, fluxes, etc., of sinusoidal waveform may also be represented by rotating vectors such as OP. Moreover, so long as their frequencies are the same, different voltages and currents may be represented on the same diagram to appropriate scales.

The expression $i = I_m \sin \omega t$ represents a sinusoidal current of maximum value I_m which passes through its zero value and is becoming positive at the instant given by $t = 0$. In general a current will have some other value at the instant $t = 0$. Suppose the value $t = 0$ is given by

$$i = I_m \sin \phi$$

then the complete expression for the current is

$$i = I_m \sin (\omega t + \phi) \qquad . \qquad . \qquad . \qquad (5.4)$$

where ϕ is called the phase angle of the current.

Fig. 5.2(*a*) shows the wave and vector diagrams for the three currents,

$$i_1 = I_{1m} \sin \left(\omega t + \frac{\pi}{4} \right)$$

$$i_2 = I_{2m} \sin \left(\omega t - \frac{\pi}{6} \right)$$

and $\qquad i_3 = I_{3m} \sin \omega t$

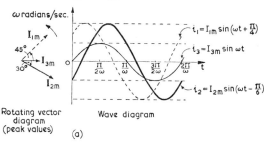

Rotating vector diagram (peak values)

Wave diagram

(a)

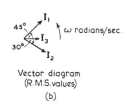

Vector diagram (R.M.S.values)

(b)

FIG. 5.2. REPRESENTATION OF SINUSOIDAL QUANTITIES HAVING THE SAME FREQUENCY

The vector diagram is drawn for the instant $t = 0$, and to the same scale as the wave diagram. It could equally well have been drawn to a scale which would have represented r.m.s. values, since there is a fixed relationship between the peak value of a sinusoidally varying quantity and the r.m.s. value (given by equation (1.13)). The vector diagram drawn to a scale of r.m.s. values is shown in Fig. 5.2(*b*), where $\mathbf{I}_1$ is the vector representing the r.m.s. value of i_1, i.e. of $I_{1m} \sin \left(\omega t + \frac{\pi}{4} \right)$. Note that the bold-face type is used to distinguish vector quantities from algebraic quantities. Thus I_1 is simply the size, or magnitude, of the vector $\mathbf{I}_1$.

The angle to the horizontal at which $\mathbf{I}_1$ is drawn in Fig. 5.2(*b*) represents the phase angle of the vector with respect to some zero of time. In the same way the vectors $\mathbf{I}_2$ and $\mathbf{I}_3$ represent the r.m.s. values and phase angles of i_2 and i_3 with respect to the same zero of time.

Since in this illustration the peak (and therefore the r.m.s.) values of i_1 and i_2 are equal, these are said to differ in phase only. This is also shown on the wave diagram of Fig. 5.2(a), where the peak values are shown of the same magnitude, but occurring at different instants of time. In the vector diagram I_1 is said to lead I_2 by the total angle of phase displacement between the two vectors, since the wave diagram shows that i_1 reaches its maximum value before i_2. Another way of expressing this is to say that I_2 lags I_1 by the total angle of phase displacement between them (in this case 75°). From Fig. 5.2(b) it is seen that I_3 differs both in magnitude and phase from both I_1 and I_2.

The fact that the three vectors I_1, I_2, and I_3 are drawn on the same vector diagram implies that the angular velocity of each of these vectors is the same, i.e. the vectors represent sinusoidally varying quantities of the same frequency. Alternating quantities of different frequencies cannot be represented on the same vector diagram.

The phase angles between the vectors on a vector diagram indicate the order in which the various quantities reach their maximum values, and enable the time intervals between these maxima to be determined.

The general expression for an alternating current is given by equation (5.4). A similar expression for the instantaneous value of an alternating voltage is,

$$v = V_m \sin (\omega t + \psi) \qquad . \qquad . \qquad . \qquad (5.5)$$

where V_m is the peak value of the voltage, and ψ (pronounced psi) is its phase angle with respect to zero time. The r.m.s. value of the voltage (V) may be represented on the same vector diagram as the currents, provided that the frequency is the same. This immediately gives a visual indication of the phase displacement between currents and voltages in any particular case.

Example 5.1

In a certain a.c. circuit supplied from 50-c/s mains the voltage has a maximum value of 250 V and the current has a maximum value of 5 A. At the instant chosen as $t = 0$ the voltage has an instantaneous value of 200 V and the current has an instantaneous value of 2 A. Develop trigonometrical expressions for the instantaneous values of the current and the voltage. Calculate the instantaneous values at the instant given by $t = 0.015$ sec and find the angle of phase difference between the current and voltage vectors (assume that the voltage and current waves are sinusoidal).

Frequency $= f = 50$ c/s

Angular velocity $= \omega = 2\pi f = 2\pi \times 50 = 314$ rad/sec

The voltage wave is of the form
$$v = 250 \sin (314t + \psi) \qquad \text{from equation (5.5)}$$
at $t = 0$, $v = 200$ V

Therefore $\qquad\qquad 200 = 250 \sin (\psi)$

and $\qquad\qquad\qquad \sin \psi = \dfrac{200}{250} = 0 \cdot 8$

Therefore $\qquad\qquad\qquad \psi = 53 \cdot 2°$

(considering only the smallest positive value of ψ)

Therefore $\qquad\qquad v = \underline{\underline{250 \sin (314t + 53 \cdot 2°)}}$

Similarly the current wave is of the form

$$i = 5 \sin (314t + \phi)$$

but at $t = 0,\ i = 2$ A

Therefore $\qquad\qquad\qquad 2 = 5 \sin \phi$

$$\sin \phi = \dfrac{2}{5} = 0 \cdot 4$$

therefore $\qquad\qquad\qquad \phi = 23 \cdot 6°$

therefore $\qquad i = \underline{\underline{5 \sin (314t + 23 \cdot 6°)}} \qquad$ from equation (5·4)

At $t = 0 \cdot 015$ sec, instantaneous voltage $= 250 \sin (314 \times 0 \cdot 015 + 53 \cdot 2°)$

$$= 250 \sin (4 \cdot 7 + 53 \cdot 2°)$$

Note that the number 4·7 is a number of radians, and that the 53·2° should correctly be expressed in radians. However it is more convenient to express the 4·7 radians as a number of degrees.

$$4 \cdot 7 \text{ rad} = 4 \cdot 7 \times \dfrac{180°}{\pi} = 270°$$

Therefore the instantaneous voltage $= 250 \sin (270° + 53 \cdot 2°) = \underline{\underline{-150 \text{ V}}}$

Similarly, instantaneous current $= 5 \sin (4 \cdot 7 + 23 \cdot 6°)$

$$= 5 \sin (270° + 23 \cdot 6°)$$

$$= \underline{\underline{-4 \cdot 58 \text{ A}}}$$

Angle of phase difference $= 53 \cdot 2° - 23 \cdot 6° = \underline{\underline{29 \cdot 6° \text{ lag}}}$

N.B. The angle is said to be lagging since, in this case, the current wave lags behind the voltage wave. The words "lag" or "lead" are applied to the current wave with respect to the voltage wave.

5.2. Kirchhoff's Laws applied to A.C. Circuits

Kirchhoff's first law states that at any instant the algebraic sum of the currents at any junction in an electrical network is zero. Referring to the junction of Fig. 5.3(a).

$$i_1 = i_2 + i_3$$

where i_1, i_2, i_3 are the instantaneous values of the currents in the three branches at a given instant and the above equation is a simple algebraic equation.

Let $\qquad i_2 = I_{2m} \sin (\omega t + \phi_2)$

and $\qquad i_3 = I_{3m} \sin (\omega t + \phi_3)$

i.e. two sinusoidal currents of the same frequency.

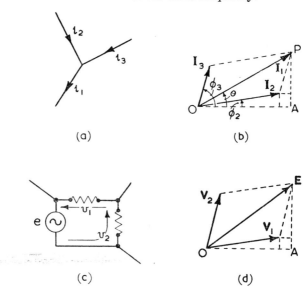

(a) \qquad\qquad (b)

(c) \qquad\qquad (d)

FIG. 5.3. KIRCHHOFF'S LAWS APPLIED TO AN A.C. CIRCUIT

$$i_1 = I_{2m} \sin (\omega t + \phi_2) + I_{3m} \sin (\omega t + \phi_3)$$

$$= I_{2m} \sin \omega t \cos \phi_2 + I_{2m} \cos \omega t \sin \phi_2$$
$$+ I_{3m} \sin \omega t \cos \phi_3 + I_{3m} \cos \omega t \sin \phi_3$$

$$= \{I_{2m} \cos \phi_2 + I_{3m} \cos \phi_3\} \sin wt + \{I_{2m} \sin \phi_2$$
$$+ I_{3m} \sin \phi_3\} \cos \omega t$$

$$= \sqrt{[\{I_{2m} \cos \phi_2 + I_{3m} \cos \phi_3\}^2 + \{I_{2m} \sin \phi_2}$$
$$+ I_{3m} \sin \phi_3\}^2] . \sin (\omega t + \theta) \qquad (5.6)$$

where $\qquad \theta = \tan^{-1} \left\{ \dfrac{I_{2m} \sin \phi_2 + I_{3m} \sin \phi_3}{I_{2m} \cos \phi_2 + I_{3m} \cos \phi_3} \right\} \qquad . \quad (5.7)$

The vectors I_2 and I_3 representing i_2 and i_3 are drawn in Fig. 5.3(*b*)
The vector OP is the vector sum of I_2 and I_3.
Now

$$OP^2 = OA^2 + AP^2$$
$$= \{I_{2m} \cos \phi_2 + I_{3m} \cos \phi_3\}^2 + \{I_{2m} \sin \phi_2 + I_{3m} \sin \phi_3\}^2$$

Therefore

$$OP = \sqrt{[\{I_{2m} \cos \phi_3 + I_{3m} \cos \phi_3\}^2}$$
$$+ \{I_{2m} \sin \phi_2 + I_{3m} \sin \phi_3\}^2]$$

Also, from the diagram, the phase angle, θ, of OP is given by equation (5.7). Thus OP is the vector representation of $i_1 = i_2 + i_3$.

$$OP = \mathbf{I}_1 = \mathbf{I}_2 + \mathbf{I}_3$$

i.e. vector $\mathbf{I}_1$ is the vector sum of $\mathbf{I}_2$ and $\mathbf{I}_3$.

This result would apply for any number of branches from the junction point. Kirchhoff's first law applies to the instantaneous currents at the junction, but if all the currents are sinusoidal and of the same frequency then the vector sum of the currents at any junction is zero.

Kirchhoff's second law states that at any instant the algebraic sum of the e.m.f.s and p.d.s round any closed loop is zero.

Referring to the closed loop of Fig. 5.3(c)

$$e = v_1 + v_2$$

where e, v_1 and v_2 are the instantaneous values of the e.m.f.s and p.d.s round the closed loop, and the above equation is a simple algebraic equation.

By a method, exactly identical to the one above for the vector sum of two currents, it may be shown that vector $\mathbf{E}$ (representing e) is the vector sum of vectors $\mathbf{V}_1$ and $\mathbf{V}_2$, representing v_1 and v_2 (see Fig. 5.3(d)).

i.e. $$\mathbf{E} = \mathbf{V}_1 + \mathbf{V}_2 \quad . \quad . \quad . \quad . \quad (5.8)$$

This result would apply for any number of e.m.f.s or p.d.s in the closed loop. Thus Kirchhoff's second law may also be stated as: "the vector sum of the e.m.f.s and p.d.s round any closed loop is zero when the e.m.f.s and p.d.s are sinusoidal and have the same frequency."

Example 5.2

Three circuit elements are connected in series (Fig. 5.4(a)), and the voltages across the circuit elements are given by

$$v_1 = 50 \sin \omega t$$
$$v_2 = 40 \sin (\omega t + 60°)$$
$$v_3 = 60 \sin (\omega t - 30°)$$

Calculate the total voltage and its phase angle with reference to v_1.

Vectors representing these voltages are shown in Fig. 5.4(b). The vector sum may be determined graphically or by the following calculation. In the calculation each vector is split into two mutually perpendicular components, the first component being parallel to the reference direction and the second perpendicular to the reference direction. The first component is then called the "in phase" component and the second the "quadrature" or "quadrate" component.

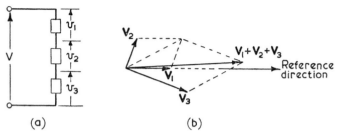

FIG. 5.4. PERTAINING TO EXAMPLE 5.2

In-phase component of $V_1 = 50$ V
Quadrature component of $V_1 = 0$
In-phase component of $V_2 = 40 \cos 60° = 20$ V
Quadrature component of $V_2 = 40 \sin 60° = 34·6$ V
In-phase component of $V_3 = 60 \cos 30° = 51·9$ V
Quadrature component of $V_3 = -60 \sin 30° = -30$ V

Adding the in-phase components and the quadrature components,

total in-phase component $= 50 + 20 + 51·9 = 121·9$ V

total quadrature component $= 34·6 - 30 = 4·6$ V

Therefore magnitude of total voltage $= \sqrt{(121·9^2 + 4·6^2)} = \underline{\underline{122 \text{ V}}}$

and phase angle with reference to $V_1 = \tan^{-1} \dfrac{4·6}{121·9} = \underline{\underline{2·2°}}$

5.3. Simple Single Element Circuits

(a) PURELY RESISTIVE CIRCUIT

Suppose that an alternating voltage given by $v = V_m \sin \omega t$ is applied to a circuit comprising a non-inductive resistance of R Ω. The instantaneous current is

$$i = \frac{v}{R} = \frac{V_m}{R} \sin \omega t \qquad . \qquad . \qquad (5.9)$$

The maximum value, I_m, of the current must occur when $v = V_m$ since R is a constant.

Therefore $\qquad\qquad I_m = \dfrac{V_m}{R} \qquad . \qquad . \qquad . \qquad . \qquad (5.10)$

and substituting for $\dfrac{V_m}{R}$ in (5.9)

$$i = I_m \sin \omega t$$

If the voltage v and current i are plotted on a wave diagram such as Fig. 5.5(c), then both waves are simple sine waves, and will "rise and fall" together, passing through their zero values at the same instant (i.e. at $t = 0$, π/ω, $2\pi/\omega$, etc.), and through their positive and negative maximum values at the same instants (i.e. at $t = \pi/2\omega$, $3\pi/2\omega$, etc). When two alternating quantities behave in this manner they are said to be "in phase." The current and voltage in a purely resistive circuit are in phase.

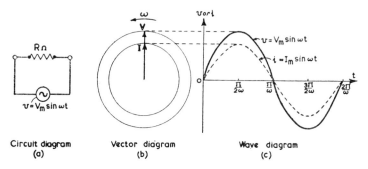

Circuit diagram   Vector diagram   Wave diagram
(a)   (b)   (c)

FIG. 5.5. NON-INDUCTIVE RESISTANCE CIRCUIT

The vector diagram (Fig. 5.5(b)) is drawn for the instant $t = \pi/2\omega$ sec. Since at this instant both voltage and current waves are passing through their maximum values, the rotating vectors **V** and **I** are perpendicular to the time axis and are parallel. As will become evident, a feature of the vector diagram which has great significance in the analysis of simple a.c. circuits is the displacement of the vectors relative to one another. The instant for which the diagram is drawn is immaterial to the present study of a.c. circuits.

(*b*) PURELY INDUCTIVE CIRCUIT

It is impossible to obtain a conductor which does not contain some resistance, but the assumption of a pure inductance gives a useful simplification.

Suppose the circuit contains only a pure inductance of L henrys. By the definition of inductance (see § 2.13) the voltage across the terminals of an inductance

$$= L \times \text{the rate of change of current}$$
$$\text{through the inductance}$$

i.e. $$v = L \cdot \frac{di}{dt}$$

Suppose a current, given by

$$i = I_m \sin \omega t$$

is established through the inductor.

Then, $v = L \cdot \dfrac{\mathrm{d}}{\mathrm{d}t}(I_m \sin \omega t)$

Therefore $v = \omega L I_m \cos \omega t$

or $v = \omega L I_m \sin (\omega t + 90°)$ . . . (5.11)

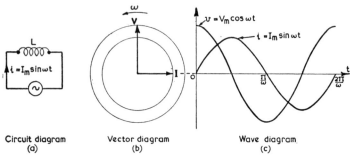

| Circuit diagram | Vector diagram | Wave diagram |
| (a) | (b) | (c) |

FIG. 5.6. PURELY INDUCTIVE CIRCUIT

If the wave diagram is now drawn (Fig. 5.6(c)) the current wave is a sine wave and the voltage wave is a cosine wave.

It is clear that in this case, unlike the case of a circuit containing resistance only, the current and voltage are not in phase. In fact the current reaches its maximum $\pi/2\omega$ seconds, or a quarter of a cycle, later than the voltage.

The vector diagram is drawn for the instant $t = 0$. The vector **I** is displaced from **V** by 90° (or $\pi/2$ radians). Although the vectors change their position from instant to instant, since they both have the same angular velocity, ω rad/sec, their displacement relative to one another is unaltered. Thus the current vector in a purely inductive circuit lags the voltage vector by 90°. It is equally true, of course, to say that the voltage leads the current by 90° in a purely inductive circuit.

From equation (5.11)

$$V_m = \omega L I_m$$

Therefore $\dfrac{V_m}{\sqrt{2}} = \dfrac{\omega L \cdot I_m}{\sqrt{2}}$

or, in r.m.s. values,

$$V = \omega L I$$

Therefore $V = 2\pi f L I$ . . . . (5.12)

ωL (or $2\pi f L$) is a constant for a given inductance and frequency and is called the inductive reactance, X_L.

Therefore $\qquad\qquad V = I \, . \, X_L \qquad . \qquad . \qquad . \quad (5.13\text{(i)})$

and $\qquad\qquad\qquad X_L = \dfrac{V}{I} \qquad . \qquad . \qquad . \qquad . \quad (5.13\text{(ii)})$

so that the units of inductive reactance are ohms, since inductive reactance is the quotient of volts and amperes.

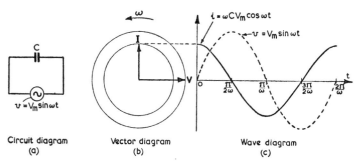

Circuit diagram (a)   Vector diagram (b)   Wave diagram (c)

FIG. 5.7. CIRCUIT CONTAINING CAPACITANCE ONLY

(c) PURELY CAPACITIVE CIRCUIT

Suppose a voltage $v = V_m \sin \omega t$ is applied to a circuit containing capacitance C farads only.

By equation (4.1) the instantaneous charge, q, on the capacitor is given by $q = Cv = CV_m \sin \omega t$. By equation (4.2(b)) the current, i, through the capacitor is given by

$$i = C \frac{\mathrm{d}v}{\mathrm{d}t} = \omega C V_m \cos \omega t$$

If the wave diagram is now drawn (Fig. 5.7(c)) the voltage wave is a sine wave and the current wave is a cosine wave. In this case again, current and voltage waves are clearly not in phase. The current reaches its positive maximum value $\pi/2\omega$ seconds, (or quarter of a cycle), before the voltage wave reaches its positive maximum value.

The vector diagram is drawn for the instant $t = 0$. In this diagram the current vector leads the voltage vector by 90°.

Now when $\cos \omega t = 1$, i reaches its maximum value, I_m

Therefore $\qquad\qquad I_m = \omega C V_m$

and $\qquad\qquad\qquad V_m = \dfrac{1}{\omega C} I_m$

and
$$\frac{V_m}{\sqrt{2}} = \frac{1}{\omega C} \cdot \frac{I_m}{\sqrt{2}}$$

or, using r.m.s. values

$$V = \frac{1}{\omega C} \cdot I$$

$$= \frac{1}{2\pi f C} \cdot I \qquad \qquad . \quad . \quad (5.14)$$

$\dfrac{1}{\omega C}$ or $\dfrac{1}{2\pi f C}$ is known as the capacitive reactance, X_c, and is a constant for a given capacitance and frequency.

Therefore $V = I \cdot X_c$.   .   .   (5.15)

and $X_c = \dfrac{V}{I}$, so that the units of capacitive reactance are ohms.

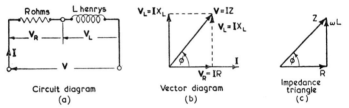

Circuit diagram   Vector diagram   Impedance triangle
(a)   (b)   (c)

FIG. 5.8. RESISTANCE AND INDUCTANCE IN SERIES

5.4. Simple Series Circuits

(a) RESISTANCE AND INDUCTANCE IN SERIES

The vector diagram of the circuit is shown in Fig. 5.8(b)). Since the current is common to both circuit elements vector I is drawn first. The vector $V_R = I \cdot R$ is in phase with I. The vector $V_L = I \cdot X_L$ leads I by 90°. V, the supply voltage, is the vector sum of V_R and V_L. The angle of phase difference between V and I is ϕ. By Pythagoras' theorem,

$$V = \sqrt{(V_R^2 + V_L^2)}$$

where V is the size of V

$$= \sqrt{(I^2 R^2 + I^2 X_L^2)}$$
$$= I\sqrt{(R^2 + X_L^2)}$$
$$= IZ$$

where Z is called the impedance of the circuit.

Therefore $Z = \dfrac{V}{I} = \sqrt{(R^2 + X_L^2)} = \sqrt{(R^2 + \omega^2 L^2)}$. (5.16)

It should be emphasized that it is the vector sum of $\mathbf{V}_R$ and $\mathbf{V}_L$ which equals the supply voltage $\mathbf{V}$. The arithmetical sum of V_R and V_L will be greater than the supply voltage V.

From equation (5.16) it is seen that Z, R, and ωL must form the sides of a right-angled triangle. This triangle will be similar to the voltage triangle of Fig. 5.8(b), and may be derived from it by dividing each vector by I. This gives the impedance triangle of Fig. 5.8(c)).

By the geometry of the vector diagram (Fig. 5.8(b))

$$\text{phase angle} = \phi = \tan^{-1}\frac{V_L}{V_R} = \tan^{-1}\frac{IX_L}{IR} = \tan^{-1}\frac{X_L}{R}\text{ lag}$$

$$(5.17\text{(i)})$$

This result could also have been obtained from the geometry of the impedance triangle (Fig. 5.8c). An alternative expression for ϕ is,

$$\phi = \cos^{-1}\frac{V_R}{V} = \cos^{-1}\frac{R}{Z} = \cos^{-1}\frac{R}{\sqrt{(R^2 + \omega^2L^2)}}\text{ lag} \qquad (5.17\text{(ii)})$$

In a purely inductive circuit the current vector lags the voltage vector by 90°; with both inductance and resistance, the current lags the voltage by some angle less than 90°, depending on the ratio of inductive reactance to resistance.

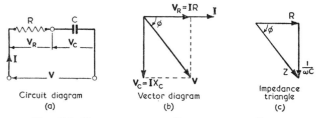

Circuit diagram	Vector diagram	Impedance triangle
(a)	(b)	(c)

FIG. 5.9. RESISTANCE AND CAPACITANCE IN SERIES

(*b*) RESISTANCE AND CAPACITANCE IN SERIES

The vector diagram is shown in Fig. 5.9; since the current, I, is common to both circuit elements vector $\mathbf{I}$ is drawn first. Vector $\mathbf{V}_R(= \mathbf{I}R)$ is in phase with vector $\mathbf{I}$, and the vector $\mathbf{V}_c(= \mathbf{I} \cdot X_c)$ lags vector $\mathbf{I}$ by 90°. Vector $\mathbf{V}$, the supply voltage vector, is the vector sum of $\mathbf{V}_R$ and $\mathbf{V}_c$. The angle of phase difference between vectors $\mathbf{V}$ and $\mathbf{I}$ is ϕ. Then,

$$V = \sqrt{(V_R^2 + V_c^2)} = \sqrt{(I^2R^2 + I^2X_c^2)} = I\sqrt{(R^2 + X_c^2)} = IZ$$

where Z is the impedance of the circuit

Therefore $\qquad Z = \dfrac{V}{I} = \sqrt{(R^2 + X_c^2)} = \sqrt{(R^2 + 1/\omega^2 C^2)} \quad \cdot \quad (5.18)$

Note that the impedance of a circuit is the voltage across the circuit per ampere flowing through it, so that it will always be measured in ohms.

In a circuit, containing both resistance and capacitance, the current leads the voltage by a phase angle ϕ which is greater than $0°$ but less than $90°$.

The impedance triangle is constructed from the voltage diagram by dividing each voltage by I as shown in Fig. 5.9(c).

By the geometry of the vector diagram,

$$\text{phase angle } \phi = \tan^{-1} \frac{V_c}{V_R} = \tan^{-1} \frac{IX_c}{IR} = \tan^{-1} \frac{X_c}{R} \text{ lead}$$

(5.19(i))

Alternatively,

$$\text{phase angle } \phi = \cos^{-1} \frac{V_R}{V} = \cos^{-1} \frac{R}{Z} = \cos^{-1} \frac{R}{\sqrt{(R^2 + X_c^2)}}$$

(5.19(ii))

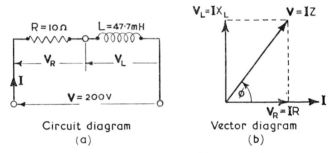

Circuit diagram
(a)

Vector diagram
(b)

FIG. 5.10. DIAGRAM FOR EXAMPLE 5.3

Example 5.3

A coil of resistance 10 Ω and inductance 47·7 mH is connected to a 200-V, 50-c/s supply. Calculate the current drawn from the supply and the angle of phase difference between the supply voltage and current vector.

Inductive reactance $= X_L = 2\pi f L = 2\pi 50 \times 47·7 \times 10^{-3} = 15 \ \Omega$

Total circuit impedance $= Z = \sqrt{(R^2 + X_L^2)} = \sqrt{(10^2 + 15^2)} = 18·0 \ \Omega$

Therefore current drawn from supply $= \dfrac{V}{Z} = \dfrac{200}{18·0} = \underline{\underline{11·1 \text{ A}}}$

Angle of phase difference, $\phi = \tan^{-1} \dfrac{X_L}{R} = \tan^{-1} \dfrac{15}{10} = \underline{56·3° \text{ lag}}$

Example 5.4

A non-inductive resistor of 75 Ω is connected in series with a pure inductor of 0·2 H across a 50-c/s supply. If the voltage across the resistor is 150 V find the voltage across the inductor and the supply voltage.

Voltage across the 75-Ω resistor $= V_R = 150$ V

Therefore current through resistor $= \dfrac{V_R}{R} = \dfrac{150}{75} = 2$ A

This current also flows through the inductor.

Reactance of inductor $= X_L = 2\pi f L = 2\pi 50 \times 0{\cdot}2 = 62{\cdot}8\ \Omega$

Therefore voltage across inductor $= V_L = IX_L = 2 \times 62{\cdot}8 = \underline{125{\cdot}6\ \text{V}}$

Supply voltage $= V = \sqrt{(V_R^2 + V_L^2)} = \sqrt{(150^2 + 125{\cdot}6^2)} = \underline{196\ \text{V}}$

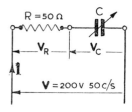 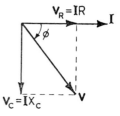

FIG. 5.11. DIAGRAM FOR EXAMPLE 5.5

Example 5.5

A resistance of 50 Ω is connected in series with a variable capacitor across a 200-V, 50-c/s supply. Calculate

(a) the current drawn from the supply, the voltage drops across the resistor and across the capacitor, and the angle of phase difference between supply voltage and current vectors, when the capacitor has a capacitance of 50 μF;

(b) the value of the capacitance when the supply current is 2 A; and

(c) the value of the capacitance when the angle of phase difference between the voltage and current vectors is 30° lead.

The vector diagram in Fig. 5.11

(a) Capacitive reactance $= X_{C_1} = \dfrac{1}{2\pi f C_1} = \dfrac{10^6}{2\pi \cdot 50 \cdot 50} = 63{\cdot}6\ \Omega$

Total impedance $= Z_1 = \sqrt{(R^2 + X_{C_1}^2)} = \sqrt{(50^2 + 63{\cdot}6^2)} = 80{\cdot}9\ \Omega$

Therefore supply current $= I = \dfrac{V}{Z_1} = \dfrac{200}{80{\cdot}9} = \underline{\underline{2{\cdot}48\ \text{A}}}$

Therefore voltage drop across resistor $= IR = 2{\cdot}48 \times 50 = \underline{124\ \text{V}}$

and voltage drop across capacitor $= IX_C = 2{\cdot}48 \times 63{\cdot}6 = \underline{158\ \text{V}}$

By equation (5.19(i)) phase angle $= \phi = \tan^{-1}\dfrac{X_C}{R} = \tan^{-1}\dfrac{63{\cdot}6}{50} = \underline{\underline{51{\cdot}8°\ \text{lead.}}}$

(b) Circuit current $= 2$ A

Thus total impedance $= Z_2 = \dfrac{V}{I} = \dfrac{200}{2} = 100\ \Omega$

and capacitive reactance $= X_{C_2} = \sqrt{(Z_2^2 - R^2)} = \sqrt{(100^2 - 50^2)} = 86{\cdot}6\ \Omega$

and capacitance $= C_2 = \dfrac{1}{2\pi f X_{C_2}} = \dfrac{10^6}{2\pi \times 50 \times 86{\cdot}6} = \underline{\underline{36{\cdot}7\ \mu\text{F}}}$

(c) Phase angle $= \phi = 30° = \tan^{-1}\dfrac{X_{C_3}}{R}$ from equation (5.19(i))

Therefore capacitive reactance $= X_{C_3} = R \tan 30° = 50 \times 0{\cdot}577 = 28{\cdot}9\ \Omega$

Therefore capacitance $= C_3 = \dfrac{1}{2\pi f X_{C_3}} = \dfrac{10^6}{2\pi \times 50 \times 28{\cdot}9} = \underline{\underline{110\ \mu\text{F}}}$

5.5. Simple Parallel Circuits

(a) RESISTANCE AND INDUCTANCE IN PARALLEL

The vector diagram of the circuit is shown in Fig. 5.12(b). Since the applied voltage is common to both circuit elements vector **V** is drawn first. The vector $\mathbf{I}_R (= \mathbf{V}/R)$ is in phase with the vector **V**.

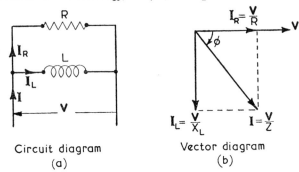

Circuit diagram   Vector diagram
(a)   (b)

FIG. 5.12. RESISTANCE AND INDUCTANCE IN PARALLEL

The vector $\mathbf{I}_L (= \mathbf{V}/X_L)$ lags the vector **V** by 90°. **I**, the current drawn from the supply is the vector sum of $\mathbf{I}_R$ and $\mathbf{I}_L$. The angle of phase difference between **V** and **I** is ϕ. The current lags the voltage by ϕ which is less than 90°. From the diagram,

$$I = \text{size of resultant current} = \sqrt{(I_R{}^2 + I_L{}^2)}$$

$$= \sqrt{\left(\frac{V^2}{R^2} + \frac{V^2}{X_L{}^2}\right)} = V \sqrt{\left(\frac{1}{R^2} + \frac{1}{X_L{}^2}\right)}$$

Therefore

$$\frac{V}{I} = Z = \frac{1}{\sqrt{\left(\dfrac{1}{R^2} + \dfrac{1}{X_L{}^2}\right)}} \;\Omega \qquad . \qquad (5.20(\text{i}))$$

where Z is the impedance of the circuit.
From equation (5.20(i))

$$\frac{1}{Z} = \sqrt{\left(\frac{1}{R^2} + \frac{1}{X_L{}^2}\right)} \qquad . \qquad . \qquad (5.20(\text{ii}))$$

In this circuit it should be emphasized that the supply current **I** is the vector sum of $\mathbf{I}_R$ and $\mathbf{I}_L$.

From the vector diagram, the phase angle ϕ between voltage and total current vectors is

$$\phi = \tan^{-1} \frac{I_L}{I_R} = \tan^{-1} \frac{V/X_L}{V/R} = \tan^{-1} \frac{R}{X_L} = \tan^{-1} \frac{R}{\omega L} \quad (5.21)$$

(b) RESISTANCE AND CAPACITANCE IN PARALLEL

The vector diagram of the circuit is shown in Fig. 5.13. Since the applied voltage is common to both circuit elements, vector $\mathbf{V}$ is drawn first. The vector $\mathbf{I}_R = \dfrac{\mathbf{V}}{R}$ is in phase with the vector $\mathbf{V}$. The vector $\mathbf{I}_c = \dfrac{\mathbf{V}}{X_c}$ leads the vector $\mathbf{V}$ by 90°. $\mathbf{I}$, the current drawn from the supply, is the vector sum of $\mathbf{I}_R$ and $\mathbf{I}_c$. The angle of phase difference between $\mathbf{V}$ and $\mathbf{I}$ is ϕ. Evidently the current leads the voltage by phase angle ϕ, which is less than 90°.

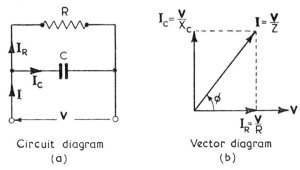

Circuit diagram
(a)

Vector diagram
(b)

FIG. 5.13. RESISTANCE AND CAPACITANCE IN PARALLEL

From the vector diagram

$$I = \sqrt{(I_R{}^2 + I_c{}^2)} = \sqrt{\left(\frac{V^2}{R^2} + \frac{V^2}{X_c{}^2}\right)} = V\sqrt{\left(\frac{1}{R^2} + \frac{1}{X_c{}^2}\right)}$$

Therefore

$$V = \frac{I}{\sqrt{\left(\dfrac{1}{R^2} + \dfrac{1}{X_c{}^2}\right)}} = IZ \qquad . \qquad . \qquad (5.22)$$

Where $Z = \dfrac{1}{\sqrt{\left(\dfrac{1}{R^2} + \dfrac{1}{X_c{}^2}\right)}}$ is the impedance of the circuit.

Also,

$$\frac{1}{Z} = \sqrt{\left(\frac{1}{R^2} + \frac{1}{X_c{}^2}\right)} = \sqrt{\left(\frac{1}{R^2} + \omega^2 C^2\right)} \qquad . \qquad (5.23)$$

Phase angle ϕ between voltage and current vectors is

$$\phi = \tan^{-1}\frac{I_c}{I_R} = \tan^{-1}\frac{V/X_c}{V/R} = \tan^{-1}\frac{R}{X_c} = \tan^{-1}\omega CR$$

$$(5.24)$$

Example 5.6

A circuit comprising a resistance of 100 Ω and a capacitance of 25 μF connected in parallel is supplied from a 200-V, 50-c/s supply. Calculate (a) the current flowing in the resistance, in the capacitance, and the total current from the supply, (b) the impedance of the circuit, and (c) the angle of phase difference between voltage and current vectors.

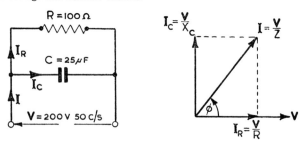

FIG. 5.14. DIAGRAM FOR EXAMPLE 5.6

(a) Current through resistor $= I_R = \dfrac{V}{R} = \dfrac{200}{100} = \underline{\underline{2 \text{ A}}}$

Capacitive reactance $= X_c = \dfrac{1}{2\pi f C} = \dfrac{10^6}{2\pi 50 \times 25} = 127 \text{ } \Omega$

Capacitor current $= I_c = \dfrac{V}{X_c} = \dfrac{200}{127} = 1{\cdot}57 \text{ A}$

Supply current $= I = \sqrt{(I_R{}^2 + I_c{}^2)} = \sqrt{(2^2 + 1{\cdot}57^2)} = \underline{\underline{2{\cdot}54 \text{ A}}}$

(b) Impedance of combined circuit $= Z = \dfrac{V}{I} = \dfrac{200}{2{\cdot}54} = \underline{\underline{78{\cdot}8 \text{ } \Omega}}$

(c) Phase difference $= \phi = \tan^{-1} \dfrac{I_R}{I_c}$

$$= \tan^{-1} \dfrac{1{\cdot}57}{2{\cdot}0} = \underline{\underline{38° \text{ lead}}}$$

5.6. Power in an A.C. Circuit

The power absorbed by a load in a d.c. circuit is given by the product VI watts. Since the r.m.s. values of alternating voltages and currents are such that they have the same power effect as the corresponding direct values of voltage and current, it might be thought that the power absorbed by a load in an a.c. circuit would be given simply by the product of the r.m.s. values of voltage and current. However it can be shown that the phase difference between the voltage and current waves in an a.c. circuit also affects the power absorbed by the load.

Consider the three cases (a) current and voltage in phase; (b) current and voltage 90° out of phase; (c) the general one when the voltage and current differ in phase by phase angle ϕ.

(a) Current and Voltage in Phase

Assume for a given load that the applied voltage is $v = V_m \sin \omega t$ and that the load current is $i = I_m \sin \omega t$. Then

$$\text{instantaneous load power} = vi$$

$$= V_m I_m \sin^2 \omega t$$

$$= V_m I_m \cdot \tfrac{1}{2}(1 - \cos 2\omega t)$$

$$= \frac{V_m I_m}{2} - \frac{V_m I_m}{2} \cos 2\omega t \quad . \quad (a)$$

Therefore

$$\text{average load power} = \frac{V_m I_m}{2} - \text{mean value of } \frac{V_m I_m}{2} \cos 2\omega t$$

and since the mean value of a cosine wave taken over a cycle is zero,

$$\text{mean load power} = \frac{V_m I_m}{2}$$

$$= \frac{V_m}{\sqrt{2}} \times \frac{I_m}{\sqrt{2}}$$

$$= VI \quad . \quad . \quad . \quad (5.25)$$

where V and I are r.m.s. values.

Thus the mean power absorbed by a load in an a.c. circuit in which the voltage and current are in phase is given in watts by the product of the r.m.s. values of voltage and current.

Fig. 5.15(a) shows the voltage, current and power waves for the case when the voltage and current are in phase. The power wave, as can be seen from equation (a), is a negative cosine wave of frequency double that of the voltage and current waves and raised above the time axis by an amount $\frac{V_m I_m}{2}$. That is to say, the power never becomes negative. This is so because the instantaneous values of current and voltage are either both positive or both negative at all instants, and therefore their product (the instantaneous power) is always positive.

(b) Current and Voltage 90° Out of Phase

Assume for a given load that the applied voltage, $v = V_m \sin \omega t$, and the load current $i = I_m \sin (\omega t \pm 90°)$. For Fig. 5.15(b) the current has been taken as leading the voltage.

Instantaneous load power $= v \cdot i$

$$= V_m I_m \sin \omega t \sin (\omega t \pm 90°)$$

$$= \pm V_m I_m \sin \omega t \cos \omega t$$

$$= \pm \frac{V_m I_m}{2} \sin 2\omega t \qquad . \qquad . \quad (b)$$

Therefore

mean load power = mean value of $\left(\dfrac{V_m I_m}{2} \sin 2\omega t \right) = 0,$ (5.26)

since the mean value of $\sin 2\omega t$ taken over a cycle is zero.

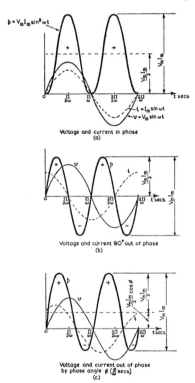

Voltage and current in phase
(a)

Voltage and current 90° out of phase
(b)

Voltage and current out of phase
by phase angle ϕ $\left(\frac{\phi}{\omega} \text{ secs}\right)$
(c)

FIG. 5.15. POWER IN AN A.C. CIRCUIT

In Fig. 5.15(b) the power wave, can be seen to be a positive sine wave of frequency double that of the voltage and current waves. The maximum value of the instantaneous power is $V_m I_m/2$ and the minimum value is $-V_m I_m/2$. In this case the load absorbs energy for a quarter of a cycle, and in the next quarter of a cycle gives back the same amount of energy. The net energy and power absorbed is therefore zero.

(c) GENERAL CASE : CURRENT AND VOLTAGE ϕ RADIANS OUT OF PHASE

Assume that for a certain load the applied voltage $v = V_m \sin \omega t$, and the load current $i = I_m \sin (\omega t \pm \phi)$

Instantaneous load power $= v \cdot i$

$$= V_m \cdot I_m \sin \omega t \sin (\omega t \pm \phi)$$

$$= V_m \cdot I_m \cdot \tfrac{1}{2} \{ \cos (\mp \phi) - \cos (2\omega t \pm \phi) \}$$

$$= \frac{V_m \cdot I_m}{2} \cdot \cos \phi - \frac{V_m I_m}{2} \cos (2\omega t \pm \phi)$$

Therefore

mean load power = mean value of

$$\left\{ \frac{V_m I_m}{2} \cos \phi - \frac{V_m I_m}{2} \cos (2\omega t \pm \phi) \right\}$$

and since the mean value of $\cos (2\omega t \pm \phi)$ over a cycle is zero, then,

$$\text{mean load power} = \frac{V_m \cdot I_m}{2} \cdot \cos \phi$$

$$= V \cdot I \cos \phi, \text{ where } V \text{ and } I \text{ are r.m.s. values.}$$

$$(5.27)$$

Fig. 5.15(c) shows the voltage, current and power waves for the case where V and I differ in phase by a phase angle ϕ. The power wave, whose peak to peak value $(V_m \cdot I_m)$ is the same as in the cases previously considered, has an intermediate position relative to the time axis, as compared with the two previous cases. Thus the load absorbs a net amount of energy, since the positive loops are greater than the negative loops.

It will be seen that the two particular cases considered previously agree with the general result obtained.

5.7. Power Factor

In a.c. circuit analysis the product of the r.m.s. values of current and voltage, VI, is referred to as the *volt-amperes*. As has been seen, this product does not in general represent the power absorbed by a load. *The power factor* is defined as that factor by which the volt-amperes must be multiplied to give the true power absorbed. Thus—

$$\text{power absorbed (watts)} = \text{volt-amperes} \times \text{power factor} \qquad (5.28)$$

Where the voltage and current waves are sinusoidal it has been shown in the previous section that,

$$\text{power absorbed} = VI \cos \phi \ \text{watts} \qquad \text{from} \quad (5.27)$$

Comparing equations (5.27) and (5.28) it is seen that the power factor when the current and voltage waves are sinusoidal is cos ϕ, i.e. the power factor is the cosine of the angle of phase difference between the current and voltage. It must be emphasized that this result obtains only when wave shapes are sinusoidal.

For the case of sinusoidal waves the power factor of a circuit is said to be leading or lagging according to whether the current in the circuit leads or lags the applied voltage.

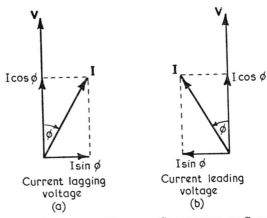

FIG. 5.16. ACTIVE AND REACTIVE COMPONENTS OF CURRENT

5.8. Active and Reactive Components of Current (Fig. 5.16)

Consider a circuit in which the current I lags (or leads) the voltage by a phase angle ϕ. For analytical purposes it is possible to consider the current as being made up of two rectangular components—

1. $I \cos \phi$, in phase with the voltage and called the active component;

2. $I \sin \phi$, 90° out of phase with the voltage and called the reactive component, or the quadrature component.

Since the power absorbed by a load in an a.c. circuit is $VI \cos \phi$ watts it is evident that all the useful energy absorbed by the load may be attributed to the component $I \cos \phi$. It is for this reason that it is called the active component.

As is evident from Fig. 5.16, when I lags behind **V**, the reactive component of current lags **V** by 90°; when I leads **V**, the reactive component of current leads **V** by 90°.

5.9. Measurement of Power in A.C. Circuits

The dynamometer wattmeter is most commonly used to measure power in a.c. circuits and only this type of instrument is considered.

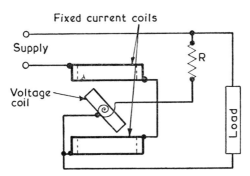

FIG. 5.17. THE DYNAMOMETER WATTMETER

The dynamometer wattmeter is similar in construction to the dynamometer ammeter (§3.4). When the dynamometer instrument is used as a wattmeter the fixed coils carry the load current, or a known fraction of it, and the moving coil carries a current proportional to the voltage across the load (see Fig. 5.17).

Let the voltage across the load at any instant be $v = V_m \sin \omega t$ and the load current at any instant be $i = I_m \sin (\omega t \pm \phi)$.

It was shown in § 3.4 that the torque on the moving coil of a dynamometer instrument is given by

$$T = K_2 i_m i_f \cos \theta \qquad \text{Nw-m}$$

where i_m is the current in moving coil and i_f the current in the fixed coil.

For wattmeter connexion of the dynamometer instrument,

$$i_m \propto v = V_m \sin \omega t$$
$$i_f \propto i = I_m \sin (\omega t \pm \phi)$$

The instantaneous torque on the moving coil, T_i, is

$$T_i = K_3 V_m I_m \sin \omega t \sin (\omega t \pm \phi) \cos \theta \qquad \text{Nw-m}$$
$$= K_3 V_m I_m \cos \theta \tfrac{1}{2} \{\cos (\pm \phi) - \cos (2\omega t \pm \phi)\}$$

The inertia of the deflecting system prevents it from following the variations in instantaneous torque and the moving coil will take up a deflexion corresponding to the average torque, T_{av}, which is

$$T_{av} = K_3 \frac{V_m I_m}{2} \cos \theta \times \text{mean value of } \{\cos \phi - \cos (2\omega t \pm \phi)\}$$

$$= K_3 \frac{V_m I_m}{2} \cos \phi \cos \theta$$

since the mean value of $\cos (2\omega t \pm \phi) = 0$

i.e. $$T_{av} = K_3 VI \cos \phi \cos \theta$$

where V and I are in r.m.s. values.

The above expression for the mean torque shows that the deflexion of the instrument is proportional to the mean power.

The scale of the instrument is not uniformly divided being crowded at each end due to the effect of the $\cos \theta$ term. Most dynamometer wattmeters for laboratory use have two current ranges obtained by connecting the fixed coils (a) in series and (b) in parallel. Further extensions of range may be obtained using current transformers. Several voltage ranges are obtained by connecting fixed resistors in series with the moving coil. Control and damping are arranged as for the dynamometer ammeter.

Example 5.7

A choke coil has an effective resistance of 10 Ω and an effective inductance of 0·1 H. It is connected to a 200-V, 50-c/s supply. Calculate (a) the impedance of the coil, (b) the current drawn from the supply (c) the power factor for the coil and (d) the power absorbed by the coil.

Resistance of coil $= R = 10 \; \Omega$

Reactance of coil $= X_L = 2\pi f L = 2\pi \times 50 \times 0·1 = 31·4 \; \Omega$

(a) Impedance of coil $= Z = \sqrt{(R^2 + X_L{}^2)} = \sqrt{(10^2 + 31·4^2)} = \underline{\underline{33 \; \Omega}}$

(b) Current drawn from supply $= \dfrac{V}{Z} = \dfrac{200}{33} = \underline{\underline{6·06 \; A}}$

Phase angle between current and voltage vectors $\Big\} = \phi = \tan^{-1} \dfrac{X_L}{R} = \tan^{-1} \dfrac{31·4}{10} = 72·4° \; \text{lag}$

(c) power factor $= \cos \phi = \cos 72·4° = \underline{\underline{0·302 \; \text{lag}}}$

(d) power absorbed $= VI \cos \phi = 200 \times 6·06 \times 0·302 = \underline{\underline{367 \; W}}$

5.10. Power and Power Factor for Various Circuits

For a pure inductance or a pure capacitance the current and voltage waves are always 90° out of phase thus the power factor and mean power absorbed are both zero.

If a resistance R Ω and a reactance X Ω are connected in series to give a total impedance Z Ω, and this is connected to a supply so that the current taken from the supply is I A, then

$$\text{supply voltage} = V = I\,Z \text{ volts}$$

Therefore

$$\text{volt-amperes drawn from supply} = V\,.\,I = I^2Z$$

Power absorbed from supply = power absorbed by resistance R (since the mean power absorbed by the reactance is zero).
Therefore

$$\text{power absorbed from the supply} = I^2R$$

and

$$\text{power factor of circuit} = \frac{I^2R}{I^2Z} = \frac{R}{Z} = \cos\phi$$

$$(5.29)$$

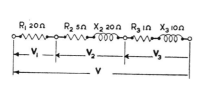
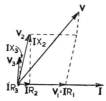

FIG. 5.18. PERTAINING TO EXAMPLE 5.8

Example 5.8

A pure resistance of 20 Ω, a coil of resistance 5 Ω and inductive reactance 20 Ω, and a second coil of resistance 1 Ω and inductive reactance 10 Ω, are connected in series to (a) a direct voltage of 100 V (b) a 50-c/s alternating voltage of 200 V. Calculate the current, the voltage drop across each unit, and the power absorbed by each unit in each case, if the reactances are given at 50 c/s.

(a) The inductances will have no effect on the direct current.

Total resistance of circuit to direct current = 26 Ω

Therefore direct current drawn $= \dfrac{100}{26} = 3\cdot85$ A

$$\begin{aligned}
\text{volt drop across pure resistance} &= 20 \times 3\cdot85 = 77 \text{ V}\\
\text{volt drop across first coil} &= 5 \times 3\cdot85 = 19\cdot2 \text{ V}\\
\text{volt drop across second coil} &= 1 \times 3\cdot85 = 3\cdot85 \text{ V}\\
\text{power absorbed by pure resistance} &= 3\cdot85^2 \times 20 = 296 \text{ W}\\
\text{power absorbed by first coil} &= 3\cdot85^2 \times 5 = 74 \text{ W}\\
\text{power absorbed by second coil} &= 3\cdot85^2 \times 1 = 14\cdot8 \text{ W}
\end{aligned}$$

(b) Under alternating current conditions the inductances will give rise to reactances depending on the frequency used. Here the reactances are $X_2 = 20\ \Omega$ and $X_3 = 10\ \Omega$.

The vector diagram for the circuit is drawn approximately to scale in Fig. 5.18; since all the components are connected in series it is most convenient to draw first the vector **I** representing the circuit current.

The voltage $\mathbf{V}_1\ (= \mathbf{I}R_1)$ is in phase with **I** since the first unit is a pure resistance $R_1\ \Omega$.

The voltage $\mathbf{V}_2\ \{= \mathbf{I}\sqrt{(R_2{}^2 + X_2{}^2)}\}$ has the component IR_2 in phase with **I** and the component IX_2 leading **I** by 90°. The voltage $\mathbf{V}_3\ (= \mathbf{I}\sqrt{(R_3{}^2 + X_3{}^2)}$ has the component IR_3 in phase with **I** and the component IX_3 leading **I** by 90°. The total voltage **V** is the vector sum of $\mathbf{V}_1$, $\mathbf{V}_2$ and $\mathbf{V}_3$.

i.e. $$\mathbf{V} = \mathbf{V}_1 + \mathbf{V}_2 + \mathbf{V}_3$$

Therefore $$V = \sqrt{\{(IR_1 + IR_2 + IR_3)^2 + (IX_2 + IX_3)^2\}}$$

$$= I\sqrt{\{(R_1 + R_2 + R_3)^2 + (X_2 + X_3)^2\}}$$

Therefore total circuit impedance $= Z = \dfrac{V}{I}$

$$= \sqrt{\{(R_1 + R_2 + R_3)^2 + (X_2 + X_3)^2\}}$$

Therefore $$Z = \sqrt{\{(20 + 5 + 1)^2 + (20 + 10)^2\}} = 39 \cdot 7\ \Omega$$

and circuit current $= \dfrac{V}{Z} = \dfrac{200}{39 \cdot 7} = 5 \cdot 03\ \text{A}$

Therefore volt drop across pure resistance $= 5 \cdot 03 \times 20 = 100 \cdot 6\ \text{V}$

volt drop across first coil $= 5 \cdot 03 \times \sqrt{(5^2 + 20^2)} = 104\ \text{V}$

volt drop across second coil $= 5 \cdot 03 \times \sqrt{(1^2 + 10^2)} = 50 \cdot 4\ \text{V}$

power absorbed by pure resistance $= 5 \cdot 03^2 \times 20 = 508\ \text{W}$

power absorbed by first coil $= 5 \cdot 03^2 \times 5 = 127\ \text{W}$

(or power $= V_2 \cdot I \cos \phi_2$ from equation (5.27)

$$= 104 \times 5 \cdot 03 \times \frac{5}{\sqrt{(5^2 + 20^2)}} = 127\ \text{W})$$

power absorbed by second coil $= 5 \cdot 03^2 \times 1 = 25 \cdot 4\ \text{W}$

(or power $= V_3 I \cos \phi_3$

$$= 50 \cdot 4 \times 5 \cdot 03 \times \frac{1}{\sqrt{(1^2 + 10^2)}} = \underline{\underline{25 \cdot 4\ \text{W}}})$$

In the above example it has been assumed that the power loss in an inductance when it is connected to an a.c. supply is due only to the resistance of the windings. This is true for an air-cored inductance but not true for an iron-cored inductance. When an alternating current is passed through an iron-cored inductance the flux in the iron core will be alternating. This gives rise to two additional causes of power loss. First, the iron is subjected to cycles of magnetization, and therefore there will be a hysteresis loss in it (§ 2.27). Second, the iron being a conductor subjected to an alternating flux will have an e.m.f. induced in it according to equation (2.3). This e.m.f. will cause a current to flow in the iron (termed an eddy current), and hence there will be a power loss dependent on the value of the eddy current and the resistance of the iron path. This eddy current loss may be reduced by employing high resistivity iron, and by using thin laminations instead of solid iron cores.

The effect of the two iron losses is to increase the apparent resistance of an iron-cored coil when it is connected to an a.c. supply. The apparent resistance on a.c. is called the effective a.c. resistance of the coil. It should be noted that both iron losses vary with the frequency of the supply and with the maximum value of flux density in the core.

Example 5.9

An iron-cored coil has a d.c. resistance of 10 Ω. When it is connected to a 250-V, 50-c/s supply the current taken is 1 A at a power factor of 0·3 lagging. Determine the inductance of the coil, its effective resistance, and the part of the effective resistance which represents the effect of iron losses.

Let R_e = effective a.c. resistance of the coil.

Then power dissipated $= I^2 R_e = VI \cos \phi$

Therefore $R_e = \dfrac{V}{I} \cos \phi = \dfrac{250}{1} \times 0\cdot3 = \underline{\underline{75\ \Omega}}$

Total circuit impedance $= Z = \dfrac{V}{I} = 250\ \Omega$

Hence from equation (5.16)

$$\omega^2 L^2 = Z^2 - R_e^2$$

Therefore $L = \sqrt{\left(\dfrac{Z^2 - R_e^2}{\omega^2}\right)} = \sqrt{\left(\dfrac{250^2 - 75^2}{(2\pi \times 50)^2}\right)} = \underline{\underline{0\cdot758\ \text{H}}}$

Resistance equivalent to iron loss $\Big\} = R_e -$ d.c. resistance $= 75 - 10 = \underline{\underline{65\ \Omega}}$

Example 5.10

Three voltmeters are used to measure the input to an inductive load in series with a non-inductive resistance of 14 Ω. The voltage across the non-inductive resistance, the load, and the combination are 70, 90 and 140 V respectively. Find (a) the impedance of the load and of the combination; (b) the power absorbed by the load; (c) the power factor of the load; (d) the reactance of the load.

Current, $I = \dfrac{V_R}{R} = \dfrac{70}{14} = 5$ A where $V_R =$ voltage across the non-inductive resistance

(a) Impedance of load $= \dfrac{V_1}{I} = \dfrac{90}{5} = \underline{\underline{18\ \Omega}}$ where $V_1 =$ load voltage.

Impedance of combination $= \dfrac{140}{5} = \underline{\underline{28\ \Omega}}$

The vector diagram for the problem is shown in Fig. 5.19—the problem is most easily continued by drawing the vector diagram to scale. Since a series circuit is considered, the current vector **I**, is first drawn in the reference direction. The vector, **V**$_R$, may also be marked off along the reference direction. Now the magnitude of the total voltage, **V**, is known to be 140 V but its

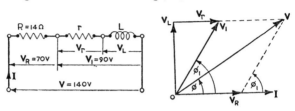

FIG. 5.19. DIAGRAM FOR EXAMPLE 5.10

phase, with reference to the current vector, is not known. The vector **V** will, however, lie in the first quadrant since the total current must lag the total voltage in an inductive circuit. A circle, centre O, and radius 140 V, to scale, may be drawn through the first quadrant and the total voltage vector, **V**, from O will terminate at some point on this circle.

Since
$$\mathbf{V} = \mathbf{V}_R + \mathbf{V}_1$$

vectors **V**$_R$ and **V**$_1$ must, when placed end to end in order, give vector **V**. Thus if a second circle is drawn through the first quadrant with centre point at the end of **V**$_R$ and with radius 90 V, to scale, the second circle will cut the first at a point which is the termination of **V**. Also the line joining the ends of the vectors **V**$_R$ and **V** will represent the vector **V**$_1$ which may also be drawn from the origin O.

Let V_L and V_r be the quadrature and in phase components of V_1.
V_r, V_L, and ϕ, the phase angle of the load, may all be found from the diagram.

(b) Power absorbed by the load $= V_r \times I$ (or $V_1 I \cos \phi$)
$$= 47 \cdot 3 \times 5$$
$$= \underline{\underline{236 \cdot 5 \text{ W}}}$$

(c) Power factor of load $= \cos \phi_1 = \cos 58° = \underline{\underline{0 \cdot 533 \text{ lag}}}$

(d) Voltage drop across effective coil resistance $= V_r = 47 \cdot 3$ V

Therefore effective coil resistance $= \dfrac{47 \cdot 3}{5} = \underline{\underline{9 \cdot 46 \ \Omega}}$

Voltage drop across effective coil reactance $= V_L = 76 \cdot 8$ V

Therefore effective coil reactance $= \dfrac{76 \cdot 8}{5} = \underline{\underline{15 \cdot 4 \ \Omega}}$

5.11. Series-parallel Circuit

Consider a circuit consisting of two branches connected in parallel, the first branch containing a resistance in series with an inductance, the second containing a resistance in series with a capacitor, shown in Fig. 5.20.

To obtain the vector diagram of this circuit it is easier, in the first place, to consider the vector diagrams of the two series branches separately. That for branch 1 is shown in Fig. 5.20(b) and that for branch 2 is shown in Fig. 5.20(c). The construction of these vectors diagrams has already been considered in § 5.4.

Now the resultant voltage **V** in each diagram is the supply voltage. Fig. 5.20(d) is obtained by superimposing Figs. 5.20(b) and 5.20(c) with the resultant voltage vectors **V** coinciding. This diagram shows

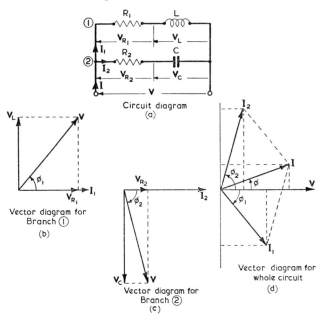

FIG. 5.20. THE SERIES-PARALLEL CIRCUIT

I_1 lagging **V** by phase angle ϕ_1, I_2 leading **V** by phase angle ϕ_2, and **I** the vector sum of I_1 and I_2 obtained by completing the parallelogram and drawing the diagonal. The angle of phase difference between **V** and **I** is ϕ. In Fig. 5.20(d) **I** is shown leading **V**, but with different values and phases for I_1 and I_2, **I** may lag **V**.

The impedance of branch $1 = Z_1 = \sqrt{(R_1{}^2 + X_L{}^2)}$

The impedance of branch $2 = Z_2 = \sqrt{(R_2{}^2 + X_c{}^2)}$

where X_L is the reactance of the inductance and X_c is the reactance of the capacitor.

$$I_1 = \frac{V}{Z_1} \; ; \cos \phi_1 = \frac{R_1}{Z_1} \; ; \text{ and } \phi_1 = \cos^{-1} \frac{R_1}{Z_1}$$

$$I_2 = \frac{V}{Z_2} \; ; \cos \phi_2 = \frac{R_2}{Z_2} \; ; \text{ and } \phi_2 = \cos^{-1} \frac{R_2}{Z_2}$$

The active components of the branch currents, and the reactive components may be summed separately. The total current may then be found by combining the resultant active and reactive components vectorially. Thus,

active component of total current = sum of active components
of branch currents

i.e. $$I \cos \phi = I_1 \cos \phi_1 + I_2 \cos \phi_2$$

Therefore $$\cos \phi = \frac{I_1 \cos \phi_1 + I_2 \cos \phi_2}{I} \qquad . \qquad . \quad (5.30)$$

Referring to Fig. 5.20(d), if $I_2 \sin \phi_2 > I_1 \sin \phi_1$, the current will lead the voltage; if $I_1 \sin \phi_1 > I_2 \sin \phi_2$ the current will lag the voltage.

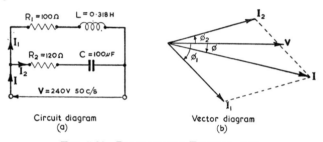

Circuit diagram
(a)

Vector diagram
(b)

FIG. 5.21. DIAGRAM FOR EXAMPLE 5.11

Example 5.11

A parallel circuit consists of two branches, one containing a coil of resistance 100 Ω and inductance 0·318 H, the other containing a resistance of 120 Ω in series with a capacitor of 100-μF capacitance. Calculate the total current and the overall power factor of the circuit if it is connected to a 240-V, 50-c/s supply. The circuit diagram is shown in Fig. 5.21.

Reactance of coil $= X_L = 2\pi fL = 2\pi \cdot 50 \times 0\cdot318 = 100 \, \Omega$

Reactance of capacitor $= X_c = \dfrac{1}{2\pi fC} = \dfrac{10^6}{2\pi \cdot 50 \times 100} = 31\cdot8 \, \Omega$

Impedance of coil branch $= Z_1 = \sqrt{(R_1^2 + X_L^2)} = \sqrt{(100^2 + 100^2)} = 141 \, \Omega$

Impedance of capacitor branch $= Z_2 = \sqrt{(R_2^2 + X_c^2)} = \sqrt{(120^2 + 31\cdot8^2)}$
$$= 124 \, \Omega$$

Current through coil branch $= I_1 = \dfrac{V}{Z_1} = \dfrac{240}{141} = 1\cdot69 \, \text{A}$

Current through capacitor branch $= I_2 = \dfrac{V}{Z_2} = \dfrac{240}{124} = 1\cdot93 \, \text{A}$

Power factor of coil branch $= \cos \phi_1 = \dfrac{R_1}{Z_1} = \dfrac{100}{141} = 0\cdot707 \, \text{lag}$

Therefore $\qquad\qquad\qquad \sin \phi_1 = 0.707$

Power factor of capacitor branch $= \cos \phi_2 = \dfrac{R_2}{Z_2} = \dfrac{120}{124} = 0.966$ lead

Therefore $\qquad\qquad\qquad \sin \phi_2 = 0.256$

In-phase component of total current $= I \cos \phi = I_1 \cos \phi_1 + I_2 \cos \phi_2$

$$= 1.69 \times 0.707 + 1.93 \times 0.966$$
$$= 3.06 \text{ A}$$

Quadrature component of total current $= I \sin \phi = -I_1 \sin \phi_1 + I_2 \sin \phi_2$

$$= -1.69 \times 0.707 + 1.93 \times 0.256$$
$$= -0.7 \text{ A}$$

(the negative sign must be introduced with the lagging quadrature component of the coil current since this is in opposition to the leading quadrature component of the capacitor current).

Total current $= I = \sqrt{(I^2 \cos^2 \phi + I^2 \sin^2 \phi)} = \sqrt{(3.06^2 + 0.7^2)} = \underline{\underline{3.14 \text{ A}}}$

Overall power factor $= \dfrac{I \cos \phi}{I} = \dfrac{3.06}{3.14} = \underline{\underline{0.975 \text{ lag}}}$

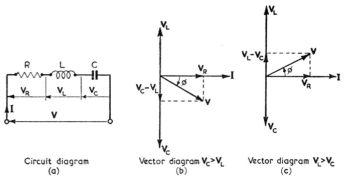

Circuit diagram	Vector diagram $V_c > V_L$	Vector diagram $V_L > V_c$
(a)	(b)	(c)

FIG. 5.22. THE GENERAL SERIES CIRCUIT

5.12. The General Series Circuit—Series Resonance

Consider a circuit containing resistance, inductance and capacitance in series, as shown in Fig. 5.22(a). The vector diagram of the circuit is obtained by first drawing vector **I** since the current is common to all circuit elements: vector $\mathbf{V}_R (=IR)$ is in phase with vector **I**; vector $\mathbf{V}_L (=IX_L)$ leads vector **I** by 90°; Vector $\mathbf{V}_c (=IX_c)$ lags vector I by 90°. **V**, the supply voltage, is the vector sum of $\mathbf{V}_R$, $\mathbf{V}_L$ and $\mathbf{V}_c$. Since $\mathbf{V}_L$ and $\mathbf{V}_c$ are in direct phase opposition, when summed they tend to cancel each other out. As a consequence it is possible for both $\mathbf{V}_L$ and $\mathbf{V}_c$ to be greater than the supply voltage **V**. It can be seen at once that two cases, at least, are possible; that when $V_c > V_L$ and that when $V_L > V_c$. These two cases are drawn in Figs. 5.22(b) and 5.22(c).

From the vector diagrams

$$V = \sqrt{\{V_R^2 + (V_L - V_c)^2\}}$$
$$= \sqrt{\{I^2R^2 + (IX_L - IX_c)^2\}}$$
$$= I\sqrt{(R^2 + (X_L - X_c)^2)} \quad . \quad . \quad . \quad (5.31)$$
$$= IZ$$

where $\quad Z = \sqrt{\{R^2 + (X_L - X_c)^2\}} \quad . \quad . \quad . \quad (5.32)$

is the impedance of the circuit.

Series Resonance

Two cases of the general series circuit have so far been considered, that when $V_c > V_L$ and that when $V_L > V_c$. A third case is, however, possible when $V_c = V_L$. When this occurs the condition is known as series resonance, and the circuit is said to resonate. The vector diagram for resonance conditions is drawn in Fig. 5.23.

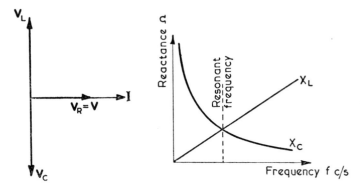

FIG. 5.23. Vector Diagram for Series Resonant Circuit

FIG. 5.24. Variation of Inductive and Capacitive Reactance with Frequency

If the general series circuit were connected to a variable frequency source at zero frequency (i.e. a direct voltage) $X_L = 2\pi f L = 0$ and $X_c = \dfrac{1}{2\pi f C} = \infty$; as the frequency of the supply is increased, X_L will increase in proportion and X_c will decrease in inverse proportion. Evidently there will be one frequency which will make $X_L = X_c$ and consequently $IX_L = IX_c$ or $V_L = V_c$, the condition for series resonance. This is illustrated in Fig. 5.24.

Another approach to the resonant conditions could be made by supplying the circuit from a constant frequency source and varying the value of one of the reactive elements, the capacitance for instance, until X_c equalled X_L.

The condition for resonance is that—

$$V_c = V_L$$

or $$IX_c = IX_L$$

or $$X_c = X_L \quad . \quad . \quad . \quad . \quad (5.33)$$

Now the impedance of a general series circuit is,

$$Z = \sqrt{(R^2 + (X_L - X_c)^2)}$$

Hence at resonance—

$$Z = R \quad . \quad . \quad . \quad . \quad (5.34)$$

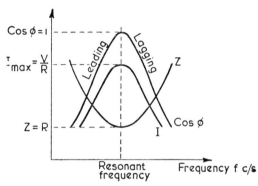

FIG. 5.25. SERIES RESONANCE CURVES

Thus at resonance the impedance is a minimum and is equal to the resistance of the circuit. The current will therefore be in phase with the voltage (a deduction supported by the vector diagram of Fig. 5.23). If the resistance of the circuit is low the current, which is a maximum at the resonant frequency since the impedance is a minimum, may reach a very high value, and in consequence the voltage across the inductance and capacitance may be many times the supply voltage. Since the current is a maximum at resonance, as is also the power factor (i.e. unity), the power absorbed by the circuit is also a maximum at resonance. The general form of curves of current, power factor, and impedance, are indicated in Fig. 5.25.

At resonance

$$X_c = X_L$$

Therefore
$$\frac{1}{\omega_0 C} = \omega_0 L$$

$$\omega_0^2 = \frac{1}{LC}$$

$$(2\pi f_0)^2 = \frac{1}{LC}$$

$$f_0 = \frac{1}{2\pi} \cdot \frac{1}{\sqrt{LC}} \qquad . \qquad . \qquad . \quad (5.35)$$

This is the resonant or natural frequency of the general series circuit.

Example 5.12

A coil of resistance of 10 Ω, an inductance of 1 H, and a capacitance of 15·83 μF are connected in series across a 100-V, variable-frequency supply.

Calculate the current drawn from the supply, the power factor, the power, the voltage across the inductance and the voltage across the capacitance when the frequency is (*a*) 35 c/s (*b*) 45 c/s (*c*) resonant.

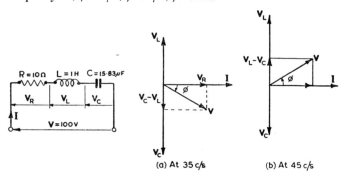

FIG. 5.26. DIAGRAM FOR EXAMPLE 5.12

The vector diagram appears in Fig. 5.26.
(*a*) at 35 c/s—

Inductive reactance $= X_L = 2\pi f L = 2\pi . 35 . 1 = 220 \ \Omega$

Capacitive reactance $= X_c = \dfrac{1}{2\pi f C} = \dfrac{10^6}{2\pi . 35 . 15\cdot83} = 286 \ \Omega$

Therefore total impedance, from equation (5.32), is

$$Z = \sqrt{\{10^2 + (220 - 286)^2\}} = 66\cdot8 \ \Omega$$

Therefore current from supply $= \dfrac{V}{Z} = \dfrac{100}{66\cdot8} = \underline{1\cdot5 \ A}$

Power factor $= \cos \phi = \dfrac{R}{Z} = \dfrac{10}{66\cdot8} = \underline{\underline{0\cdot15 \ \text{lead}}}$

Power absorbed $= V \cdot I \cdot \cos \phi = 100 \times 1\cdot5 \times 0\cdot15 = \underline{\underline{22\cdot5 \text{ W}}}$

Voltage across inductance $= V_L = IX_L = 220 \times 1\cdot5 = \underline{\underline{330 \text{ V}}}$

Voltage across capacitance $= V_c = IX_c = 286 \times 1\cdot5 = \underline{\underline{429 \text{ V}}}$

(b) at 45 c/s—

Inductive reactance $= X_L = 2\pi fL = 2\pi \times 45 \times 1 = 283 \ \Omega$

Capacitive reactance $= X_c = \dfrac{1}{2\pi fC} = \dfrac{10^6}{2\pi \cdot 45 \cdot 15\cdot83} = 223 \ \Omega$

Therefore total impedance $= Z = \sqrt{\{10^2 + (283 - 223)^2\}} = 60\cdot9 \ \Omega$

Therefore current from supply $= \dfrac{V}{Z} = \dfrac{100}{60\cdot9} = \underline{\underline{1\cdot64 \text{ A}}}$

Power factor $= \cos \phi = \dfrac{R}{Z} = \dfrac{10}{60\cdot9} = \underline{0\cdot164 \text{ lag}}$

Power drawn from supply $= VI \cos \phi = 100 \times 1\cdot64 \times 0\cdot164$

$$= \underline{\underline{26\cdot9 \text{ W}}}$$

Voltage across inductance $= V_L = IX_L = 283 \times 1\cdot64 = \underline{\underline{464 \text{ V}}}$

Voltage across capacitance $= V_c = IX_c = 223 \times 1\cdot64 = \underline{\underline{366 \text{ V}}}$

(c) at resonant frequency—

Resonant frequency $= f_0 = \dfrac{1}{2\pi\sqrt{LC}} = \dfrac{1}{2\pi}\bigg/\Big\{\dfrac{10^6}{1 \times 15\cdot83}\Big\} = 40 \text{ c/s}$

Inductive reactance $=$ capacitance reactance (in magnitude)

$$= 2\pi fL = 2\pi \times 40 \times 1 = 251 \ \Omega$$

Total impedance $=$ resistance (since the reactances cancel) $= 10 \ \Omega$

Therefore current drawn from supply $= \dfrac{V}{Z} = \dfrac{100}{10} = \underline{\underline{10 \text{ A}}}$

and power factor $= \underline{\underline{1}}$

Total power $= VI = 100 \times 10 = \underline{1,000 \text{ W}}$

Voltage across inductance $=$ voltage across capacitance

$$= IX_L = 10 \times 251 = \underline{\underline{2,510 \text{ V}}}$$

5.13. The General Parallel Circuit—Parallel Resonance

As has already been pointed out, it is impossible to obtain a circuit element containing inductance only, since any inductive winding must contain some resistance. The general parallel circuit is therefore normally taken as a coil of resistance R and inductance L, in parallel with a capacitor of capacitance C, as shown in Fig. 5.27(a).

To obtain the vector diagram, vector **V** is drawn first. Vector $\mathbf{I}_c \left(= \dfrac{V}{X_c}\right)$ leads **V** by 90°. Vector $\mathbf{I}_L$, the coil current, will lag **V** by a phase angle ϕ_L, which will be greater than $0°$ and less than $90°$ since the coil contains both resistance and inductance. Vector $\mathbf{V}_R(=\mathbf{I}_L R)$ is in phase with $\mathbf{I}_L$. Vector $\mathbf{V}_L(=I_L X_L)$ leads vector $\mathbf{I}_L$ by $90°$. The vector sum of $\mathbf{V}_R$ and $\mathbf{V}_L$ is evidently the supply voltage $\mathbf{V}$. The main current $\mathbf{I}$ is the vector sum of $\mathbf{I}_c$ and $\mathbf{I}_L$. The angle of phase difference between $\mathbf{V}$ and $\mathbf{I}$ is ϕ.

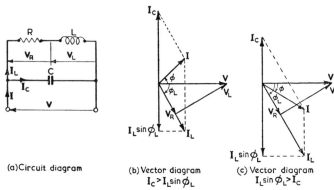

(a) Circuit diagram

(b) Vector diagram
$I_c > I_L \sin \phi_L$

(c) Vector diagram
$I_L \sin \phi_L > I_c$

FIG. 5.27. THE GENERAL PARALLEL CIRCUIT

Two cases, at least, are possible—(a) when $I_c > I_L \sin \phi_L$, in which case the main current will be leading; (b) when $I_L \sin \phi_L > I_c$, in which case the main current will be lagging. The vector diagrams corresponding to these two conditions are given in Figs. 5.27(b) and 5.27(c).

$$\text{The impedance of the coil} = Z_L = \sqrt{(R^2 + X_L{}^2)}$$

The coil current $$I_L = \frac{V}{Z_L} \; ; \; \text{and} \cos \phi_L = \frac{R}{Z_L} \, .$$

Also $$I_c = \frac{V}{X_c}$$

Since the current through the capacitive branch has no active component of current,

$$\text{total active component of current} = I_L \cos \phi_L,$$
and

$$\text{total reactive component of current} = I_c \sin 90° - I_L \sin \phi_L$$

$$= I_c - I_L \sin \phi_L$$

Therefore

$$\text{total supply current} = \sqrt{\{(I_L \cos \phi_L)^2 + (I_c - I_L \sin \phi_L)^2\}}$$

$$(5.36)$$

PARALLEL RESONANCE

In the above analysis either $I_c > I_L \sin \phi_L$ or $I_c < I_L \sin \phi_L$, but a third special case is possible when $I_c = I_L \sin \phi_L$ and this is known as the parallel resonant condition.

I_c and $I_L \sin \phi_L$ may be thought to become equal in the following manner. Suppose the general parallel circuit is supplied from a variable frequency source. At zero frequency (i.e. a direct applied voltage) the inductive reactance will be zero and the coil current, I_L, will, consequently, be a maximum and in phase with V. The capacitive reactance will be infinite and I_c, consequently, zero. As the frequency of the supply increases, the inductive reactance will increase, and the coil current I_L will fall in value and will lag V by a progressively greater amount. On the other hand the capacitive reactance will be reduced as the frequency increases, and I_c will increase in value. Evidently there is one frequency, the resonant frequency, which will bring $I_L \sin \phi_L$ and I_c into equality. The vector diagram for the parallel resonant condition is shown in Fig. 5.28.

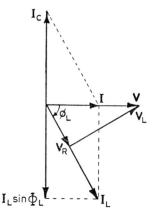

FIG. 5.28. VECTOR DIAGRAM FOR PARALLEL RESONANT CIRCUIT

At resonance, when $I_c = I_L \sin \phi_L$, the total current I can have no resultant reactive component and is therefore in phase with V. Thus, like the series resonant circuit, the parallel resonant circuit has a unity power factor. For given values of the circuit elements the current taken by the circuit at the resonant frequency is a minimum, unlike the series resonant circuit, where the resonance current is a maximum.

From Fig. 5.28,

$$\cos \phi_L = \frac{V_R}{V} = \frac{I_L R}{I_L Z_L} = \frac{R}{\sqrt{(R^2 + X_L^2)}}$$

$$\sin \phi_L = \frac{V_L}{V} = \frac{I_L X_L}{I_L Z_L} = \frac{X_L}{\sqrt{(R^2 + X_L^2)}}$$

The condition for parallel resonance is that

$$I_c = I_L \sin \phi_L$$

Therefore $\quad \dfrac{V}{X_c} = \dfrac{V}{\sqrt{(R^2 + X_L{}^2)}} \cdot \dfrac{X_L}{\sqrt{(R^2 + X_L{}^2)}}$

$$\omega_0 C = \dfrac{\omega_0 L}{R^2 + \omega_0^2 L^2}$$

$$R^2 + \omega_0^2 L^2 = \dfrac{L}{C} \qquad \qquad . \quad . \quad . \quad . \quad (5.37)$$

$$\omega_0^2 L^2 = \dfrac{L}{C} - R^2$$

$$\omega_0 = \sqrt{\left(\dfrac{1}{LC} - \dfrac{R^2}{L^2} \right)}$$

Therefore $\quad f_0 = \dfrac{1}{2\pi} \sqrt{\left(\dfrac{1}{LC} - \dfrac{R^2}{L^2} \right)} \qquad . \quad . \quad . \quad (5.38)$

This is the resonant or natural frequency of the general parallel circuit. If R is small, (which is often so), then

$$f_o \doteqdot \dfrac{1}{2\pi} \sqrt{\left(\dfrac{1}{LC} \right)} \qquad . \quad . \quad . \quad (5.39)$$

i.e. the same expression as for the general series circuit.
Also from Fig. 5.28

$$I = I_L \cos \phi_L$$

$$\dfrac{V}{Z} = \dfrac{V}{\sqrt{(R^2 + X_L{}^2)}} \cdot \dfrac{R}{\sqrt{(R^2 + X_L{}^2)}}$$

$$Z = \dfrac{R^2 + \omega^2 L^2}{R}$$

and substituting $\dfrac{L}{C}$ for $R^2 + \omega^2 L^2$ (see equation (5.37)),

$$Z = \dfrac{L}{CR} \ \Omega \qquad . \quad . \quad . \quad (5.40)$$

Thus the equivalent impedance of the general parallel circuit at resonance is $\dfrac{L}{CR}$ Ω.* Since at resonance the current is a minimum this must represent the maximum impedance of the circuit.

The above expression for the equivalent impedance of the parallel resonant circuit throws some light on the physical nature of resonance.

* This is a pure resistance, often called the dynamic resistance of the resonant circuit.

In the ideal case, when $R = 0$, the impedance which the circuit presents to the supply is infinite and no current will flow from the supply. Nevertheless an alternating current will flow around the local circuit connecting the capacitance and inductance and will serve to transfer energy from the electric field of the capacitor to the magnetic field of the inductor and back again. Since there is no resistance in the circuit this continual energy transfer is achieved without energy loss. In actual cases, where the oscillatory circuit (as it is called) contains resistance, current is drawn from the supply and the energy associated with the supply current makes good the loss in the oscillatory circuit.

The phenomenon of parallel resonance is of considerable practical importance. It forms the fundamental basis of the tuned circuit in electronics and what is virtually a parallel resonance circuit is used for power factor improvement purposes.

Example 5.13

A coil of 20-Ω resistance and 0·25-H inductance is connected in parallel with a variable capacitor across a 100-V, 50-c/s supply. Calculate the capacitance of the capacitor to make the supply current a minimum, the effective impedance of the circuit, the current drawn from the supply, and the power absorbed.

The current drawn from the supply will be a minimum at resonance. The resonant frequency is given by

$$f_0 = \frac{1}{2\pi}\sqrt{\left(\frac{1}{LC} - \frac{R^2}{L^2}\right)} = 50 \text{ c/s}$$

where L is the coil inductance and C is the parallel capacitance

Therefore $\dfrac{1}{LC} = 4\pi^2 f_0^2 + \dfrac{R^2}{L^2} = 4\pi^2 . 50^2 + \dfrac{20^2}{0·25^2} = 105,000$

$$C = \frac{1}{105,000 . L} = \frac{10^6}{105,000 \times 0·25} = \underline{\underline{38 \ \mu F}}$$

Effective impedance $Z = \dfrac{L}{CR} = \dfrac{0·25 \times 10^6}{38 \times 20} = \underline{\underline{329 \ \Omega}}$

Current $I = \dfrac{V}{Z} = \dfrac{100}{329} = \underline{\underline{0·304 \text{ A}}}$

Power $= VI \cos \phi = 100 \times 0·304 = \underline{\underline{30·4 \text{ W}}}$

Also, at resonance,

$$\text{capacitive reactance } X_c = \frac{10^6}{2\pi 50·38} = 83·8 \ \Omega$$

$$\text{Capacitor current} = \frac{V}{X_c} = \frac{100}{83·8} = 1·194 \text{ A}$$

The ratio of supply current to capacitive current at resonance is called the current magnification of the circuit.

Current magnification $= \dfrac{1·194}{0·304} = \underline{\underline{3·93}}$

5.14. The kVA Method for Parallel Loads

Suppose a load having a power factor $\cos \phi$ takes a current I amperes from a supply of V volts.

$$\text{Volt-amperes from supply} = VI$$

Since this is usually a large number it is more convenient to adopt the unit kilo-volt-amperes (kVA) for the measurement of volt-amperes.

Therefore

$$\text{volt-amperes from supply} = \frac{VI}{1000} \text{ kVA}$$

$$\text{Power drawn from supply} = \frac{VI}{1000} \cos \phi \text{ kW}$$

$$\text{Reactive volt-amperes} = \frac{VI}{1000} \sin \phi \text{ kVAR}$$

The "R" is conventionally included in the unit symbol for reactive volt-amperes to distinguish between reactive volt-amperes and total volt-amperes.

Evidently,

Power drawn from supply (kW) = total volt-amperes (kVA) $\times \cos \phi$

Reactive volt-amperes (kVAR) = total volt-amperes (kVA) $\times \sin \phi$

A very common calculation is the determination of the required capacity of the generator or other apparatus to supply a number of loads which are connected in parallel and which are therefore all operating at the same voltage. This type of calculation is shortened by the adoption of the following kVA method.

Suppose a system of voltage **V** supplies load currents $\mathbf{I_1}$, $\mathbf{I_2}$, $\mathbf{I_3}$, etc., at power factors $\cos \phi_1$, $\cos \phi_2$, $\cos \phi_3$, etc., respectively. Active component of total current,

$$I_a = I_1 \cos \phi_1 + I_2 \cos \phi_2 + I_3 \cos \phi_3 + \ldots$$

Reactive component of total current,

$$I_q = I_1 \sin \phi_1 + I_2 \sin \phi_2 + I_3 \sin \phi_3 + \ldots$$

$$\text{Total current} = I = \sqrt{(I_a{}^2 + I_q{}^2)}$$

Now if each term in the above calculation is multiplied by a factor $V/1000$, where V is the common supply voltage, then the calculation would become as follows—

A system of voltage V supplies loads of kVA_1, kVA_2, kVA_3, etc.

at power factors $\cos \phi_1$, $\cos \phi_2$, $\cos \phi_3$, etc., respectively.

$$\text{Total power} = kW_1 + kW_2 + kW_3 + \ldots$$

$$\text{Total reactive volt-amperes} = kVAR_1 + kVAR_2 + kVAR_3 + \ldots$$

$$\text{Total volt-amperes} = \sqrt{\{(kW_1 + kW_2 + kW_3 + \ldots)^2}$$
$$+ (kVAR_1 + kVAR_2 + kVAR_3 + \ldots)^2\}$$

$$(5.41)$$

It will be seen that calculations may be performed in terms of kVA, kW and kVAR in place of total current, active component of current and reactive component of current respectively.

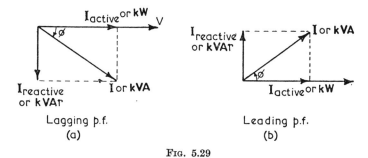

Lagging p.f.
(a)

Leading p.f.
(b)

FIG. 5.29

Vector diagrams may also be drawn. These will be basically the current vector diagrams but with each current vector multiplied by a scale factor of $V/1000$. Fig. 5.29 shows typical diagrams for lagging and leading power factor cases.

It should be specially noted that leading kVAR are taken as positive while lagging kVAR are taken as negative.

Example 5.14

A single phase a.c. generator supplies the following loads—
1. Lighting load of 20 kW at unity p.f.
2. Induction motor load of 100 kW at p.f. 0·707 lagging.
3. Synchronous motor load of 50 kW at p.f. 0·9 leading.
Calculate the total kW and kVA delivered by the generator and the power factor at which it works.

Using the suffixes 1, 2, and 3 to indicate the different loads we have—

$$kVA_1 = \frac{kW_1}{\cos \phi_1} = \frac{20}{1} = 20 \ \text{kVA}$$

$$kVA_2 = \frac{kW_2}{\cos \phi_2} = \frac{100}{0\cdot707} = 141\cdot4 \ \text{kVA}$$

$$kVA_3 = \frac{kW_3}{\cos \phi_3} = \frac{50}{0\cdot9} = 55\cdot6 \ \text{kVA}$$

These loads are represented, approximately to scale, in Fig. 5.30. The three kVAs are not in phase and the total kVA cannot therefore be found by arithmetical addition. The simplest way to find the vector sum of the kVAs is to determine their rectangular components, i.e., the kWs and $kVAR$s of each load, which may be summed arithmetically. The total kW and $kVAR$ may then be combined to obtain the total kVA.

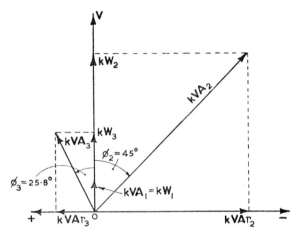

FIG. 5.30. DIAGRAM FOR EXAMPLE 5.14

$$kVAR_1 = kVA_1 \sin \phi_1 = 20 \times 0 = 0$$

$$kVAR_2 = kVA_2 \sin \phi_2 = -141\cdot4 \times 0\cdot707 = -100 \text{ kVAR}$$

$$kVAR_3 = kVA_3 \sin \phi_3 = +55\cdot6 \times 0\cdot436 = +24\cdot3 \text{ kVAR}$$

$kVAR_2$ and $kVAR_3$ are in opposite directions, $kVAR_2$ being a lagging and $kVAR_3$ a leading $kVAR$.

Total kW $= 20 + 100 + 50 = \underline{170 \text{ kW}}$

Total $kVAR = 0 - 100 + 24\cdot3 = -75\cdot7$ kVAR

Total kVA $= \sqrt{\{(kW)^2 + (kVAR)^2\}}$

$= \sqrt{\{170^2 + 75\cdot7^2\}}$

$= \underline{\underline{186 \text{ kVA}}}$

Power factor $= \dfrac{kW}{kVA} = \dfrac{170}{186} = \underline{\underline{0\cdot914 \text{ lagging}}}$

The power factor must be lagging since the resultant $kVAR$ is lagging.

It is often more convenient to adopt the tabular method shown on p. 189 in order to solve problems of this nature.

Load	kW	cos ϕ	kVA	sin ϕ	kVAR
1	20	1	20	0	0
2	100	0·707	141·4	0·707	−100
3	50	0·9	55·6	0·436	+24·2
Total	170				−75·8

The total kVA and overall power factor are then obtained as above.

EXAMPLES 5

1. A circuit consists of an inductance of 0·0318 H and a resistance of 5 Ω connected in series. Calculate its resistance, reactance and impedance for frequencies of 25 c/s and 50 c/s.

Ans. 5Ω, 5 Ω, 7·07 Ω; 5 Ω, 10 Ω, 11·2 Ω.

2. A resistance of 50 Ω is connected in series with a capacitor of 50 μF across a 200-V, 50-c/s supply. Calculate the values of the current and the p.d.s across the resistance and the capacitor.

Ans. 2·47 A; 123·5 V; 157·3 V.

3. A coil of resistance 10 Ω and inductance 0·1 H is connected in series with a capacitor of capacitance 150 μF across a 200-V, 50-c/s supply. Calculate (a) the inductive reactance, (b) the capacitive reactance, (c) the impedance, (d) the p.d. across the coil and the capacitor respectively. (*O.N.C.*)

Ans. 31·4 Ω, 21·25 Ω, 14·3 Ω, 462 V, 298 V.

4. A capacitor of 80 μF takes a current of 1 A when the alternating p.d. is 250 V. Find (a) the frequency and (b) the resistance to be connected in series with the capacitor to reduce the current to 0·5 A at this frequency.

Ans. 7·98 c/s; 433 Ω.

5. A circuit takes a current of 8 A at 100 V, the current lagging by 30 degrees behind the applied voltage. Calculate the values of the equivalent resistance and reactance of the circuit. (*O.N.C.*)

Ans. 10·81 Ω; 6·25 Ω (inductive).

6. A 4·7-H inductor, which has a resistance of 20 Ω, a 4-μF capacitor and a 100-Ω, non-inductive resistor are connected in series to a 100-V, 50-c/s supply. Calculate the time intervals between the positive peak value of the supply voltage and the next peak value of power. (*L.U.,* 1949)

Ans. 2·3 msec.

7. Explain with the aid of diagrams the physical conditions in an a.c. circuit which may cause the current either to lag or lead the applied voltage.

A coil has an inductance of 0·2 H and a resistance of 12 Ω. If a voltage of 200 V at a frequency 50 c/s is applied, calculate the energy stored in the magnetic field during the quarter period when the current is rising from zero to a maximum value. Prove the formula. (*L.U.,* 1950)

Ans. 1·95 J.

8. Explain why the current taken by a capacitor leads a quarter of a cycle in front of the applied voltage.

A capacitor having a capacitance of 20 μF is connected in series with a non-inductive resistance of 120 Ω across a 100-V, 50-c/s supply. Calculate (a) the current (b) the phase difference between the current and the supply voltage and (c) the power. Also, draw the vector diagram.   (*L.U.* 1940)

Ans. 0·501 A; 52·9°; 30·2 W.

9. A coil of resistance 15 Ω and inductance 0·05 H is connected in parallel with a non-inductive resistance of 20 Ω. Find (a) the current in each branch, (b) the total current and (c) the phase angle of the whole arrangement for an applied voltage of 200 V at 50 c/s.   (*O.N.C.*)

Ans. 9·22 A; 10 A; 17·7 A; 22·1°.

10. Show that the current drawn by an inductance lags behind the applied voltage by 90 degrees.

When a voltage of 240 V at 50 c/s is applied to a coil A, the current drawn is 10 A and the power dissipated is 450 W. When the same supply is connected to coil B, the current is 15 A and the power dissipated is 950 W.

Calculate (a) the inductance of each coil, and (b) the current and power taken when the two coils are connected in series across the above supply.   (*O.N.C.*)

Ans. 75·8 mH; 49·2 mH; 5·97 A; 311 W.

11. A coil has a resistance of 5 Ω and an inductance of 31·8 mH. Calculate the current taken by the coil and the power factor when connected to 240-V, 50-c/s mains. Draw the vector diagram. If a non-inductive resistance of 10 Ω is then connected in series with the coil, calculate the new value of the resultant current and its power factor.   (*O.N.C.*)

Ans. 21·4 A; 0·447 lagging; 13·33 A; 0·833 lagging.

12. A parallel circuit consists of two branches, one containing a coil of resistance 120 Ω and inductance 0·25 H, the other a non-inductive resistance 75 Ω in series with a capacitor of 50-μF capacitance. The circuit is connected to a 240-V, 50-c/s supply

(a) Calculate the total current and overall power factor.

(b) Draw to scale the vector diagram for the circuit.   (*O.N.C.*)

Ans. 3·31 A; 0·99 lead.

13. An iron-cored choking coil takes 5 A at a power factor of 0·6 when supplied at 100 V, 50 c/s. When the iron core is removed and the supply reduced to 15 V at the same frequency, the current rises to 6 A at a power factor of 0·9.

Determine (a) the iron loss in the core (b) the copper loss at 5 A (c) the inductance of the choking coil with core when carrying 5 A.   (*O.N.C.*)

Ans. 244 W; 56·2 W; 0·0509 H.

14. Three voltmeters are used to measure the power input to an inductive load in series with a resistance. The voltages across the non-inductive resistance, the load and the combination are 75 V, 80 V, and 140 V respectively. The current is 4 A.

Find (a) the impedance of the load and of the combination (b) the power absorbed by the load (c) the power factor of the load.   (*O.N.C.*)

Ans. 20 Ω; 35 Ω; 202 W; 0·633 lagging.

15. State what is meant by resonance in a series circuit consisting of capacitance and inductance and find the frequency at which resonance occurs in terms of the circuit constants.

A choking coil is connected in series with a capacitor of capacitance 20 μF. With a constant supply voltage of 200 V it is found that the circuit takes its maximum current of 50 A when the supply frequency is 50 c/s. Calculate the resistance and inductance of the choking coil and the voltage across the capacitor. (*O.N.C.*)

Ans. 4 Ω; 0·504 H; 7,970 V.

16. A large coil of inductance 1·405 H and resistance 40 Ω is connected in series with a capacitor of capacitance 20 μF. Calculate the frequency at which the circuit resonates. If a voltage of 100 V is applied to the circuit at the resonant condition, calculate the current drawn from the supply and the voltage across the coil and the capacitor. (*O.N.C.*)

Ans. 30 c/s; 2·5 A; 670 V; 663 V.

17. A coil of 20-Ω resistance has an inductance of 0·2 H and is connected in parallel with a capacitor of 100 μF capacitance. Calculate the frequency at which the circuit will act as a non-inductive resistance of R Ω. Find also the value of R. (*O.N.C.*)

Ans. 31·8 c/s; $R = 100$ Ω.

18. An inductive circuit, in parallel with a non-inductive circuit of 20 Ω is connected across a 50 c/s supply. The inductive current is 4·3 A and the non-inductive current is 2·7 A. The total current is 5·8 A.

Find (*a*) the power absorbed by the inductive resistance
(*b*) its inductance
(*c*) the p.f. of the combined circuits. (*L.U.*, 1939)

Ans. 78·6 W; 0·0376 H; 0·719 lag.

19. A series circuit consisting of a resistance of 12 Ω, an inductance of 0·3 H and a variable capacitor, is connected to an alternator of which the voltage is 100 V and the frequency 50 c/s. Calculate the capacitance which will give maximum current. If another capacitor, C, is now connected across the terminals of the whole circuit, calculate its capacitance in order that the total current may be a minimum when the frequency is increased to 60 c/s the voltage remaining constant.

Draw a vector diagram approximately to scale, for each case, showing the voltages and currents in the different parts of the circuit. (*L.U.*, 1948)

Ans. 33·8 μF; 76·9 μF.

20. A variable capacitor is connected in series with a circuit consisting of non-inductive resistance of 50 Ω, in parallel with a coil across a 200-V, 50-c/s supply. The coil has an inductance of 0·2 H and a negligible resistance. Calculate (*a*) the capacitance of the capacitor when the p.f. of the whole circuit is unity and (*b*) the corresponding p.d. across the capacitor. Draw a vector diagram representing the voltage and the currents. (*L.U.*, 1945)

Ans. 131 μF; 159 V.

21. Two alternators, running in parallel, supply the following loads—
3,000 kW at p.f. 0·8 lagging
2,000 kW at p.f. 0·9 lagging
1,500 kW at unity p.f.
750 kW at p.f. 0·8 leading
1,500 kW at p.f. 0·95 leading.

The alternators share the load so that one machine delivers 5,000 kW at power factor 0·92 lagging. Find the load on the other machine, and the power factor of the total load. (*O.N.C.*)

Ans. 3,750 kW; 0·973 lag.

CHAPTER 6

Simple Three-phase Circuits

WHEN SINGLE-PHASE (1-phase) alternating current was first applied to electric motors, it was found to be unsatisfactory, on account of (a) the poor power factors of the machines, (b) the pulsating torques and (c) the inability of the machines to start from rest without additional apparatus. These disadvantages are overcome by the three-phase (3-phase) system, in which the machine has three separate windings which are supplied with currents $2\pi/3$ radians (120°) out of phase with one another. Economies are effected both in the size of generators and motors for given outputs, and also in the quantities of copper required for 3-phase transmission as against the 1-phase system.

6.1. Single-phase and 3-phase A.C. Generators (Alternators)

In Chapter 2, it was seen that when a coil was rotated in a uniform magnetic field a sinusoidally varying e.m.f. appeared across the terminals. This forms the basis of the simplest 1-phase alternator; a sketch is given in Fig. 6.1(a) of this alternator and the voltage wave-form produced. Consider now three similar coils which are mounted on the same axis as shown in Fig. 6.1(b), the planes of the coils being displaced by $2\pi/3$ rad (120°) from one another. The coils are designated red, yellow, and blue (R, Y, B). The starts of each coil are indicated by the subscript s, and the finishes by the subscript f. The starts and finishes of each coil are brought out to slip-rings on the shaft, six slip-rings being required. When the coils are rotated at a constant speed in the uniform magnetic field, they will have their maximum e.m.f.s induced at different instants in time. Thus the maximum positive e.m.f. in the yellow coil will take place when the shaft has rotated 120° from the position in which there was maximum positive e.m.f. in the red coil. This corresponds to an electrical displacement of $2\pi/3$ rad between the e.m.f.s in the two coils, the red coil e.m.f. leading the yellow by $2\pi/3$ rad for anti-clockwise rotation in the view shown. In the same way, there will be a phase displacement of $2\pi/3$ rad between the e.m.f. generated in the yellow coil and that generated in the blue coil.

If the coils are identical, the same maximum e.m.f. will be induced

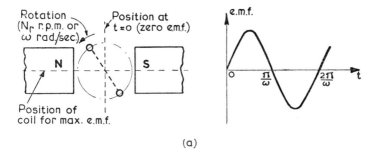

(a)

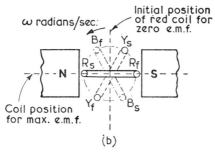

(b)

FIG. 6.1. THE SIMPLE ALTERNATOR

in each one. Let this be E_m. The instantaneous voltage in the red coil will then be given by the expression,

$$e_R = E_m \sin \omega t \qquad . \qquad . \qquad . \qquad (6.1)$$

where $\omega =$ angular velocity of the coils.

Since the yellow e.m.f. lags this by $2\pi/3$ rad, the instantaneous e.m.f. across the yellow slip-rings will be

$$e_Y = E_m \sin \left(\omega t - \frac{2\pi}{3} \right) \qquad . \qquad . \qquad . \qquad (6.2)$$

and that across the blue slip-rings will be

$$e_B = E_m \sin \left(\omega t - \frac{4\pi}{3} \right) \qquad . \qquad . \qquad (6.3(i))$$

since the e.m.f. in the blue coil lags that in the yellow by a further $2\pi/3$ rad, i.e. it lags e_R by $4\pi/3$ radians. Note that $4\pi/3$ lag is equivalent to $2\pi/3$ lead so that e_B may be written as,

$$e_B = E_m \sin\left(\omega t + \frac{2\pi}{3}\right) \qquad . \qquad . \quad (6.3(\text{ii}))$$

These e.m.f.s. are called the *phase e.m.f.s.*

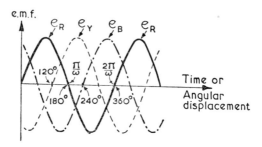

FIG. 6.2. PHASE RELATIONSHIPS FOR 3-PHASE VOLTAGES

The three e.m.f. waves are drawn out in Fig. 6.2 to a base of time, or angular displacement of the coils. They are plotted on the same base line to show their inter-relation in time. These sinusoidal quantities may also be represented by vectors, which give the effective values of voltage and show their phase relation to one another (Fig. 6.3).

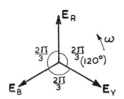

FIG. 6.3. 3-PHASE VOLTAGE
VECTOR DIAGRAM

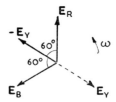

FIG. 6.4. EFFECT OF INCORRECT
CONNEXION OF THE YELLOW PHASE

It is of interest to note what happens if the start and finish of one of the coils are reversed, (say the yellow coil). In this case, the vector e.m.f. measured at the slip-rings of the yellow coil will be reversed, so that the vector $\mathbf{E}_Y$ in the vector diagram will be drawn in the opposite direction to that in Fig. 6.3. This is shown in Fig. 6.4, the result being a three-phase system in which the voltages are displaced by $\pi/3$ rad (60°). This type of 3-phase system is never employed.

6.2. Mesh Connexion

Fig. 6.5 shows the three coils of the simple generator supplying three separate loads. The e.m.f.s are reckoned conventionally

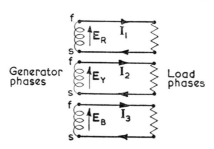

FIG. 6.5. THREE LOADS SUPPLIED BY A 3-PHASE, 6-WIRE SYSTEM

positive from start to finish in the windings. This supply requires six wires, and is equivalent to three separate 1-phase supplies from one generator. For the mesh- (or delta-) connected system each adjacent pair of wires is connected together (Fig. 6.6). The current

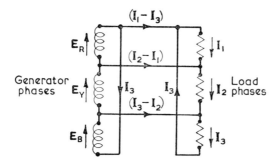

FIG. 6.6. THREE LOADS SUPPLIED BY A 3-WIRE, 3-PHASE SYSTEM

in each line will then be the vector difference between the phase currents. This arrangement effects a considerable saving of copper. The conventional way of showing a mesh-connected generator and load is shown in Fig. 6.7. From this it is seen that, with three mesh-connected coils, the three phase e.m.f.s are in the same direction round the mesh. There is, however, no resultant e.m.f. acting round this closed mesh since, at any instant,

$$e_R + e_Y + e_B = E_m \sin \omega t + E_m \sin \left(\omega t - \frac{2\pi}{3} \right) + E_m \sin \left(\omega t + \frac{2\pi}{3} \right)$$

$$= E_m \sin \omega t + E_m \left(\sin \omega t \cos \frac{2\pi}{3} - \cos \omega t \sin \frac{2\pi}{3} \right)$$

$$+ E_m \left(\sin \omega t \cos \frac{2\pi}{3} + \cos \omega t \sin \frac{2\pi}{3} \right) = 0$$

Since $\cos \dfrac{2\pi}{3} = \cos 120° = -\tfrac{1}{2}$

therefore $e_R + e_Y + e_B = 0$.   .   .   (6.4)

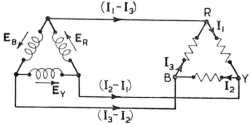

FIG. 6.7. 3-PHASE, DELTA-CONNECTED LOAD SUPPLIED FROM A
3-PHASE DELTA-CONNECTED GENERATOR

Hence there will be no circulating current in the mesh.

FIG. 6.8.   VECTOR
SUM   OF   PHASE
E.M.F.s ROUND A
CLOSED MESH

The fact that the vector sum of the three phase e.m.f.s is zero may also be realized by consideration of the vector diagram. If the three vectors of Fig. 6.3 are placed end to end in order, representing the sum of the three phase voltages taken in order, then, as shown in Fig. 6.8 the three vectors form a closed triangle, indicating that the resultant voltage is zero.

The connexions between phases are normally made inside the generator, so that only three slip-rings are required.

6.3. Star Connexion

In the mesh connexion the windings are connected from the finish of one coil to the start of the next. In the star connexion, all the starts are connected together and the three finishes are brought out to three slip-rings. The common point may be brought out to a fourth slip-ring. Fig. 6.9 shows the conventional diagram of this arrangement. The fourth wire acts as a common return for the currents in the three phases. This is called the 4-wire star connexion. If the volt drops in the connecting lines are neglected, the load voltages $\mathbf{V}_{Ro'}$, $\mathbf{V}_{Yo'}$, and $\mathbf{V}_{Bo'}$ will be equal to the generated phase e.m.f.s, and the star or neutral point of the load (O') will be at the same potential as the star, or neutral, point of the generator.

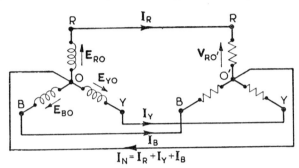

FIG. 6.9. 3-PHASE, 4-WIRE, STAR-CONNECTED LOAD SUPPLIED FROM A STAR-CONNECTED GENERATOR

The voltage across each generator winding is called the phase voltage (V_{ph}). This is the voltage between each line and neutral. The voltage between two lines is called the line voltage (V_l).

If the load is balanced (i.e. all phase impedances identical) the current in each line will be the same, and for a resistive load (i.e. unity power factor) these currents will be in phase with the phase voltages. Thus,

$$\mathbf{I}_R = \frac{\mathbf{V}_{Ro'}}{R_L}$$

where R_L is the load resistance.

At any instant,

$$i_R = \frac{E_{Ro\ max} \sin \omega t}{R_L} = I_m \sin \omega t$$

Similarly

$$i_Y = I_m \sin \left(\omega t - \frac{2\pi}{3} \right)$$

and

$$i_B = I_m \sin \left(\omega t - \frac{4\pi}{3} \right)$$

Therefore neutral wire current is,

$$i_N = i_R + i_Y + i_B$$

$$= I_m \left\{ \sin \omega t + \sin\left(\omega t - \frac{2\pi}{3}\right) + \sin\left(\omega t - \frac{4\pi}{3}\right) \right\}$$

$$= I_m \times 0$$

$$= 0 \qquad . \qquad . \qquad . \qquad . \qquad . \qquad . \qquad . \qquad . \qquad (6.5)$$

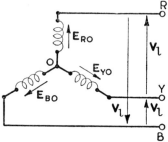

Fig. 6.10. 3-Phase, 3-Wire System

This result holds for all balanced loads, even when the power factor is not unity, hence the neutral current for a balanced load will always be zero. The neutral wire may therefore be removed without affecting the system, giving the 3-wire star connexion shown in Fig. 6.10. Note that the load may be connected either in star or in mesh, irrespective of the generator connexion.

6.4. Vector Diagram for Mesh Connexion with Balanced Loads

In the mesh connected generator (Fig. 6.11(a)) the voltage between any two lines will be equal to the voltage generated by one phase.

Therefore $\qquad\qquad V_l = E_{ph}$ $\qquad$. $\qquad$. $\qquad$. $\qquad$. $\qquad$ (6.6)

i.e. $\qquad\qquad$ line voltage $=$ phase voltage

The voltages between successive pairs of lines will thus be displaced from one another by $2\pi/3$ rad (120°), as shown in Fig. 6.11(b). Suppose the load is such that the current delivered by each phase winding lags the phase voltage by ϕ rad, then, since the load is balanced, these currents will all be equal in magnitude, and will be displaced by $2\pi/3$ rad from one another. These currents are drawn in Fig. 6.11(b) and from them the currents in the three lines can be found. The current in any line will be, by Kirchhoff's first law, the vector difference between successive phase currents. Thus,

$$\mathbf{I}_R = \mathbf{I}_1 - \mathbf{I}_3; \; \mathbf{I}_Y = \mathbf{I}_2 - \mathbf{I}_1 \text{ and } \mathbf{I}_B = \mathbf{I}_3 - \mathbf{I}_2$$

The vector subtraction is shown in Fig. 6.11(c) and follows the normal rules, i.e. the vector to be subtracted is reversed, and then added to the first vector.

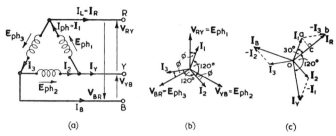

(a)   (b)   (c)

FIG. 6.11. VOLTAGE AND CURRENT RELATIONS FOR A MESH-CONNECTED SYSTEM

The phase angle between I_1 and $-I_3$ is $\pi/3$ rad (60°), hence the vector I_R lags behind I_1 by $\frac{1}{2} \times \pi/3$ rad $= \pi/6$ rad (30°). In the triangle OaB, $Oa = I_1$, $ab = -I_3$, so that $Oa = ab$. Hence the triangle is isosceles. If ac is perpendicular to Ob, then,

$$Ob = 2 \times Oc = 2 \times Oa \cos \frac{\pi}{6} = 2Oa \frac{\sqrt{3}}{2} = \sqrt{3}I_1$$

Therefore $I_R = \sqrt{3}I_1$, and lags it by 30°.

Thus for a mesh connexion with a balanced load the line current (I_l) is $\sqrt{3}$ times the phase current (I_{ph}),

i.e.
$$I_l = \sqrt{3} . I_{ph} \qquad . \qquad . \qquad . \qquad (6.7)$$

It may be seen from the geometry of Fig. 6.11(c) that the phase displacement between successive line currents is also $2\pi/3$ rad.

The power delivered by the generator is the sum of the powers delivered by each phase. If the load is balanced,

total power $= 3 \times$ phase power

$\qquad = 3 \times E_{ph} \times I_{ph} \times \cos \phi$ (where $\cos \phi =$ power factor of each load phase)

$\qquad = 3 \times V_l \times \dfrac{I_l}{\sqrt{3}} \times \cos \phi$

Therefore

Power $= \sqrt{3} . V_l I_l \cos \phi$ watts $\qquad . \qquad . \qquad . \qquad (6.8)$

6.5. Vector Diagram for Star Connexion with Balanced Load

Fig. 6.12(a) shows the diagram of a 3-phase generator with the windings star connected. The conventional positive directions of current and voltage are shown. The load current is assumed to lag the phase voltage by ϕ rad, and from the figure the current in each line must be the same as the phase current,

i.e. $$I_l = I_{ph} \qquad . \qquad . \qquad . \qquad . \qquad (6.8)$$

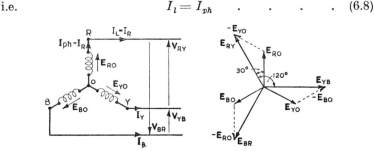

(a)   (b)

FIG. 6.12. LINE AND PHASE VOLTAGE RELATIONS FOR A
STAR-CONNECTED SYSTEM

The generated e.m.f.s will have phase displacements of 120°, as shown in the vector diagram of Fig. 6.12(b). Now the line voltages will be the vector differences between successive phase voltages. Vector differences are taken because the conventional positive directions of the e.m.f.s in a generator are from the star point outwards for each phase. The vector subtraction is performed in the same way as for currents in the mesh connected system, giving

$$\mathbf{V}_{RY} = \mathbf{E}_{Ro} - \mathbf{E}_{Yo}; \quad \mathbf{V}_{YB} = \mathbf{E}_{Yo} - \mathbf{E}_{Bo}; \quad \mathbf{V}_{BR} = \mathbf{E}_{Bo} - \mathbf{E}_{Ro}$$

From the geometry of the figure (similar to that already derived for mesh currents), $\mathbf{V}_{RY}$ is equal in magnitude to $\sqrt{3}$ times E_{Ro} and *leads* it by $\pi/6$ rad (30°). Also, successive line voltages are displaced 120° from one another. Hence for a star-connected system,

$$V_l = \sqrt{3}E_{ph} \qquad . \qquad . \qquad . \qquad . \qquad (6.9)$$

The power developed in the generator will be three times the power developed in each phase and if the load is balanced,

$$\text{total power} = 3 \times E_{ph} \times I_{ph} \times \cos\phi$$

$$= 3 \times \frac{V_l}{\sqrt{3}} \times I_l \times \cos\phi$$

i.e. $$\text{power} = \sqrt{3}V_lI_l \cos\phi \qquad . \qquad . \qquad . \qquad (6.10)$$

This expression is the same as that for the power developed in the mesh connected system, so that $\sqrt{3} \cdot V_l I_l \cos \phi$ represents the power in any balanced 3-phase system.

In the analysis of the star and mesh connected systems it has been assumed that the order in which successive phase e.m.f.s reach their maximum is $R \rightarrow Y \rightarrow B$. This is called the phase sequence of the system. The standard positive phase sequence in Great Britain is $R \rightarrow Y \rightarrow B$.

If the red and yellow coils were interchanged, the sequence would be $R \rightarrow B \rightarrow Y$. It is important, where interconnexion between generating stations is employed, that the phase sequences of each individual station should be the same, otherwise a short circuit will result.

6.6. Loading of 3-Phase Systems

As already mentioned, the load on a 3-phase system may be either star or mesh connected. The normal consumer's supply voltage is from 400 to 440 V between lines, giving approximately from 230 to 250 V between line and neutral. It is usual for distribution to be by the 4-wire system. The motor loads are usually supplied with the full line voltage, and all three phases, but lighting and heating loads are

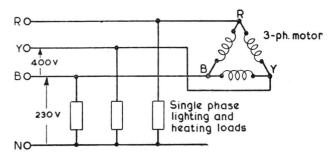

Fig. 6.13. Single-phase Loads Taken from a 3-Phase System

normally connected between one line and neutral, giving the equivalent of a 1-phase supply. If these 1-phase loads are adjusted so that approximately one-third of the total is taken between each line and neutral then this is equivalent to a balanced star-connected system. Domestic consumers are supplied with 1-phase voltage from a 3-phase system by this means. Fig. 6.13 shows three 1-phase loads connected to a 3-phase supply, along with a 3-phase motor. If each 1-phase load takes the same power then the system is balanced.

In the same way as in a single-phase system, the a.c. load for a 3-phase system is usually given in terms of kVA and power factor, and not simply in kW.

Since $kW = kVA \times \cos \phi$, where $\cos \phi =$ power factor of load,

$$\text{then total } VA = \frac{\text{total power (watts)}}{\cos \phi}$$

$$= \frac{\sqrt{3} V_l I_l}{\cos \phi} \cos \phi$$

i.e. $\qquad\qquad$ total $VA = \sqrt{3} V_l I_l$ $\qquad$. $\qquad$. $\qquad$. (6.11)

In the same way the VAR in a 3-phase balanced system are given by,

$$VAR = \sqrt{3} V_l I_l \sin \phi = (VA) \sin \phi . \qquad . \quad (6.12)$$

The overall power factor of any given load is given by the expression—

$$\text{power factor} = \frac{\text{total power}}{\text{total volt-amperes}}$$

$$= \frac{W}{VA} = \frac{kW}{kVA} \qquad . \qquad . \qquad (6.13)$$

Example 6.1

A 3-phase alternator supplies a total load of 25 MW at a line voltage of 32 kV. Calculate the currents in the windings for (a) star (b) mesh connexion, if the load power factor is (i) 0·8 lagging (ii) unity.

(a) *Star*

(i) 0·8 lagging; $\cos \phi = 0\cdot8$

From equation (6.8) power $= \sqrt{3} . V_l I_l \cos \phi$

Therefore $I_l = \dfrac{25{,}000{,}000}{\sqrt{3} . 32{,}000 . 0\cdot8} = \underline{566 \text{ A}} = I_{ph} =$ winding current

(ii) Unity power factor : $\cos \phi = 1$

Therefore $I_l = \dfrac{25{,}000{,}000}{\sqrt{3} . 32{,}000 . 1} = \underline{452 \text{ A}} = I_{ph}$

(b) *Mesh*

As for the star connexion the line currents will be 566 and 452 A for 0·8 lagging and unity power factors respectively.

For mesh connexion $\qquad\qquad I_{ph} = \dfrac{I_l}{\sqrt{3}}$

Winding currents are

(i) $\quad \dfrac{566}{\sqrt{3}}$, i.e. $\underline{327 \text{ A}}$, and $\qquad$ (ii) $\quad \dfrac{452}{\sqrt{3}}$, i.e. $\underline{261 \text{ A}}$

It should be noted that for the same line voltage the e.m.f. generated in each phase of a mesh connected alternator will require to be the full line voltage, while the e.m.f. generated per phase for star connexion need only be $1/\sqrt{3}$ of the line voltage. This means that for the same e.m.f. generated per phase the star connexion will give the larger line voltage. Since it is found to be more economic to generate at a high voltage the star connexion is usually employed in practice.

Example 6.2

Three similar coils each having a resistance of 5 Ω and an inductance of 0·02 H are connected (a) in star (b) in delta to a 440-V, 3-phase, 50-c/s supply Calculate the line current and total power absorbed in each case.

Reactance of coil $= 2\pi fL = 2\pi \times 50 \times 0{\cdot}02 = 6{\cdot}28 \ \Omega$

Impedance $Z = \sqrt{(R^2 + X_L{}^2)} = \sqrt{(5^2 + 6{\cdot}28^2)} = 8{\cdot}05 \ \Omega$

Power factor of each coil $= \dfrac{R}{Z} = \dfrac{5}{8{\cdot}05} = 0{\cdot}622$ lagging

(a) *Star*

From equation (6.10) $\qquad V_{ph} = \dfrac{V_l}{\sqrt{3}} = \dfrac{440}{\sqrt{3}} = 254 \text{ V}$

Therefore $I_{ph} = \dfrac{V_{ph}}{Z_e} = \dfrac{254}{8{\cdot}05} = 31{\cdot}6 \text{ A} = I_l$

From equation (6.8), power $= \sqrt{3} \cdot V_l \cdot I_l \cdot \cos \phi$
$$= \sqrt{3} \cdot 440 \cdot 31{\cdot}6 \cdot 0{\cdot}622 = \underline{15{,}000 \text{ W}}$$

(b) *Delta*

From equation (6.6), $\qquad V_{ph} = V_l$

Therefore $I_{ph} = \dfrac{V_{ph}}{Z} = \dfrac{440}{8{\cdot}05} = 54{\cdot}6 \text{ A}$

From equation (6.7), $\qquad I_l = \sqrt{3} \ I_{ph} = \underline{94{\cdot}8 \text{ A}}$

From equation (6.8) power $= \sqrt{3} \cdot 440 \cdot 94{\cdot}8 \cdot 0{\cdot}622 = \underline{45{,}000 \text{ W}}$

Note that the kVA delivered to three equal impedances which are mesh-connected to a 3-phase supply is always three times the kVA delivered to them if they are star connected.

Example 6.3

A 440-V, 3-ph, 50-c/s system supplies the following loads—

(a) a 50-kVA motor load at 0·8 lagging
(b) a 15-kW balanced lighting load
(c) a 10-kVA balanced welding load at 0·3 lagging.

Find the total kVA, the overall power factor, and the line current.

This type of problem is best solved by constructing a table and filling in the appropriate values.

Load	kVA	$\cos \phi$	kW $(= kVA \cos \phi)$	$\sin \phi$	kVAR $(= kVA \sin \phi)$
Motor	50	0·8 lag	40	0·6	30
Lighting	15	1	15	0	0
Welding	10	0·3 lag	3	0·954	9·54
Total			58		39·54

Let ϕ be the overall phase angle. Then,

$$\tan \phi = \frac{\text{total } kVAR}{\text{total } kW} = \frac{39 \cdot 5}{58} = 0 \cdot 682$$

Therefore $\phi = 34° \; 18'$, lagging

overall p.f. $= \cos \phi = \underline{0 \cdot 826 \text{ lagging.}}$

Total kVA supplied $= \dfrac{\text{total } kW}{\text{overall p.f.}} = \dfrac{58}{0 \cdot 826} = \underline{\underline{70 \cdot 3 \text{ kVA}}}$

Since $kVA = \dfrac{\sqrt{3} V_l I_l}{1,000}$, then $I_l = \dfrac{kVA \cdot 1,000}{\sqrt{3} \cdot V_l} = \dfrac{70 \cdot 3 \cdot 1,000}{\sqrt{3} \cdot 440} = \underline{\underline{92 \cdot 3 \text{ A}}}$

6.7. Power Factor Improvement

Three-phase heating and lighting loads are supplied at power factors from 0·95 lagging to unity, whereas motor loads usually have lagging power factors of between 0·65 and 0·9 lagging. For 1-phase supplies the motor power factor may be as low as 0·4, and electric welding units have even lower power factors. Thus the overall load on a supply system is in the vast majority of cases at a lagging power factor. For the 1- and 3-phase cases, the power factor ($\cos \phi$) is given by

$$\cos \phi = \frac{kW}{kVA}, \text{ or } kVA = \frac{kW}{\cos \phi}$$

In the 1-phase case

$$kVA = \frac{VI}{1,000}, \text{ or } I = \frac{1,000 \; kVA}{V}$$

and for the balanced 3-phase case

$$kVA = \frac{\sqrt{3} V_l I_l}{1,000}, \text{ or } I_l = \frac{1,000 \; kVA}{\sqrt{3} V_l}$$

i.e. kVA is directly proportional to current.

The disadvantage of a low power factor is that the current required for a given power is increased. This leads to the following undesirable conditions—

1. Large kVA for a Given Power

Alternators, switchgear, transformers and cables are all limited in their current carrying capacity by the permissible temperature rise (proportional to I^2). Thus they may be fully loaded with respect to kVA (all a.c. equipment is rated on a kVA basis because of the temperature rise limitation) without delivering their full power. This means that it is possible for existing plant to increase its earning capacity (proportional to power supplied) if the overall power factor can be raised.

2. POOR VOLTAGE REGULATION

The voltage regulation of a system is the change in voltage between the no load and the loaded condition. When a load with a lagging power factor is switched on, there is a large drop in the supply voltage due to increased volt drops in the supply lines and transformers. This drop in voltage reduces the starting torque of motors and expensive voltage stabilizing gear may be required to keep the consumer's voltage fluctuation within the statutory limits.

For these reasons the supply undertakings try to keep the overall power factor at well above 0·8 lagging. Commercial consumers are encouraged to have a high power factor by special penalty tariffs, which relate the cost of energy supplied to the power factor. Domestic consumers are assumed to have almost unity power factor.

Example 6.4

A 30-MVA, 11-kV, 3-phase, alternator supplies full load at a lagging power factor of 0·6. Find the percentage increase in earning capacity if the power factor is raised to 0·9.

The earning capacity is proportional to the kW (or MW) supplied. The load refers to the MVA rating.

MW supplied at 0·6 lagging $= MVA \times$ p.f. $= 30 \times 0·6 = 18$ MW

MW supplied at 0·9 lagging $= 30 \times 0·9 = 27$ MW

Percentage increase in earning capacity $= \dfrac{27 - 18}{18} \times 100 = \underline{\underline{50 \text{ per cent}}}$

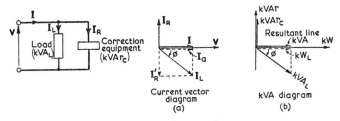

FIG. 6.14. POWER FACTOR CORRECTION

Fig. 6.14(a) shows the current vector diagram for a 1-phase load supplied at a lagging power factor, cos ϕ. The load current, $\mathbf{I}_L$, may be split up into an active component, $\mathbf{I}_A$ in phase with the supply voltage $\mathbf{V}$, and a reactive component, $\mathbf{I}'_R$, in quadrature with $\mathbf{V}$. If, now, power factor correction equipment is installed in parallel with the load, taking a current $\mathbf{I}_R$ leading $\mathbf{V}$ by 90°, such that $I_R = I'_R$, then the resulting line current will be equal to the active component of load current only. The equivalent kVA diagram is shown in Fig. 6.14(b). The leading $kVAR$ of the correction equipment is exactly equal to lagging $kVAR$ of the load, so that the resulting kVA will be at unity p.f., and will be equal to the load power, kW_L. This means that the resultant load will be supplied at unity power factor, i.e. the power factor has been improved from $\cos \phi$ lagging to unity.

Power factor correction equipment includes the following—

(a) Synchronous Motors (synchronous capacitor). These machines take leading $kVAR$, when they are over-excited, especially when running idle. They are used to correct power factor in bulk, and have the advantage that the amount of correction may be varied by altering the excitation.

(b) Static Capacitors. These are usually installed to correct the power factor of a group of motors, or a small industrial concern. They are almost loss free (phase angle 90° leading), but are not variable, so that on light loads they may over-compensate. Automatic switching of capacitor banks may be used to overcome this.

(c) Phase Advancers. These are fitted to individual machines and adjust the p.f. towards unity.

The economic degree of correction to be applied varies with the tariff arrangements between consumer and supply authority. If power is purchased on a kVA basis or where $kVAR$ are charged for as well as kWh, it is usually advisable to correct to from 0·95 to 0·98. Where a bonus payment is offered for power factors over 0·8 or 0·9 the correction should give slightly better power factors than the limit stated.

Example 6.5

A load of 400 h.p. is supplied by a 440-V, 3-phase, 50-c/s motor of 0·9 efficiency, through a cable of resistance 0·03 Ω per core. The motor has a power factor of 0·7 lagging. Calculate (a) the kVAR rating and the capacitance/phase of a mesh-connected capacitor bank to correct this power factor to 0·95 lagging and (b) the percentage reduction in cable copper loss.

Fig. 6.15 shows the circuit and vector diagram for the problem.

(a) Motor input $= \dfrac{\text{Output}}{\text{Efficiency}} = \dfrac{400 \times 0\cdot746}{0\cdot9} = 332 \text{ kW}$

At power factor 0·7 lagging—

$$\cos \phi_1 = 0\cdot7; \quad \sin \phi_1 = 0\cdot715$$

Motor $kVA = kVA_1 = \dfrac{kW}{\cos \phi_1} = \dfrac{332}{0\cdot7} = 474 \text{ kVA}$

Motor $kVAR = kVA_1 \sin \phi_1 = 474 \times 0\cdot715 = 338$ kVAR lagging

At power factor 0·95 lagging—

The power supplied (Oa in Fig. 6.15) must be the same, but the $kVAR$ will be reduced from ac to ab.

$$\cos \phi_2 = 0\cdot95; \quad \tan \phi_2 = 0\cdot329$$

$$ab = Oa \tan \phi_2 = 332 \times 0\cdot329 = 109 \text{ kVAR}$$

Therefore capacitor $kVAR$ required $= 338 - 109 = \underline{229 \text{ kVAR}}$

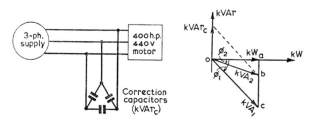

FIG. 6.15. PERTAINING TO EXAMPLE 6.5

Capacitor line current $= \dfrac{229{,}000}{\sqrt{3} \times 440} = 301$ A

Since the capacitors are mesh-connected,

current through each capacitor $= \dfrac{301}{\sqrt{3}} = 174$ A

Reactance/phase $= X_c = \dfrac{440}{174} = 2\cdot54 \ \Omega$

Capacitance/phase $= C = \dfrac{1}{2\pi f X_c} = \dfrac{10^6}{2\pi \times 50 \times 2\cdot54} = \underline{1{,}260 \ \mu F}$

(b) Original line current $= I_{l1} = \dfrac{474 \times 1{,}000}{\sqrt{3} \times 440} = 623$ A

Original copper loss/conductor $= I_{l1}{}^2 R = 623^2 \times 0\cdot03 = 11{,}640$ W

kVA with capacitors connected $= \dfrac{kW}{\cos \phi_2} = \dfrac{332}{0\cdot95} = 349$

New line current $= \dfrac{349{,}000}{\sqrt{3} \times 440} = 458$ A

New copper loss $= 458^2 \times 0\cdot03 = 6{,}300$ W per conductor.

Therefore per cent reduction $= \dfrac{11{,}640 - 6{,}300}{11{,}640} \times 100 = \underline{45\cdot9 \text{ per cent}}$

Example 6.6

Calculate the additional balanced lighting load which the cable in Example 6.5 can supply when the capacitors are connected and find the resulting overall power factor.

Basic Electrical Engineering

The total kVA which the cable can supply will be 474 kVA. With the capacitors connected, the kVA supplied is 349 kVA at a power factor of 0·95 lagging. The lighting load is assumed to be at unity power factor, and Fig.

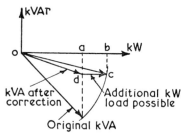

Fig. 6.16. Vector Diagram for Example 6.6

6.16 shows the vector diagram. The solution is easily obtained by means of a table as follows—

Load	kVA	cos ϕ	kW	sin ϕ	kVAR
Motor	474	0·7 lag	332	−0·715	−338
Capacitor	229	0 lead	0	1·0	+229
Lighting		1	x	0	0
			$(332 + x)$		−109

From the vector diagram $332 + x = Ob$

and $109 = bc$

Also $\qquad Oc$ = resultant kVA = 474

$$Ob^2 + bc^2 = Oc^2$$

$$(332 + x)^2 + (109)^2 = 474^2$$

$$332 + x = \sqrt{(474^2 - 109^2)} = 461$$

Therefore $\qquad x = 129$

Therefore additional lighting load (for original cable loading) = 129 kW

EXAMPLES 6

1. Deduce the relationship between phase and line voltages in a 3-phase, star-connected system. Each phase of a star-connected load consists of a non-reactive resistance of 100 Ω in parallel with a capacitor of capacitance 31·8 μF.

Calculate the line current, the power absorbed, the total kVA, and the power factor when connected to a 416-V, 3-phase, 50-c/s supply. (*O.N.C.*)

Ans. 3·39 A; 1·73 kW; 2·44 kVA; 0·707.

2. Show that the power in a balanced, 3-phase circuit is given by $\sqrt{3}\ VI \cos \phi$, where V and I are line values and $\cos \phi$ is the power factor.

Calculate the power absorbed by three similar choking coils each of resistance 150 Ω and inductance 1·275 H when (a) star- (b) delta-connected to a 440-V, 3-phase, 25-c/s supply. *(O.N.C.)*

Ans. 463 W; 1,390 W.

3. Show that the power in a balanced 3-phase circuit is given by $\sqrt{3}\ VI \cos \phi$, where V and I are line values and $\cos \phi$ is the power factor.

Calculate the active and reactive components of the current in each phase of a star-connected 5,000-V, 3-phase alternator supplying 3,000 kW at power factor 0·8. *(O.N.C.)*

Ans. 346 A; 260 A.

4. Derive the relationship between the line and phase currents in a 3-phase delta-connected generator supplying a balanced load.

A delta-connected generator feeds an induction motor which is star connected for starting and delta connected for running. If the starting motor phase current is 20 A and the running motor phase current is 10 A, calculate the generator phase current in each case.

Ans. 11·6 A; 10 A.

5. Explain with vector diagrams how a capacitor can be used to raise the power factor of a lagging load.

A 3-phase, 440-V, 50-c/s circuit takes a current of 200 A at a lagging power factor of 0·6. Calculate the kVA rating of the capacitor-bank required to raise the resultant power-factor to 0·866 lagging.

Ans. 69 kVA.

6. Show, with the aid of a vector diagram, how a capacitor may be used to improve the overall power factor of a lagging load.

A 440-V, 3-phase, induction motor drives a pump which delivers 1,000 gal/min of water against a head of 150 ft. At this load the power factor of the motor is 0·707 and the overall efficiency of the set is 45 per cent. Calculate the kVA rating of the capacitors required to raise the power factor to 0·866 lagging (1 gal water weighs 10 lb). *(O.N.C.)*

Ans. 32 kVA.

7. Explain why an electricity supply undertaking prefers to supply energy at a high power factor. In what way is the industrial consumer encouraged to improve his power factor?

A factory takes the following balanced loads from a 440-V, 3-phase, 50-c/s supply—

    (a) a lighting load of 20 kW.

    (b) a continuous motor load of 50 kVA at 0·8 p.f. lagging.

    (c) an intermittent welding load of 30 kVA at 0·5 p.f. lagging.

Calculate the kVA rating of the capacitor bank required to improve the power-factor of loads (a) and (b) together to unity. Give also the value of the capacitor required in each phase, if a star-connected bank is employed.

What is the new overall power factor if, after correction has been applied, the welding load is switched on? *(O.N.C.)*

Ans. 30 kVA; 490 μF; 0·945 lagging.

CHAPTER 7

The Direct Current Machine

ALL ELECTROMAGNETIC machines may be regarded as energy convertors, either converting mechanical into electrical energy (generators), or electrical into mechanical energy (motors), or electrical energy at one voltage into electrical energy at another voltage (transformers). The operation of all rotating electromagnetic machines depends on two basic principles, (a) the induction of e.m.f. in a circuit undergoing a change of flux linkages, and (b) the force or torque imposed on a current-carrying circuit situated in a magnetic field. As has been seen in Chapter 2, the numerical value of such an e.m.f. in a complete circuit is given by the equation,

$$e = \frac{\mathrm{d}}{\mathrm{d}t} (\Phi N) \text{ volts} \qquad . \qquad . \qquad . \quad (7.1)$$

and the numerical value of the torque by,

$$T = I \cdot \frac{\mathrm{d}}{\mathrm{d}\theta} (\Phi N) \text{ newton-metres} \qquad . \quad (7.2)$$

It should be clearly understood that both of the fundamental actions referred to above apply equally to generators and motors.

The simplest electromagnetic machine consists of a single coil rotating in a steady magnetic field, provided either by a current-carrying coil or by a permanent magnet. Fig. 7.1 illustrates such an arrangement. The coil is attached to the shaft and has its ends brought out to slip-rings which are insulated from the shaft and from one another. Brushes make contact with the slip-rings.

With the direction of the flux and the rotation as shown in Fig. 7.1(a), the direction of the induced e.m.f. as obtained from the Right Hand Rule, will be as shown in Fig. 7.1(b). As the coil rotates the e.m.f. induced in any particular coil side will be reversed every half revolution. At the instant when the coil is in the plane XX (Fig. 7.1(a)) the coil is linking a maximum amount of flux, but the rate of change of flux linkages is zero, and there is no e.m.f. induced in the coil. This condition is repeated after a rotation of 180° from this position. The voltage at the slip-rings is therefore an alternating voltage. If a load resistance is connected across the slip-rings the machine is a simple alternating current generator. Mechanical

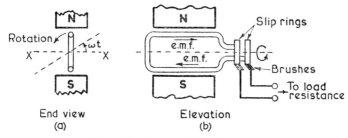

End view
(a)

Elevation
(b)

FIG. 7.1. SIMPLE A.C. GENERATOR

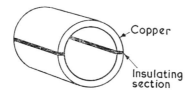

FIG. 7.2. THE TWO-PART COMMUTATOR

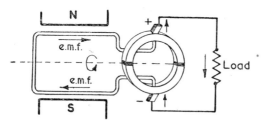

FIG. 7.3. OPERATION OF A TWO-PART COMMUTATOR

energy is supplied to rotate the coil and, neglecting losses, this energy is transformed into electrical energy, which is dissipated in the form of heat in the load resistance.

To obtain a uni-directional current from the coil the slip-rings would have to be replaced by a two-part commutator. This is illustrated in Fig. 7.2 and consists essentially of a hollow cylinder of copper split in half, each half being insulated from the other and from the spindle. Two brushes make alternate contact with each part of the commutator as it rotates. Fig. 7.3 illustrates the way in which the commutator works. The arrows in this diagram indicate the direction of current flow. Although the direction of the current in the rotating coil reverses each half revolution, the direction of the current through the load remains unaltered. However, though the current is uni-directional, it is not steady but fluctuates in value as the coil rotates.

7.1. The Drum-wound Machine

The simple machine which has already been described has the following disadvantages— (i) the large air gap will cause the magnetic

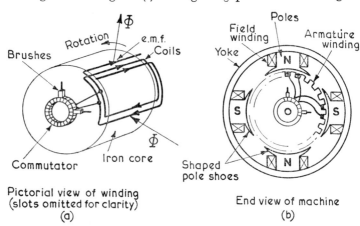

FIG. 7.4. THE DRUM-WOUND MACHINE WITH FOUR POLES

circuit to have a high reluctance, (ii) the winding is not suitable for large power outputs, and (iii) the output voltage fluctuates.

The drum-wound machine, in which the output (or armature) winding is accommodated in longitudinal slots on a laminated iron core, overcomes these disadvantages. The method of winding is indicated in Fig. 7.4. The return loop of each coil is brought back in a slot which is approximately one pole pitch round the armature from the first side of the coil. In this way the coils will link a maximum amount of flux. The iron core serves the double purpose of affording mechanical support to the winding and of offering a low reluctance path to the magnetic flux.

The magnetic flux of the machine is provided by the electro-magnetic effect of coils (called field coils) which surround polar projections, which are normally bolted on to the yoke, or outer casing. Each coil on the armature winding has a connexion to an individual commutator segment. Between each pair of brushes on the commutator there will thus be a large number of armature coils in series. Since these coils will be distributed round the armature, the average e.m.f. between the brushes will be almost constant, irrespective of the position of the armature. This effect is further increased by shaping the pole pieces so that the e.m.f. which is generated in any one coil is not sinusoidal, as in the simple generator, but is flat-topped, as shown in Fig. 7.5.

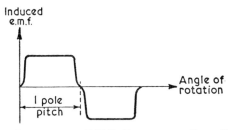

FIG. 7.5. WAVEFORM OF E.M.F. INDUCED IN EACH COIL DUE TO SHAPING OF POLE SHOES

Drum windings for d.c. machines are double layer windings, where each slot accommodates at least two coil sides, one at the top of the slot, and the other at the bottom. The coils themselves are of constant width, or span, and usually contain several turns each. They may be preformed prior to their insertion in the slots. Two types of drum windings will be considered, namely the simple lap winding, and the simple wave winding.

7.2. Developed Winding Diagrams

As has already been mentioned, armature coils may contain many turns, but in order to simplify the work, only single-turn coils and

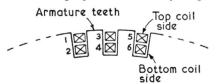

FIG. 7.6. METHOD OF NUMBERING COIL SIDES

two coil sides per slot will be considered. The results obtained may easily be adapted to take into account more complicated windings.

A coil side lies either along the bottom of a slot, or along the top of a slot and each coil (two coil sides) will have one bottom and one top coil side. Since single-turn coils are assumed, there will be as many armature conductors as coil sides. Fig. 7.6 illustrates the method of numbering the coil sides, top coil sides being odd and bottom ones even. The coil sides are numbered in order round the armature.

In the conventional way of representing a developed armature winding, full lines represent top coil sides, and dotted lines represent bottom coil sides. It will be realized that when the conductors are laid into the slots on a cylindrical rotor, the left-hand conductors in a developed diagram will become adjacent to the right-hand ones. (See Figs. 7.8, and 7.9.)

7.3. The Lap Winding

Fig. 7.7 shows the arrangement of the coils in a progressive lap winding, and Fig. 7.8 shows the developed diagram of the winding.

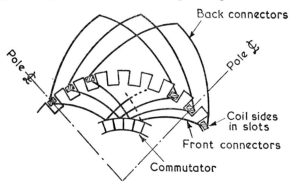

FIG. 7.7. RADIAL VIEW OF PART OF A LAP WINDING

In the lap winding a coil side runs down the top of a slot and pitches round the back of the armature (i.e. the end remote from the commutator). It then enters the bottom of another slot about a pole pitch further round the armature. Emerging from the slot the coil pitches back to a commutator segment adjacent to the one from which the other end of the coil started. If the lap winding is progressive this commutator segment will be one segment further round the commutator in the same direction as the back pitch. If it is a retrogressive lap winding the end of the coil will finish in a commutator segment on the other side of the first. The second coil will start from the commutator segment at which the first coil finished. This coil will enter a slot adjacent to the slot in which the beginning of the first coil is situated. If the winding is progressive this will be one slot further on; if retrogressive it is one slot further back.

The front pitch (y_f) of the winding is the difference (measured in conductor numbers) between the two coil sides attached to any one commutator segment. For example in Fig. 7.8(a) the front pitch is $12 - 3 = 9$ conductors. In Fig. 7.8(b) the front pitch is $14 - 1 = 13$ conductors.

The back pitch (y_b) of the winding is the difference (measured in conductor numbers) between the conductors joined by any back connector. For example in Fig. 7.8(a) the back pitch is $12 - 1 = 11$

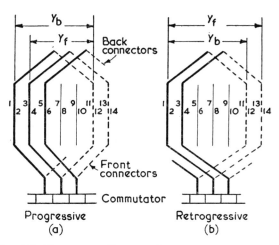

FIG. 7.8. DEVELOPED VIEW OF PART OF A LAP WINDING

conductors, and in Fig. 7.8(b) the back pitch is $14 - 3 = 11$ conductors. It will be noticed that in a progressive lap winding the back pitch is greater than the front pitch, while in a retrogressive lap winding the front pitch is greater than the back.

The total pitch is $y_t = y_b - y_f = 2$ for a progressive winding, or $y_t = y_b - y_f = -2$ for a retrogressive winding.

Since each coil has one side at the top of a slot and the other side at the bottom of a slot, both front and back pitches must be odd. In addition, both pitches must be about one pole pitch in value (reckoned in conductor numbers).

Let Z = number of armature conductors, and p = number of pole pairs.

A pole pitch measured in conductor numbers will be $y_p = \dfrac{Z}{2p}$ conductors

Hence
$$\left.\begin{aligned} y_f &= \frac{Z}{2p} - 1 \\ y_b &= \frac{Z}{2p} + 1 \end{aligned}\right\} \text{for progressive} \qquad . \qquad . \quad (7.3)$$

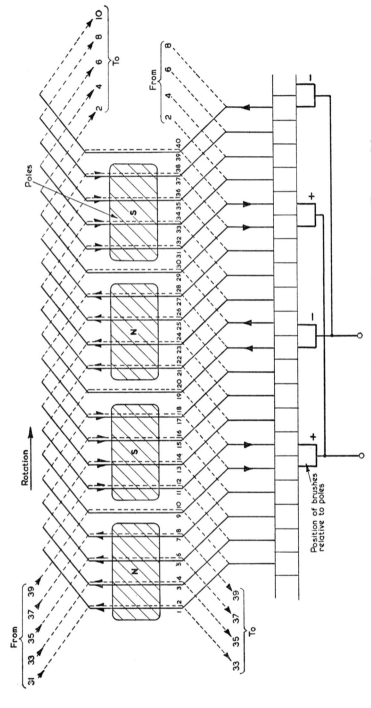

Fig. 7.9. Developed Lap Winding Showing Brush Positions for Example 7.1

and
$$y_f = \frac{Z}{2p} + 1 \\ y_b = \frac{Z}{2p} - 1 \Bigg\} \text{ for retrogressive } \qquad . \qquad . \quad (7.4)$$

This shows that $\frac{Z}{2p}$ must be an even number to make the winding possible.

Example 7.1

Design a 4-pole lap winding suitable for an armature containing 20 slots. Assume single turn coils with 2 conductors per slot.

Number of armature coils = number of slots = 20

Number of armature conductors = 2 × Number of coils = 40

Pole pitch $= \dfrac{Z}{2p} = \dfrac{40}{2 \times 2} = \underline{\underline{10 \text{ conductors}}}$

(since a 4-pole machine has 2-pole pairs).

y_f and y_b must be odd, must differ by two, and must be approximately 10. Suitable values are $y_b = 11$ and $y_f = 9$. This will result in a progressive lap winding as shown developed in Fig. 7.9. Starting with conductor 1 add on the back pitch (11) to obtain the conductor which is linked to conductor 1 by the end connector, i.e. $1 + 11 = 12$. Next deduct from this number the front pitch (9) which gives 3 as the conductor which is joined to the same commutator segment as conductor 12. Conductor 3 will connect with conductor 14 through the next end connector, and conductor 14 will connect with conductor 5 at the next commutator segment. In this manner the winding will continue until all the conductors have been connected together. It will be found that the last conductor to be connected (10) will join the free end of conductor 1 at which the winding commenced. The whole winding is then one complete loop, and is called a closed winding. D.c. machines must have closed windings for satisfactory commutation.

It remains now to ascertain the position and number of brushes required. These, like the field poles, remain fixed in space as the commutator and winding revolve. It is of the first importance that the brushes are in the correct position relative to the field poles. The position of the field poles is marked on the developed diagram of Fig. 7.9 and it is assumed that the flux under the north pole passes perpendicularly into the plane of the paper, i.e. the poles are assumed to be above the plane of the paper. The arrowhead marked "rotation" shows the direction of motion of the conductors. By the Right Hand Rule the direction of the induced e.m.f. in each conductor is now marked, the conductors which lie between poles having no e.m.f. induced in them.

Traversing the winding in order from conductor 1, it will be found that the e.m.f. in each conductor is in the direction in which it is traversed until conductor 9 is reached. There is no e.m.f. induced in either conductor 9 or the next conductor in order (20). Beyond conductor 20 the induced e.m.f.s in the conductors are in opposition to the direction in which the winding is traversed. Hence a brush should connect with the commutator segments connected to conductors 9 and 20. This will be a positive brush since the induced e.m.f.s in the windings are directed towards it.

Continuing round the winding from conductor 20 it is found that all the induced e.m.f.s are in opposition to the direction of traverse until conductors 19 and 30 are reached. In these conductors there is no induced e.m.f. and in succeeding conductors the e.m.f. is in the direction in which the winding is traversed. A brush should connect with the commutator segments connected to conductors 19 and 30. This will be a negative brush, since the induced e.m.f.s are directed away from it.

In the same way a second positive brush should be placed on the segments joined to conductors 29 and 40, and a second negative brush should be placed on the segments joined to conductors 39 and 10. The two positive brushes are connected to the positive terminal of the machine, and the two negative brushes to the negative terminal.

It will be realised that as the armature rotates the conductors which are directly connected to a given brush will change, but since the position of the poles is fixed, the e.m.f. induced in a conductor at a given point in space will not change, and thus there will always be the same e.m.f. directed towards each brush. Hence the voltage between brushes is constant and a d.c. machine is produced.

The following points are evident with regard to the above winding and may be taken as true for all lap wound machines—

1. There are as many brushes as there are poles.

2. The brushes are connected to the conductors which instantaneously lie between the poles, and have no e.m.f. induced in them.

3. The armature winding is divided into a number of sections, the number of sections being equal to the number of brushes, i.e. equal to the number of poles. Hence the number of conductors in each section will be $Z/2p$.

4. The total e.m.f. appearing between the positive and negative brushes is,

$$E = \text{average e.m.f. per conductor} \times \frac{Z}{2p}$$

5. Round the complete armature winding the resultant e.m.f. is zero, so that there will be no circulating current round the closed winding.

6. Each section of the armature winding is connected via the brushes to the machine terminals, so that the sections of the winding are in parallel. Since all the sections are identical there will be an equal share of the total armature current in each.

Let $2a =$ the number of parallel sections into which the armature is divided, then for a lap winding,

$$2a = 2p$$

and
$$\frac{p}{a} = 1 \qquad . \qquad . \qquad . \qquad . \qquad . \qquad (7.5)$$

The current in each armature conductor will be the total armature current divided by $2a$.

7.4. The Wave Winding

In the wave winding successive coils "wave" forward under successive poles instead of "lapping" back on themselves as in the lap winding. The two windings are similar in that they are both closed windings, and they may be regarded as alternatives. Fig. 7.10 illustrates the principle of the wave winding. A simple winding with single turn coils and only two conductors per slot will be examined.

Conductor 1 at the top of the first slot is connected to a bottom conductor approximately one pole pitch further round the armature. This is the back pitch (or coil pitch) and is y_b conductors. y_b must be an odd integer so that a top conductor and a bottom conductor will be joined. The number of this second conductor will be $y_b + 1$.

At the front of the armature the second conductor is joined to a third, which must be a top conductor approximately a pole pitch further round the armature. The pitch will be y_f (front pitch), which must again be an odd integer.

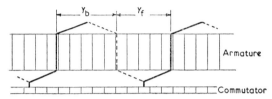

FIG. 7.10. ELEMENTS OF THE WAVE WINDING (DEVELOPED VIEW)

Hence number of third conductor is $y_b + y_f + 1$.

Hence total pitch of one coil $= y_t = y_b + y_f$, and y_t must be an even integer since y_b and y_f are odd integers; y_t is approximately two pole pitches.

The winding then continues round the armature making a pitch of y_t for each pole pair. When one tour of the armature has been completed the winding should connect to either the next top conductor (progressive) or to the preceding top conductor (retrogressive) so that ultimately all the conductors will be connected in a single closed winding. Thus if there are p pole pairs, and Z conductors, then, total pitch in one tour of the armature is

$$py_t = p(y_f + y_b) = Z \pm 2$$

$$y_f + y_b = \frac{Z \pm 2}{p} \qquad . \qquad . \quad (7.6)$$

and $\dfrac{Z \pm 2}{p}$ must be an even integer.

If these conditions are fulfilled then a closed wave winding will be produced. It may be noted that y_f and y_b need not necessarily differ by two as in the lap winding, and are in fact frequently the same.

Example 7.2

Design a 4-pole wave winding for an armature with 21 slots. Assume single turn coils and two conductors per slot.

Number of armature conductors $= 2 \times 21 = 42$

From equation (7.6), $y_f + y_b = \dfrac{Z \pm 2}{p} = \dfrac{42 \pm 2}{2} = 22$

taking $+2$ on the assumption that a progressive winding is desired. Since $(y_f + y_b)$ is even the winding will close, and will include all conductors. It should be noted that 20 slots would not have given a possible wave winding.

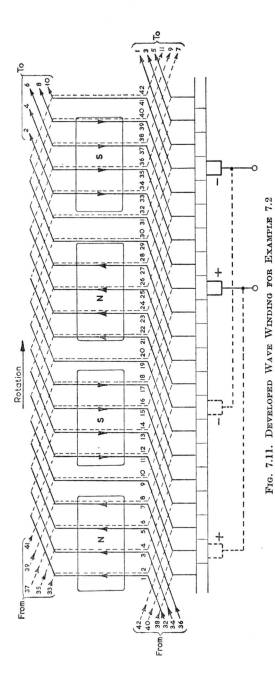

FIG. 7.11. DEVELOPED WAVE WINDING FOR EXAMPLE 7.2

Now make $y_f = y_b = 11$, i.e. an odd number, and approximately one pole pitch. A developed diagram of the winding is shown in Fig. 7.11. Conductor 1 connects at the back to conductor 12 (i.e. $1 + 11$) which, in turn, connects at the front to conductor 23, and so on round the armature until the winding is complete. Each end of each coil also connects to a commutator segment as shown. For the given polarities and direction of rotation the e.m.f. direction in each conductor may be determined from the Right Hand Rule.

To determine the brush position relative to the poles the armature winding should be toured in order from conductor 1. It will be found that the induced e.m.f.s are all in the direction in which the winding is toured until conductors 9, 20, 31, and 42, are reached. These have instantaneously no induced e.m.f.s. Beyond these conductors the e.m.f.s are reversed until conductors 19, 30, 41, and 10 are reached, these having instantaneously no e.m.f. induced in them. The positive brush should make contact with the commutator segments either at the junction of conductors 20 and 31, or at the junction of 40 and 9. (The junctions 9 to 20 and 31 to 42 are at the back of the armature.) It is not necessary to have more than one positive and one negative brush with the wave winding, but frequently more are used in machines with more than one pole pair. In the same way the negative brush (or brushes) should make contact with either (or both) the commutator segments connected at the junction of conductors 30 and 41 (and 10 and 21).

The following points are evident with regard to the above winding and may be taken as applicable to all simple wave windings—

1. Only two brushes are essential—though parallelled brushes may be added. The total number of brushes may be made up to equal the number of poles.

2. The brushes are connected to the conductors which instantaneously lie between poles, and have no e.m.f. induced in them.

3. The armature winding is divided into two sections, this being independent of the number of parallel brushes added. Hence the number of conductors in each section will be $Z/2$.

4. The total e.m.f. appearing between the positive and negative terminals is equal to the average e.m.f. per conductor $\times Z/2$.

5. Round the complete winding the resultant e.m.f. is zero, so that within the closed winding there will be no circulating current.

6. If $2a$ is the number of parallel sections in the winding, then for all wave windings $a = 1$.

Hence
$$\frac{p}{a} = p, \qquad . \qquad . \qquad . \qquad . \qquad . \quad (7.7)$$

and current in any armature conductor $= \dfrac{\text{total armature current}}{2a}$

$$= \tfrac{1}{2} \times \text{total armature current}$$

7.5. Choice of Winding

For simplicity the windings which have been considered have had single turn coils but in practice multi-turn coils are often used. The limit to the number of armature coils which can be accommodated in a machine of a given size depends mainly on the number of segments which may be accommodated in the commutator. In multi-polar machines the number of coils in series in each armature path is less in the lap than in the wave wound armature. The current-carrying capacity of the lap winding is correspondingly greater, while the terminal voltage of the wave winding will be larger.

In small machines the current-carrying capacity of the armature is not generally critical and in order to achieve suitable voltages wave windings are often used. In large machines, on the other hand, suitable voltages are easily obtained because of the relatively large number of armature conductors available, and the current-carrying capacity is more critical. Hence in large machines lap windings are often employed.

In some cases neither the simple lap nor the simple wave winding provides a satisfactory solution, and in such cases it is necessary to use a more complicated type of armature winding.

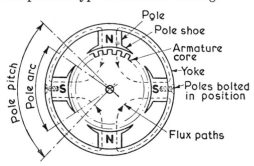

FIG. 7.12. MAGNETIC CIRCUIT FOR A 4-POLE D.C. MACHINE

7.6. E.M.F. induced in a D.C. Armature

Let E = average e.m.f. between brushes (volts)

Z = total number of armature conductors

Φ = flux per pole (webers)

p = number of pole pairs

a = number of pairs of parallel paths in the armature

n_r = speed in r.p.s.

N = number of turns = $Z/2$.

Fig. 7.12 shows the general arrangement of the magnetic circuit and flux distribution in a 4-pole machine.

From equation (2.3)

$$e = \frac{\mathrm{d}}{\mathrm{d}t}(\Phi N) \text{ volts}$$

where e is the e.m.f. in a coil of N turns linked by a flux Φ webers i.e. the instantaneous e.m.f. is equal to the instantaneous rate of change of flux linkage. The average induced e.m.f. will thus be equal to the average rate of change of flux linkage.

Consider a single turn moving through one pole pitch, as in Fig.
7.13.

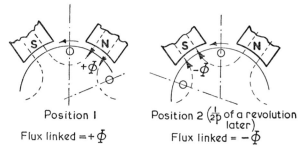

Position I

Flux linked $= +\Phi$

Position 2 $\left(\frac{1}{2p}\text{ of a revolution later}\right)$

Flux linked $= -\Phi$

FIG. 7.13. PERTAINING TO THE E.M.F. INDUCED IN A D.C. ARMATURE

Flux linked by coil initially $= +\Phi$ Wb

Flux linked by coil after moving one pole pitch $= -\Phi$ Wb

Therefore change of flux $= 2\Phi$ Wb

Time taken for the coil to make one complete revolution $\left.\right\} = \dfrac{1}{n_r}$ sec

Therefore time taken for the coil to move through one pole pitch $\left.\right\} = \dfrac{1}{2pn_r}$ sec

Average e.m.f. induced in one turn $= \dfrac{\text{change of flux}}{\text{time taken}} = \dfrac{2\Phi}{1/2pn_r}$ V

Now the number of armature turns in series in any one armature path is equal to half the total number of conductors (since each turn consists of two conductors), divided by the number of paths in parallel,

i.e. number of series-connected turns in any one armature path $\left.\right\} = \dfrac{1}{2}\cdot\dfrac{Z}{2a}$

Therefore average induced e.m.f.,

$$E = \frac{2\Phi}{1/2pn_r} \times \frac{1}{2}\cdot\frac{Z}{2a}$$

i.e. $$E = \Phi Z n_r \frac{p}{a} \quad \text{V} \qquad . \qquad . \qquad . \qquad (7.8)$$

For a simple lap-wound armature $\dfrac{p}{a} = 1$

For a simple wave-wound armature $a = 1$

For any particular machine, Z, p, and a are constants, giving the important proportionality,

$$E \propto \Phi n_r \qquad . \qquad . \qquad . \qquad . \qquad (7.9)$$

Example 7.3

The armature of a 6-pole machine has a wave winding containing 748 conductors. Calculate the e.m.f. generated when the flux per pole is 0·015 Wb, and the speed is 1,000 r.p.m.

At what speed must the armature be driven to generate an e.m.f. of 400 V if the flux per pole is reduced to 0·01 Wb?

What is the flux per pole if an e.m.f. of 500 V is generated at a speed of 900 r.p.m.?

For a wave winding $a = 1$, i.e. there are only two parallel paths. Hence by equation (7.8),

$$E = \frac{0 \cdot 015 \times 748 \times 1,000}{60} \times \frac{3}{1} = \underline{\underline{562 \text{ V}}}$$

Where quantities subscripted 1 refer to original conditions and those subscripted 2 refer to new conditions, then by proportionality (7.9)

$$\frac{E_1}{E_2} = \frac{\Phi_1 n_1}{\Phi_2 n_2}$$

and $\qquad n_2 = \dfrac{\Phi_1}{\Phi_2} \times \dfrac{E_2}{E_1} \times n_1 = \dfrac{0 \cdot 015}{0 \cdot 01} \times \dfrac{400}{562} \times 1,000 = \underline{\underline{1,070 \text{ r.p.m.}}}$

In the same way,

$$\frac{E_1}{E_3} = \frac{\Phi_1 n_1}{\Phi_3 n_3}$$

Therefore $\qquad \Phi_3 = \dfrac{500}{562} \times \dfrac{1,000}{900} \times 0 \cdot 015 = \underline{\underline{0 \cdot 0148 \text{ Wb}}}$

7.7. Torque Developed in a D.C. Armature

Let T = average torque developed (newton-metres)

Z = total number of armature conductors

Φ = flux per pole (webers)

p = number of pole pairs

a = number of pairs of parallel paths

I_a = total armature current (amperes)

Then from equation (2.7),

$$T = I \frac{\mathrm{d}}{\mathrm{d}\theta} (\Phi N) \text{ Nw-m}$$

where I is the current per coil, and N is the number of turns linked by the flux. That is, the torque produced in any position is equal to the coil current times the angular rate of change of flux linkage. Consider a single turn moving through one pole pitch (Fig. 7.13).

Flux linked by coil initially $= +\Phi$ Wb

Flux linked by coil after moving through one pole pitch $= -\Phi$ Wb

Thus change of flux $= 2\Phi$ Wb

Angular movement for one pole pitch $= \dfrac{2\pi}{2p}$ rad

Therefore average torque for one turn $= \dfrac{\text{change of flux}}{\text{angular change}} \times I$

$$= I\,\frac{2\Phi}{2\pi/2p} \quad \text{Nw-m}$$

Now the number of armature coils will be equal to half the total number of armature conductors,

Total average torque developed $= \dfrac{Z}{2} \times I\,\dfrac{2\Phi}{2\pi/2p}$

$$= \frac{\Phi Z I}{2\pi} \times 2p \quad \text{Nw-m}$$

But the coil current $I = \dfrac{\text{total armature current } I_a}{\text{number of parallel paths } (2a)}$

Therefore $\qquad I = \dfrac{I_a}{2a}$

Therefore total average torque developed $= \dfrac{\Phi Z I_a}{2\pi} \times \dfrac{p}{a}$ Nw-m (7.10)

For any particular machine, Z, p, and a are constants, giving the important proportionality,

$$T \propto \Phi I_a \qquad . \qquad . \qquad . \qquad . \qquad (7.11)$$

An alternative derivation of the torque equation may be made direct from the e.m.f. equation (7.8) as follows—

If the e.m.f. generated in a rotating armature is E volt when the current flowing is I_a ampere, then the power entering or leaving the armature is EI_a watt. If losses are neglected this power must be the mechanical power leaving or entering the armature, i.e. torque times angular velocity in radians per second

Therefore $\qquad EI_a = T \times$ (angular velocity),

where T is the torque developed in newton-metres.

Therefore $\qquad T = \dfrac{EI_a}{\text{angular velocity}}$ Nw-m

and hence by equation (7.8)

$$T = \frac{\Phi Z n}{60} \times \frac{p}{a} \times \frac{I_a}{2\pi \times n/60}$$

$$= \frac{\Phi Z I_a}{2\pi} \times \frac{p}{a} \text{ Nw-m} \qquad . \qquad . \qquad . \qquad (7.10)$$

The output torque in a motor will be less than this due to losses, and similarly the driving torque in a generator will be greater than this.

Example 7.4

The armature of a d.c. machine has a mean diameter of 55 cm and an effective length of 25 cm. The armature has a wave winding consisting of 488 conductors. The ratio of pole arc to pole pitch is 0·7. The mean flux density under the poles is 0·854 Wb/m². Calculate the torque developed (in lb(wt)-ft) when the armature current is 243 A. Find also the torque developed if the armature current falls to 200 A and the mean flux density to 0·8 Wb/m².

In order to apply equation (7.10) it is first necessary to find the flux per pole for the given conditions.

Let $2p$ = number of poles.

$$\text{Armature area/pole} = \frac{\text{Total armature area}}{2p} = \frac{\pi \times 55 \times 25}{2p} \times 10^{-4} \text{ m}^2$$

The area of armature actually under each pole will be the total area times the ratio of pole arc to pole pitch (see Fig. 7.12).

Therefore $\quad$ effective area $= \dfrac{\pi \times 55 \times 25}{2p} \times 10^{-4} \times 0\cdot7 = \dfrac{0\cdot303}{2p} \text{ m}^2$

and $\qquad$ total flux/pole $= \Phi = B \times A = 0\cdot845 \times \dfrac{0\cdot303}{2p} = \dfrac{0\cdot256}{2p} \text{ Wb}$

Equation (7.10) may now be applied to find the torque. Hence,

$$T = \frac{0\cdot256}{2p} \times \frac{488 \times 243}{2\pi} \times \frac{p}{1} \times \frac{1}{1\cdot36} = \underline{1{,}780 \text{ lb(wt)-ft}}$$

If the current falls to 200 A, and the flux density to 0·8 Wb/m², then by equation (7.11), the new torque developed is,

$$T_2 = T_1 \times \frac{\Phi_2 I_{a2}}{\Phi_1 I_{a2}} = 1{,}780 \times \frac{0\cdot8}{0\cdot854} \times \frac{200}{243} = \underline{\underline{1{,}380 \text{ lb(wt)-ft}}}$$

7.8. Generator and Motor Action

All electromagnetic machines are energy converters. Generator action occurs when the machine converts mechanical energy into electrical energy; motor action occurs when electrical energy is converted into mechanical. As an energy converter the d.c. machine is not 100 per cent efficient, since there are energy losses in the machine. These losses will be considered later.

ENERGY RELATIONSHIPS

When the machine runs as a generator, converting mechanical energy into electrical, all the losses must be supplied to the machine in the form of mechanical energy. When the machine runs as a motor, all the losses must be supplied to the machine in the form of electrical energy.

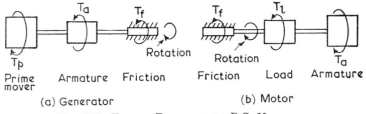

FIG. 7.14. TORQUE RELATIONS IN D.C. MACHINES

TORQUE RELATIONSHIPS

When a d.c. machine runs as a generator the driving torque is applied by the prime mover. The prime mover torque T_p, must be great enough to overcome the torque T_a, produced in the armature, and the friction torque T_f, both of which oppose the prime mover torque. Thus—

$$T_p = T_a + T_f \quad \text{for a generator}$$

When the d.c. machine runs as a motor the torque T_a, developed by the machine must be great enough to overcome the load torque T_l and the friction torque, both of which oppose the developed torque. Thus—

$$T_a = T_l + T_f \text{ for a motor}$$

(See Fig. 7.14).

VOLTAGE RELATIONSHIPS

When an armature of resistance R_a Ω carries current of I_a A, there will be a volt drop in the armature winding equal to $I_a R_a$ V. This means that the generated e.m.f. in the winding will, when the armature carries current, differ from the terminal voltage.

When the machine runs as a generator, the generated e.m.f. E, must be sufficient to supply both the terminal voltage V, and the $I_a R_a$ drop. Hence—

$$E = V + I_a R_a \quad \text{for a generator} \qquad . \qquad . \quad (7.12)$$

When the machine runs as a motor, the external terminal voltage V, must overcome the generated e.m.f. E, and the $I_a R_a$ drop, both of which oppose V. Hence—

$$V = E + I_a R_a \quad \text{for a motor}$$

or,
$$E = V - I_a R_a \quad . \quad . \quad . \quad . \quad (7.13(\text{i}))$$

These relationships are represented in Fig. 7.15.

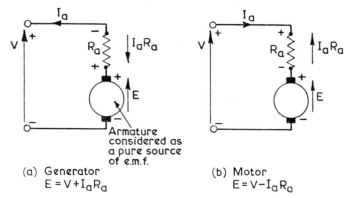

(a) Generator
$E = V + I_a R_a$

(b) Motor
$E = V - I_a R_a$

Fig. 7.15. Voltage Relations in D.C. Machines

The relationship between the e.m.f. E, induced in the armature winding, and the external terminal voltage V, is significant. When $E > V$ the machine acts as a generator, and when $V > E$ the machine acts as a motor.

It will be noticed that the relationship between the generated e.m.f. and the terminal voltage deduced for a d.c. machine is analogous to that derived for the e.m.f. and terminal voltage of an accumulator (§ 1.8).

The mechanism by which the motor regulates its electrical input may now be examined. For a motor, equation (7.13) may be rewritten as—

$$I_a = \frac{V - E}{R_a} \quad . \quad . \quad . \quad (7.13(\text{ii}))$$

As the load on the motor increases, the speed tends to decrease, and hence the e.m.f. will fall in value. By equation (7.13(ii)), I_a rises in value to accommodate the increased load. The reverse process occurs when the load is thrown off the motor—E increases and I_a falls in consequence. Similar relationships apply to generators.

The e.m.f. induced in a motor armature is frequently referred to as the "back e.m.f." In effect it controls the input current to the motor, according to the load imposed on the machine. It is because of the existence of this back e.m.f. that electric motors do not normally require flywheels or devices analogous to throttle governors.

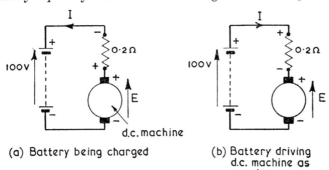

(a) Battery being charged

(b) Battery driving d.c. machine as a motor

FIG. 7.16. PERTAINING TO EXAMPLE 7.5

Example 7.5

A battery of large accumulators has negligible internal resistance, and a constant terminal voltage of 100 V. A d.c. machine has its armature directly connected across the battery terminals; the armature resistance of the machine is $0.2\ \Omega$. The field winding is supplied from an external source. Calculate the input power and the value of the generated e.m.f. if the battery charging current is to be 30 A. Find also the e.m.f. and machine output power when the machine is used as a motor and draws a current of 30 A from the battery. Mechanical and electrical losses other than copper loss are to be neglected.

Fig. 7.16 shows the currents and voltages for the generating and motoring conditions.

(a) Generating

By equation (7.12) generator e.m.f.,

$$E = V + I_a R_a = 100 + 30 \times 0.2 = \underline{106\ \text{V}}$$

Therefore input power $= EI_a = 106 \times 30 = 3,180\ \text{W}$

or, input power = power absorbed by battery + heat loss.

$$V_a I_a + I_a^2 R_a = 100 \times 30 + 30^2 \times 0.2 = \underline{3,180\ \text{W}}$$

(b) Motoring

By equation (7.13) motor e.m.f. $= E = V - I_a R_a = 100 - 30 \times 0.2 = \underline{\underline{94\ \text{V}}}$

Therefore output power $= EI_a = 94 \times 30 = 2,820\ \text{W}$

or alternatively, output power = battery output power − heat loss

$$= VI_a - I_a^2 R_a = 100 \times 30 - 30^2 \times 0.2$$
$$= \underline{2,820\ \text{W}}$$

It should be clearly noted that the current direction changes but the e.m.f. and terminal voltage directions remain the same when the operation changes from generator action to motor action or vice versa.

In practice the circuit would contain some protective device to prevent the armature of the machine from short-circuiting the battery when the machine was at rest, and hence had no armature e.m.f.

7.9. Armature Reaction in the D.C. Machine

Fig. 7.17(a) shows the flux distribution in a two-pole machine when the armature winding carries no current. The magnetic neutral axis (m.n.a.) is the line drawn at right angles to the mean direction of the flux which passes through the centre of the armature.

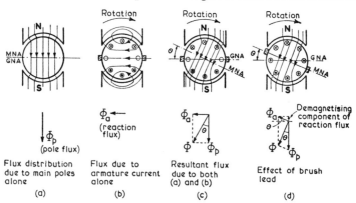

Flux distribution due to main poles alone

(a)

Flux due to armature current alone

(b)

Resultant flux due to both (a) and (b)

(c)

Effect of brush lead

(d)

FIG. 7.17. ARMATURE REACTION IN A D.C. GENERATOR

The geometrical neutral axis (g.n.a.) bisects the angle between the centre line of adjacent poles. In the case shown the m.n.a. and the g.n.a. coincide.

When the armature winding carries current it effectively forms a current-carrying coil and has therefore a magnetic field associated with it. To study this effect it is necessary to consider generators and motors separately, since, with the same rotation and polarities the current directions will be reversed.

GENERATORS

Fig. 7.17(b) shows a cross-section of a d.c. generator with a given rotation and polarity, the magnetic field due to the armature currents only being shown. The directions of the e.m.f.s induced in the armature conductors may be found by application of the R.H. rule and are shown by the dot and cross convention. With the brushes in their normal positions the armature currents will be in the same directions as the armature conductor e.m.f.s, and will also be represented by the same dots and crosses. These currents will set up a magnetic field as illustrated, the direction of the lines of force being found by the R.H. screw rule.

Comparing Fig. 7.17(a) with 7.17(b) it will be observed that the main and armature magnetic fields are at right angles to one another.

The resultant flux is due to the combined action of both fields, and is shown for the generator case in Fig. 7.17(c). The magnetic field is seen to be twisted in the direction of rotation. Since the armature current varies with the load on the machine the degree of twist will be greatest on heavy loads and negligible on light loads. The figure also shows that the m.n.a. will not now coincide with the g.n.a.

This cross-magnetizing effect of armature reaction, as it is called, has a secondary weakening effect on the total flux. As a result of the displacement of the field the value of the flux density is increased in the *trailing* pole tips and decreased in the *leading* pole tips. This effect is clearly shown in Fig. 7.17(c). Since the permeability of iron is not constant it will decrease in the trailing pole tips (where the flux density is greatest) and increase in the leading pole tips (where the flux density is least). The increase under the leading pole tip will, however, not be so great as the decrease under the trailing pole tip, and the average reluctance of the magnetic circuit of the machine will therefore be increased, causing some decrease in the flux.

For correct commutation the brushes should properly make contact with armature coils which are momentarily experiencing no change of flux linkage and consequently have no e.m.f. induced in them. The brushes should therefore make contact with coils lying in the m.n.a. To achieve this in a generator the brushes must be given a forward lead, i.e. they must be moved forward in the direction of rotation from the g.n.a. to the m.n.a.

Although this allows satisfactory commutation it leads to direct demagnetization of the main field, with a consequent reduction in flux. This is shown in the diagram of Fig. 7.17(d), where the armature flux has shifted round by the same electrical angle as the brushes, and hence has a component opposing the main field.

MOTORS

For a motor with the same polarity and direction of rotation as is shown for the generator in Fig. 7.17, the direction of the induced e.m.f.s will be the same, but the armature currents will flow in the opposite directions. This means that the direction of the armature reaction field will be reversed and hence the resultant field will be twisted in the opposite direction to that shown for a generator. This is indicated in the m.m.f. diagram of Fig. 7.18(a). The m.n.a. will thus move round an angle θ against the direction of rotation. The leading pole tips will have an increased flux density and the trailing pole tips a decreased flux density, giving rise (as in the case of a generator) to a slight weakening of the main field.

For best commutation the brushes must be given a backward lag in order to bring the coils connected to them into (or just beyond) the m.n.a. As in the generator, this gives rise to a demagnetizing component of armature reaction flux tending further to weaken the main field, as is shown in Fig. 7.18(b).

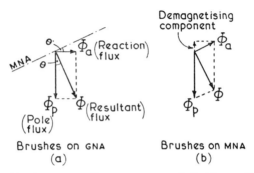

FIG. 7.18. ARMATURE REACTION IN A D.C. MOTOR WHOSE POLARITY AND ROTATION ARE THE SAME AS FOR THE GENERATOR IN FIG. 7.17

The preceding results appertain to a 2-pole machine but are in fact true for any number of pole pairs. Fig. 7.19 illustrates the magnetic fields associated with a 6-pole generator. In (a) the magnetic field of the armature current is omitted. For the rotation and polarities shown the directions of the induced e.m.f.s in the

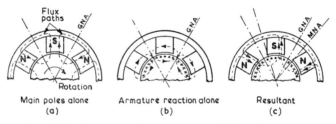

FIG. 7.19. ARMATURE REACTION IN A 6-POLE GENERATOR

armature conductors are deduced by the R.H. rule. Since the machine is taken to be generating, the directions of the armature currents are the same as the directions of the e.m.f.s. The magnetic field due to the armature currents alone is shown in Fig. 7.19(b), while (c) shows the combined field. It can be seen that the results are the same as those derived for the 2-pole machine.

7.10. Commutation

From Figs. 7.9 and 7.11 for lap and wave windings respectively, it will be observed that in all cases a brush is connected via commutator segments, to coils which have opposing e.m.f.s, i.e. the e.m.f.s in the coils connected to a brush are either all directed towards the brush (positive brush) or all directed away from the brush (negative brush). Further, the direction of the e.m.f. in a coil reverses as the coil passes a brush.

If the machine is generating, then the armature currents will be in the same direction as the armature e.m.f.s. Hence the current in the coils connected to a brush are either all towards the brush (positive brush) or all directed away from the brush (negative brush). The direction of the current in a coil will therefore reverse as the coil passes a brush.

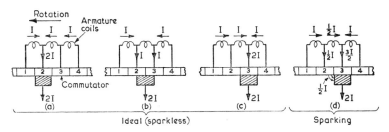

FIG. 7.20. TO ILLUSTRATE THE ACTION OF A COIL UNDERGOING COMMUTATION

If the machine is motoring, then the armature currents will be in the opposite direction to the armature e.m.f.s, so that in this case also the currents in the coils are either all directed away from a brush (positive brush) or towards a brush (negative brush).

In both cases the current in a coil reverses as the coil passes a brush. This is termed commutation. The ideal process of commutation is illustrated in Fig. 7.20. In (a) the brush is just about to make contact with the second commutator segment joined to the central coil, so that this coil is just about to undergo commutation. The full current per conductor $\left(I = \dfrac{I_a}{2a}\right)$ flows through the coil. In (b) the coil is short circuited by the brush so that no current flows in the coil. In (c) the brush has just broken contact with the commutator segment of the central coil and the current in this coil is now reversed and of full value I amperes.

If, at the instant when the brush breaks contact with the commutator segment connected to the coil undergoing commutation, the current in the coil has not reached its full value of I in the reverse direction (due, say, to the self inductance of the coil), the result will be sparking between the commutator segment and the brush. This is shown in Fig. 7.20(d). In this diagram it is assumed that the value of the current in the commutated coil reaches only $I/2$ in the reverse direction at the end of commutation. The remaining portion of the current per conductor ($I/2$) still flows to the commutator segment marked 2. Along this path, however, there is no direct connection to the brush. The current therefore takes a path through the air between the commutator segment and the brush, and sparking results.

The criterion of good commutation is that it should be sparkless, and this depends on accomplishing the current reversal during the time of commutation, i.e. the time during which the coil is short circuited. This is clearly not easily accomplished since the rate of change of current is likely to be quite high, and the inductance of the coil is quite considerable. It is essential that the commutated coil shall not have an e.m.f. induced in it tending to maintain the current in its original direction, if the current reversal is to occur in the time of commutation. On the other hand it would obviously give faster current reversal if an e.m.f. were induced in the commutated coil in such a direction as to oppose the original direction of the current flow.

RESISTANCE COMMUTATION

In early machines brushes were made of copper but carbon brushes have been found much more satisfactory. The essential difference between a copper and a carbon brush is that the copper brush has a small resistance while the carbon brush has a large resistance, compared with the resistance of an armature coil. The resistance of the carbon brush is largely contact resistance, hence, as the area of the contact between brush and commutator segment diminishes, the resistance increases. As the brush passes over the commutator segment therefore, more and more of the current which has been passing through the brush takes the alternative path through the coil. When the break between the brush and the commutator segment finally occurs, all the current is passing through the coil and commutation is achieved sparklessly.

If the resistance of the coil were negligible, the resistance of the brush entirely contact resistance, and if the coil experienced no e.m.f. as it underwent commutation, then "straight line" commutation would result. That is to say, the rate of change of current in the coil would be constant and the graph of coil current against time would be a straight line. These ideal conditions are represented in Fig. 7.21.

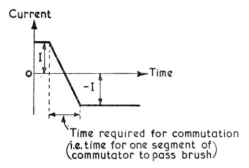

FIG. 7.21. IDEAL RESISTANCE COMMUTATION

E.M.F. COMMUTATION

Because straight line commutation is not actually achieved in practice, it is often advantageous to have an e.m.f. induced in the commutated coil, provided the e.m.f. is in a direction which assists the change of current. If the machine is a generator the brushes should be given a slight forward lead, so that the commutated coil has an e.m.f. in the direction of the coil current after commutation. If the machine is a motor, the brushes should be given a slight backward lag for the same reason.

When the armature reaction is also considered, it will be seen that if the brushes are left in the g.n.a. then the commutated coil will not merely have no e.m.f. induced in it, but will have an e.m.f. in the wrong direction for good commutation, i.e. opposing the change of current. With the brushes in the m.n.a. the commutated coil will have no e.m.f. in it, so that to produce a commutating e.m.f. the brushes should be moved slightly further round the machine than the m.n.a.

In older machines the brush gear was mounted on a rocker ring which shifted the whole brush gear as a unit. The rocker ring position was adjusted by means of a hand wheel and the brush position was altered as the load on the machine changed. Since the strength of the armature field depends upon the armature current the position of the m.n.a. changes as the load changes, so that to obtain good commutation at all loads, the brush position would have to be altered every time the load changed.

E.M.F. Commutation by Interpoles

In modern machines of more that a few kW or h.p. rating, the brushes are fixed on the g.n.a., and good commutation is achieved by the use of interpoles. Interpoles are small poles placed symmetrically between the main poles. The current passing through the coils wound on the interpoles is the armature current, since the interpole coils are connected in series with the armature. The m.m.f. (i.e. ampere-turns) of the interpoles is therefore proportional to the armature current. The armature reaction field is also proportional to the armature current. Interpoles may thus be made to compensate correctly for all conditions of loading. The method of connexion is indicated in Fig. 7.22(a).

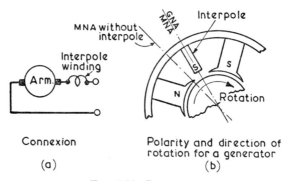

Connexion

(a)

Polarity and direction of rotation for a generator

(b)

Fig. 7.22. Interpoles

The interpole m.m.f. may be arranged to be equal and opposite to the armature m.m.f. in the region of the commutated coil. As a result the coil has no e.m.f. induced in it. Frequently the interpole m.m.f. is made greater than the armature m.m.f. in the zone of commutation. This has the effect of inducing an e.m.f. in the commutated coil in such a direction as to oppose the current in the coil at the start of commutation, and to assist its growth in the opposite direction.

The practice of overwinding the interpole (i.e. interpole m.m.f. > armature m.m.f.) is analogous to giving the brushes lead or lag beyond the m.n.a. into the fringe of the oncoming main pole in a generator, or of the receding main pole in a motor. In a generator the polarity of the interpole is that of the oncoming main pole while in a motor it is that of the receding main pole. The connexions for a generator are illustrated in Fig. 7.22(b).

It should be noted that since the interpole windings carry the armature current, then when a machine changes from generator to motor (with consequent reversal of current), the polarities of the interpoles will also change, as is required for good commutation. A machine may be used as a motor or a generator without change to the interpole connexions.

7.11. Armature Reaction Ampere-turns

The armature reaction in a 2-pole machine will be considered first, and the results will then be applied to a multipolar machine. Let

$$Z = \text{total number of armature conductors}$$

and $\qquad p = \text{total number of pole pairs (1 in this case)}$

Then the number of conductors under one pole pitch will be $Z/2p$. Since the direction of the current in the armature conductors is opposite on opposite sides of a brush, these conductors will effectively form a coil whose axis is along the brush axis. Pairs of conductors each on opposite sides of the brush axis may be thought of as forming a turn of the equivalent coil.

Therefore $\qquad$ total number of turns on effective coil $= Z/2p$

current carried by each turn $=$ conductor current $= I_a/2a$,

where I_a is the total armature current, and a is the number of pairs of parallel armature paths. Then,

$$\text{total ampere-turns on effective coil} = \frac{I_a Z}{2a \cdot 2p}$$

i.e. $\qquad$ armature reaction ampere-turns $= \dfrac{I_a Z}{2a \cdot 2p} \qquad$. (7.14)

If interpoles are added to this machine, one at each end of the g.n.a., then the total ampere-turns on the interpoles would require to be $I_a Z/(2a \cdot 2p)$ for the cancellation of the armature reaction in the commutation zone. Half of this would be required for each interpole, so that the number of turns on each interpole would be $\frac{1}{2}Z/(2a \cdot 2p)$. A slightly larger number might be used to provide a commutating e.m.f.

Before proceeding any further it is convenient to explain the conception of electrical degrees. As a coil moves through one pole pitch, the e.m.f. induced in it is reversed. If the e.m.f. is represented vectorially this would be equivalent to reversing the direction of the vector, i.e. moving it through $180°$. One pole pitch is thus said to correspond to 180 electrical degrees ($^{\circ}E$). For a machine with p pole pairs,

$$\theta_e = p\theta_m$$

where θ_m is the actual mechanical angle and θ_e is the corresponding electrical angle.

For a 2-pole machine $\theta_e = \theta_m$

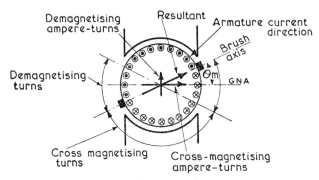

FIG. 7.23. ARMATURE REACTION AMPERE-TURNS IN A 2-POLE MACHINE

Fig. 7.23 shows the armature of a machine in which the brushes have been moved through θ_m° from the g.n.a. The armature m.m.f. will be directed along the brush axis, so that it will have two mutually perpendicular components, one along the g.n.a. and the other along the axis of the main field. The conductors which are situated within $\pm\theta_m^{\circ}$ from the g.n.a. will form a coil whose axis is along the axis of the main field, and these conductors will therefore give rise to the demagnetising ampere-turns. Since one pole pair corresponds to 360 electrical degrees, and the brush shift to $\theta_e = p \cdot \theta_m$ electrical degrees, the fraction of the total ampere-turns which will produce demagnetization is

$$\frac{4\theta_e}{360} = \frac{p\theta_m}{90}$$

Therefore demagnetizing AT/pole pair

$$= \frac{ZI_a}{2a\,2p} \times \frac{\theta_e}{90}$$

$$= \frac{ZI_a}{2a \cdot 2p} \cdot \frac{p\theta_m}{90} = \frac{ZI_a}{a} \times \frac{\theta_m}{360} \quad . \quad . \quad . \quad (7\;15)$$

Since the remaining ampere-turns are cross-magnetizing, these must be

$$\text{cross-magnetizing AT} = \frac{ZI_a}{2a \cdot 2p} - \frac{ZI_a}{a} \cdot \frac{\theta_m}{360} \quad . \quad . \quad (7.16)$$

MULTIPOLAR MACHINES

Consider one of the flux paths shown in Fig. 7.19(b). The armature reaction m.m.f. will act round this path. The number of armature turns setting up this m.m.f. will be equal to the number of armature conductors under one pole pitch, i.e. $Z/2p$ as in the 2-pole machine.

Therefore   total armature AT/pole pair $= \dfrac{ZI_a}{2a \cdot 2p}$

To cancel these ampere-turns in the commutating zone, the number of ampere-turns on each interpole will have to be

$$\text{interpole AT} = \frac{1}{2} \cdot \frac{ZI_a}{2a \cdot 2p}$$

Note that only conductors under a north pole need be considered since the conductors under south poles may be regarded as the return sides of coils whose first sides lay under a north pole.

The armature reaction in a multipolar machine may thus be computed from the same equation (equation (7.14)) as was derived for a 2-pole machine. The demagnetizing and cross-magnetizing components may also be computed from equations (7.15) and (7.16)

Example 7.6

A 350-kW, 440-V, 6-pole, d.c. generator has a lap-wound armature of 576 conductors. If the brushes are given a lead of 4 commutator segments, calculate the value of the armature demagnetizing and cross-magnetizing ampere-turns per pole on full load. The armature coils are single turn.

Total number of commutator segments $= \dfrac{576}{2} = 288$ since single-turn coils are used.

Angular lead of brushes $= 360° \times \dfrac{4}{288}$ °M

$$= 5°M = 3 \times 5°E$$

$$= 15°E$$

Full load armature current, $I_a = \dfrac{350 \times 10^3}{440} = 795$ A

From equation (7.14),

total armature AT/pole pair $= \dfrac{576 \times 795}{6 \times 6} = 12{,}700$

From equation (7.15)

$$\text{demagnetizing AT/pole pair} = \text{total AT} \frac{\theta_e}{90} = 12,700 \times \frac{15}{90}$$

Therefore demagnetizing AT/pole $= \frac{1}{2} \times 12,700 \times \dfrac{15}{90} = \underline{1,060}$

Cross-magnetizing AT/pole $= \frac{1}{2}(12,700 - 2,120) = \underline{5,300}$

Example 7.7

A 350-kW, 6-pole, 440-V, shunt generator has a lap wound armature of 576 conductors. Calculate the turns required on each interpole if the interpole air gap is 0·8 cm, and the flux density under the interpole is to be 0·35 Wb/m². Make an addition of 10 per cent to the interpole m.m.f. required to establish the flux in the air gap, to allow for the iron parts of the interpole magnetic circuit.

From the previous example, full load current = 795 A, and armature AT/pole pair = 12,700.

Thus 6,350 AT will be required on each interpole to cancel the armature reaction m.m.f. In addition, ampere-turns will be required to establish the desired flux in the interpole air gap.

Interpole AT to establish

interpole flux in air gap $= H_a l_a = \dfrac{B_a}{\mu_o} \cdot l_a$ from § 2.25

$$= \frac{0 \cdot 35}{4\pi \times 10^{-7}} \times 0 \cdot 8 \times 10^{-2} = \underline{2,230}$$

Interpole AT to establish flux in iron parts of magnetic circuit $= 0 \cdot 1 \times 2,230$
$$= 223$$

Therefore total interpole AT $= 6350 + 2230 + 223 = 8803$

Interpole exciting current $= I_a = 795$ A

Therefore number of interpole turns $= \dfrac{8803}{795} = 11 \cdot 1$ $\underline{\text{say 11 turns}}$

7.12. Methods of Exciting D.C. Generators

The magnetic field in a d.c. machine is normally supplied by electromagnetic means, i.e. by current-carrying coils wound round polar projections. Excitation is the term applied to the production of a magnetic field in the machine. There are two general methods of excitation, namely separate excitation and self excitation. The latter method may be broken down into three sub-sections—shunt excitation, series excitation and compound excitation. Compound excitation may be either "short shunt" or "long shunt".

(i) Separate Excitation

Fig. 7.24 shows the connexion diagram for a separately excited generator. For this method of excitation a separate d.c. supply is required, i.e. a source other than the generator itself.

From equation (7.12),

$$E = V + IR_a$$

where E is the generated e.m.f., V is the terminal voltage, R_a is the armature resistance, and I is the load current. It should be noted that in Fig. 7.24 the e.m.f., (E) is shown as existing across the armature, and the armature resistance is shown external to the armature. This is a conventional representation which has some convenience and may be regarded as an equivalent circuit of the machine. In fact, of course, it is the voltage V which appears across the armature.

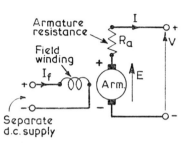

Separate excitation has the obvious disadvantage of requiring an external supply, but since the output voltage may be controlled more easily and over a wider range (from zero to a maximum) this type of excitation finds many applications.

Fig. 7.24. SEPARATELY EXCITED D.C. GENERATOR

(ii) SHUNT EXCITATION

In the shunt excited generator the field winding is connected in parallel with the load and is thus supplied by the armature of the machine itself (Fig. 7.25). In general the m.m.f. (ampere-turns) required to establish the flux in the machine may be obtained by a large number of different combinations of field current and turns. To reduce the field current loading on the armature it is advantageous to make the field current low. Therefore shunt field windings are low current windings having a large number of turns, a high resistance and incidentally a high inductance.

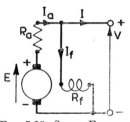

Fig. 7.25. SHUNT EXCITED D.C. GENERATOR

If an armature rotates when there is no magnetic field no e.m.f. will be induced in it. In the shunt generator the armature supplies the field, and hence it might be thought that the machine would not excite. However, there will normally be some residual magnetism in the poles which will produce a small field. This will induce a small e.m.f. in the armature windings and this in turn will cause a small field current. This field current will increase the flux per pole and the e.m.f. of the machine will build up. The build up of e.m.f. will be limited, among other factors, by saturation in the magnetic circuit of the machine. (See § 7.14.)

If, for any reason (e.g. when the machine is first constructed) there is no residual magnetism, the shunt generator will not excite. Moreover, even if there is residual magnetism it must be of the correct polarity. If the initial field current were to cause an m.m.f. opposing the residual magnetism, this would be cancelled out and the machine would fail to excite.

From Fig. 7.25 it can be seen that,

$$I_f = \frac{V}{R_f}$$

$$I_a = I + I_f$$

and from equation (7.12) $\quad E = V + I_a R_a,$

where E is the generated e.m.f., V is the terminal voltage, R_a the armature resistance, R_f the shunt field resistance, I_a the armature current, I_f the shunt field current and I the load current.

(iii) SERIES EXCITATION

In the series excited generator the field winding is connected in series with the load. The field current is therefore the main load current. This means that the field current must be relatively high, so that relatively few turns per pole are required. Thus the series field has a few turns of large cross-section conductor (frequently copper strip), having a low resistance and a comparatively low inductance.

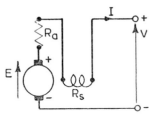

FIG. 7.26. THE D.C. SERIES
GENERATOR

In the same way as the shunt generator, the series machine will not excite if there is no residual magnetism in the poles, or if the initial field m.m.f. acts in opposition to the residual magnetism.

In Fig. 7.26, E is the generated e.m.f., V the terminal voltage, R_a the armature resistance, R_s the series field resistance, and I the main load current. As well as the usual IR_a drop there is an additional series drop in this case of IR_s. Hence,

$$E = V + I(R_a + R_s)$$

(iv) COMPOUND GENERATOR

In the compound generator the flux is provided partly by a shunt field winding and partly by a series field winding, the shunt and series coils being mounted on the same (main) poles. Normally the majority of the field m.m.f. is provided by the shunt field. The two windings may be connected to aid one another (cumulative compounding), or they may oppose one another (differential compounding).

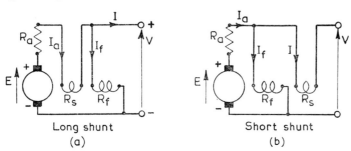

Long shunt   Short shunt
(a)   (b)

FIG. 7.27. THE D.C. COMPOUND-WOUND GENERATOR

In the long shunt compound generator, (Fig. 7.27),

$$I_f = \frac{V}{R_f}$$

$$I_a = I + I_f$$

$$E = V + I_a(R_a + R_s)$$

while in the short shunt compound generator, voltage across shunt field $= (V + IR_s)$

Therefore

$$I_f = \frac{V + IR_s}{R_f}$$

$$I_a = I + I_f$$

$$E = V + I_aR_a + IR_s$$

where E is the generated e.m.f., V the terminal voltage, R_a the armature resistance, R_f the shunt field resistance, R_s the series field resistance, and I_f the shunt field current.

Example 7.8

A 350-kW, 6-pole, short shunt compound d.c. generator runs at 600 r.p.m. and delivers full load at 440 V. The armature has a lap winding of 576 conductors. The resistances of the armature, series field, and shunt field are

0·01 Ω, 0·02 Ω, and 70 Ω respectively. The volt drop per brush may be taken as 1 V. Calculate the flux per pole.

From Example 7.7,

main load current, $I = 795$ A

Voltage across shunt field $= V + IR_s = 440 + 795 \times 0·02 = 456$ V

Shunt field current, $I_f = \dfrac{456}{R_f} = \dfrac{456}{70} = 6·5$ A

Armature current, $I_a = I + I_f = 795 + 6·5 = 802$ A

Generated e.m.f., $E = V + I_a R_a + I R_s + $ brush volt drop

The brush volt drop is 1 V per brush. Since the armature is 6-pole lap-wound, there will be six brushes but three of these are connected in parallel to form the positive terminal and the other three are connected in parallel to form the negative terminal. The total brush drop is therefore 2 V.

Therefore $E = 440 + 802 \times 0·01 + 795 \times 0·02 + 2 = 466$ V

By equation (7.8),

$$\text{flux/pole, } \Phi = E \times \frac{1}{Zn_r} \times \frac{a}{p} = 466 \times \frac{60}{576 \times 600} \times \frac{3}{3}$$
$$= \underline{\underline{0·0807 \text{ webers}}}$$

7.13. Characteristics of the Separately Excited D.C. Generator

The characteristics of the separately excited d.c. generator may be considered in two parts, namely the open circuit or magnetic characteristic, and the load characteristic.

(a) OPEN CIRCUIT CHARACTERISTICS

These characteristics refer to the no load conditions of the generator.

Suppose that the field current, I_f, of a separately excited generator is held constant, and the speed, n_r, is varied. Then from equation (7.9),

$$E \propto \Phi n_r$$

Also, since I_f is constant Φ will be constant, and hence,

$$E \propto n_r$$

The graph of E to a base of n_r is thus a straight line, if I_f is constant. If another higher value of field current, I_{f2}, is chosen and this is held constant, another straight line characteristic will be obtained which will slope more steeply. These characteristics are shown in Fig. 7.28(a).

Suppose now that the speed is held constant and that the field current, I_f, is varied. Then from equation (7.9),

$$E \propto \Phi \text{ since } n_r \text{ is constant}$$

Φ will vary as I_f varies in accordance with the *B-H* curve of the magnetic circuit. Thus the E/I_f characteristic will resemble a *B-H* curve for iron modified by the existence of the air gaps. If the value of the constant speed is increased, the steepness of the curve will also

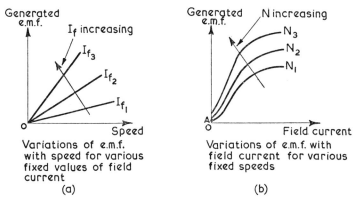

Variations of e.m.f. with speed for various fixed values of field current

(a)

Variations of e.m.f. with field current for various fixed speeds

(b)

FIG. 7.28. OPEN CIRCUIT CHARACTERISTICS OF A SEPARATELY EXCITED D.C. GENERATOR

increase, as is shown by the family of curves of Fig. 7.28(*b*). When I_f is zero the residual magnetism in the poles will give rise to the small initial e.m.f. shown.

(*b*) LOAD CHARACTERISTICS

Suppose that the generator is connected to a load, and that the load current, I, is varied. Again from equation (7.9),

$$E \propto \Phi n_r$$

If I_f and n_r are maintained constant it might appear at first as if E would remain constant. However, even if I_f remains constant the effective value of the flux per pole will be decreased by the armature reaction. The E/I characteristic, which is called the internal characteristic, will therefore droop as shown in Fig. 7.29. The V/I characteristic (the external characteristic) is obtained by subtracting the appropriate armature volt drop, IR_a, from the internal characteristic. Hence the external characteristic will also be a drooping curve as shown. In the figure the decrease in voltage from zero to full load is overemphasized for clarity. The voltage may, if desired, be maintained constant by adjustment of the field current and/or the speed.

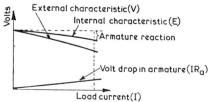

FIG. 7.29. LOAD CHARACTERISTIC OF SEPARATELY EXCITED D.C. GENERATOR

7.14. Characteristics of the Shunt Generator

In this, as in the previous case, there will be an open circuit and a load characteristic.

(a) OPEN CIRCUIT CHARACTERISTIC

If a shunt generator is run at a constant speed with the field separately excited an E/I_f curve is obtained which will be similar to that obtained for the separately excited machine. This is shown in Fig. 7.30. It will be remembered that the build up of e.m.f. in a shunt generator depends on the residual magnetism in the machine (see § 7.12) which will establish the small initial e.m.f. OP in the armature winding. This small e.m.f. circulates a field current which in turn produces additional flux to reinforce the original residual flux, provided that the field windings are correctly connected. If the field resistance is below a critical value the build up of e.m.f. will take place.

Consider the instant in time when the field current has the value OA (Fig. 7.30(a)). At this instant the total e.m.f. available is AC. Now if the field current is to increase further in value some of the e.m.f. AC must be available to overcome the e.m.f. of self induction, $L\dfrac{\mathrm{d}I_f}{\mathrm{d}t}$, which will be produced in the field winding during the growth of current, and which will oppose further current growth. Not all of the e.m.f. AC is, however, available to overcome $L\dfrac{\mathrm{d}I_f}{\mathrm{d}t}$ since the field circuit has a resistance R_f and consequently a voltage drop $I_f R_f$ (AB in the figure), which must be supplied by the e.m.f. AC. Thus an amount AB of the e.m.f. AC is absorbed by the volt drop $I_f R_f$ and the remainder, BC, is available to overcome $L\dfrac{\mathrm{d}I_f}{\mathrm{d}t}$. Since this surplus voltage is available, it is possible for the field current to increase above the value OA. At D, however, the available e.m.f., OE, is all absorbed by the $I_f R_f$ drop; the field current cannot therefore increase further, and steady state conditions are reached.

If the shunt field resistance is increased, then the slope of the line OD in Fig. 7.30(a) will increase, since this line represents the voltage-

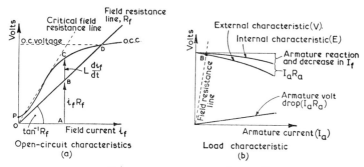

FIG. 7.30. CHARACTERISTICS OF A SHUNT GENERATOR

current relationship for the field winding (it is called the field resistance line). When OD becomes tangential to the curve OCC, conditions become unstable, and if the shunt field resistance is increased beyond this point the generator will fail to excite, since all the available e.m.f. is immediately absorbed by the $I_f R_f$ drop. This is a third reason why a shunt generator may fail to excite. (The other two reasons are given in § 7.12(ii).)

It should be noted that the critical value of the field resistance is dependent on the speed at which the generator is driven. The stable e.m.f. (given by the point D in Fig. 7.30(a)) and the critical resistance will both increase with speed.

As the field resistance of a shunt generator is increased from a value which is less that the critical resistance, the operating point, D, will move down the open circuit characteristic curve towards the origin, and the generated e.m.f. will fall slightly until the critical resistance is reached. When the field resistance exceeds the critical value for a given speed, the generated e.m.f. will suddenly fall to a very low value. Thus the voltage of a shunt generator may only be controlled over a small range near the normal operating value. This may be sufficient where a particular output voltage is required, but the small range of control makes the machine unsuitable for a variable voltage supply.

(b) LOAD CHARACTERISTICS

The load characteristic of the shunt generator is similar in form to that of the separately excited machine. As before, the armature reaction diminishes the effective flux per pole as the load current increases, and hence the generated e.m.f., E, will fall slightly even if the speed remains constant. In addition the field current, I_f, will fall as the load current increases, since the terminal voltage falls and $I_f = V/R_f$. The E/I_a graph (or internal characteristic) will therefore take the drooping form shown in Fig. 7.30(b), due both to the armature reaction and to the fall in I_f. The V/I characteristic (or external characteristic) is obtained by subtracting the armature volt drop, $I_a R_a$, from the internal characteristic.

Summarizing, there are three reasons why the terminal voltage of the shunt generator falls as the armature current increases. These reasons are

(i) reduction in effective flux due to armature reaction;

(ii) internal armature volt drop $I_a R_a$;

(iii) reduction in the value of I_f since the terminal voltage falls for reasons (i) and (ii).

If the field resistance line is plotted on the load characteristic diagram its intersection with the external characteristic gives the open circuit voltage of the machine, since on no load the armature current, I_a, is the field current, I_f. Thus the open circuit voltage is represented by point B in Fig. 7.30(b).

7.15. Characteristics of the Series Generator

Since the field current of the series generator is the load current, the machine will generate only the small e.m.f. OA (Fig. 7.31) when it is on open circuit, this e.m.f. being due to the residual magnetism in the poles. As the load increases the flux in the machine increases, and the e.m.f. and terminal voltage will both grow. In the absence of armature reaction the E/I_a (or internal) characteristic would be proportional to the flux/current characteristic of the magnetic circuit of the machine. Because of armature reaction, however, the internal characteristic, although it is of the same general shape will lie below the flux/current curve. The V/I (or external) characteristic is obtained by subtracting the appropriate armature volt drop from the internal characteristic.

Point C on the external characteristic (Fig. 7.31) corresponds to the conditions that the load current, I, is OB and the external terminal voltage is BC. If O and C are joined the slope of the resulting line is equal to the resistance of the load. As the load resistance is increased both V and I fall, and the slope of the load resistance line increases. If the load resistance is progressively increased a stage is reached when the load resistance line becomes tangential to the V/I characteristic. When this occurs conditions become unstable and the corresponding value of the load resistance may be called the critical load resistance of the series generator. If the load resistance is increased beyond this value the generator will not excite.

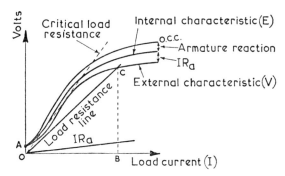

FIG. 7.31. CHARACTERISTICS OF THE SERIES GENERATOR

The above considerations assume that the generator is driven at constant speed. For any fixed current the generated e.m.f. is proportional to the speed, and hence the critical resistance will depend on the speed.

7.16 The Compound Generator

As the load current of a shunt generator increases, its terminal voltage falls. In the series generator, on the other hand, an increase in the load current is accompanied by a rise in the terminal voltage. It follows that by a judicious combination of shunt and series excitation an approximately constant voltage generator will be obtained. This is done by putting a relatively small number of series turns on each main field pole. As the load current grows the m.m.f. from the additional series turns is arranged to aid the shunt field m.m.f., and may be made to compensate for the loss of flux due to armature reaction and the drop in voltage due to internal resistance. This is called cumulative compounding.

The resulting V/I characteristic will first tend to rise, but will finally droop on account of saturation and the internal volt drops in the machine. For these reasons it is common practice to arrange that the series field m.m.f. is sufficient, at full load, to make the terminal voltage equal to the open circuit voltage. The machine is then said to be level-compounded (Fig. 7.32).

It is, of course, possible to further increase the series field. When this is done a rising V/I characteristic is obtained. This is referred to as over-compounding. If the series field m.m.f. opposes the shunt field m.m.f. a drooping characteristic is obtained, and this is referred to as differential-compounding.

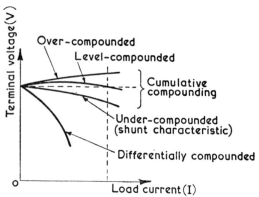

FIG. 7.32. CHARACTERISTICS OF THE COMPOUND GENERATOR

7.17. Choice of a Generator

The usual requirement of an electrical supply system is that it should operate at an approximately constant voltage. The characteristics of the series and differentially compounded generators are unsuitable for this purpose, but the separately excited, shunt and cumulatively compounded generators are all suitable.

The separately excited generator has the advantage of ease of control of the output voltage over a wide range but has the disadvantage of requiring a separate supply for the field winding. This supply is usually derived from a shunt or compound generator (called the exciter) which is mounted on the main generator shaft.

The cumulative compound machine has the advantage of an inherent constant voltage characteristic. Sometimes an over-compounded cumulative generator is used so that the increasing machine voltage will compensate for the increased volt drops in the distribution network when the load current becomes larger.

Series generators are sometimes used as series boosters in d.c. distribution networks. Differential compounding is sometimes resorted to in welding generators.

Example 7.9

The following figures were obtained from an open circuit test on a shunt generator driven at 1,000 r.p.m. with its field separately excited.

Terminal voltage, V (volts)	104	119	130	138	145
Field current, I_f (amperes)	1·0	1·5	2·0	2·5	3·0

If the field resistance is 50 Ω determine—
(a) the terminal voltage on open circuit when the speed is 1,000 r.p.m.
(b) the terminal voltage on open circuit when the speed is 750 r.p.m.
(c) the additional field resistance required so that the machine builds up to 89 V when the speed is 750 r.p.m.

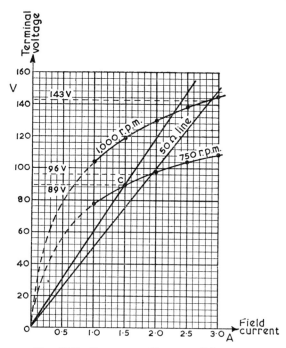

FIG. 7.33. GRAPH FOR EXAMPLE 7.9

(a) The V/I_f characteristic is plotted in Fig. 7.33 for 1,000 r.p.m. When 2 A flows through the field winding the voltage drop across it is 100 V. The line joining the origin with the point (2 A, 100 V) is therefore the field resistance line. This line is produced to cut the V/I_f characteristic. The intersection occurs at 143 V, and hence the open circuit terminal voltage at 1,000 r.p.m. is 143 V.

(b) From equation (7.9),

$$E \propto \Phi n,$$

Hence for a constant field current the e.m.f. will be directly proportional to the speed. Consider $I_f = 1 \cdot 0$ A. Then the e.m.f. generated at 1,000 r.p.m. is, from the graph, 104 V. Hence,

$$\frac{E_{750}}{E_{1,000}} = \frac{750}{1000}$$

where E_{750} is the e.m.f. when the field current is $1 \cdot 0$ A and the speed is 750 r.p.m.

Therefore $\qquad E_{750} = \dfrac{750}{1,000} \times E_{1000} = \dfrac{750}{1,000} \times 104 = 78$ V

Repeating this procedure for each value of field current the following table is obtained—

Field current (amperes)	1·0	1·5	2·0	2·5	3·0
Terminal voltage at 750 r.p.m. (volts)	78	89	97·5	103·5	108·7

This characteristic is then drawn, and its intersection with the 50-Ω line is determined. Hence from the graph, the terminal voltage on open circuit is 96 V at 750 r.p.m.

(c) Locate the point C on the open circuit characteristic for 750 r.p.m. corresponding to 89 V. The corresponding field current is 1·5 A.

$$R_f = \frac{V}{I_f} = \frac{89}{1 \cdot 5} = 59 \cdot 3 \ \Omega$$

Hence the additional field resistance which is required so that the machine builds up to 89 V at 750 r.p.m. is $59 \cdot 3 - 50 = \underline{\underline{9 \cdot 3 \ \Omega}}$

Example 7.10

A d.c. shunt generator runs at 400 r.p.m. and delivers 500 kW to bus-bars having a constant voltage of 400 V. Assuming that the field current is 5 A and that it remains constant, and neglecting the effects of armature reaction, estimate the speed at which the generator must run if the load on it is to be reduced to 300 kW. The armature resistance is 0·015 Ω.

Initial output current $= I_1 = \dfrac{500 \times 10^3}{400} = 1{,}250$ A

Final output current $\ = I_2 = \dfrac{300 \times 10^3}{400} = 750$ A

Initial e.m.f. $= E_1 = V + (I_1 + I_f)R_a = 400 + 1{,}255 \times 0 \cdot 015 = 418 \cdot 8$ V

Final e.m.f. $\ = E_2 = V + (I_2 + I_f)R_a = 400 + 755 \times 0 \cdot 015 = 411 \cdot 3$ V

Since the flux is constant, then from equation (7.9)

Final speed $n_2 =$ initial speed $\times \dfrac{E_2}{E_1} = 400 \times \dfrac{411 \cdot 3}{418 \cdot 8} = \underline{\underline{393 \text{ r.p.m.}}}$

The above example illustrates how the load on any one of a number of generators which supply a common constant voltage bus-bar may be varied.

7.18. Characteristics of the Shunt Motor

Direct current motors are classified according to their method of excitation in the same way as are generators. Fig. 7.34 shows the connexion diagram for the shunt motor. It should be noted that the field current is not drawn from the armature but is taken from the supply. Only operation from constant voltage supplies will be considered.

In Fig. 7.34 the symbols have the same significance as for the shunt generator.
Then,

$$I_f = \frac{V}{R_f}$$

$$I = I_a + I_f$$

and from equation (7.13),

$$V = E + I_a R_a$$

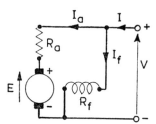

Fig. 7.34. The D.C. Shunt Motor

Speed Characteristic

$$E \propto \Phi n_r$$

Therefore

$$V - I_a R_a \propto \Phi n_r$$

or

$$n_r \propto \frac{V - I_a R_a}{\Phi} \qquad . \qquad . \qquad . \qquad (7.17)$$

If the $I_a R_a$ drop is neglected,

$$n_r \propto \frac{1}{\Phi} \text{ , since } V \text{ is constant}$$

If the effect of armature reaction is neglected, the flux will remain constant and hence the speed will be constant. Actually there will be a tendency for the speed to fall as the load current grows due to the increased volt drops. The shunt motor is very nearly a constant speed machine.

Torque Characteristic

From equation (7.11),

$$T \propto \Phi I_a$$

and since Φ is very nearly constant,

$$T \propto I_a$$

i.e. for the shunt motor the torque is approximately proportional to the armature current. The characteristics of the shunt motor are shown in Fig. 7.35. It should be noted that OC represents the no load current and CD represents the torque to overcome internal losses. The load torque for any given armature current will always be less than the total torque by an amount which is equal to the torque which must be produced to supply losses in the machine.

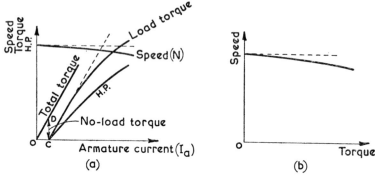

FIG. 7.35. CHARACTERISTICS OF THE SHUNT MOTOR

7.19. Characteristics of the Series Motor

Fig. 7.36 shows the connexion diagram for the series motor. The symbols have the same significance as for the series generator.

$$I = I_a$$

and $\quad V = E + I_a(R_a + R_s) \quad (7.18)$

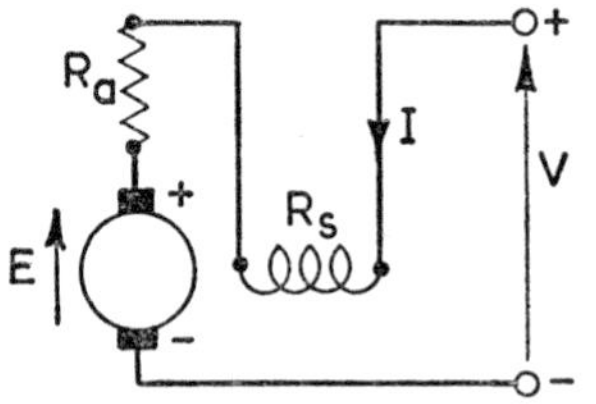

SPEED/CURRENT CHARACTERISTIC

As for a shunt motor,

$$n_r \propto \frac{V - I_a(R_a + R_s)}{\Phi}$$

FIG. 7.36. THE D.C. SERIES MOTOR

and since V is constant and on the assumption of negligible $I_a R$ drop,

$$n_r \propto \frac{1}{\Phi}$$

Now the series motor, unlike the shunt machine, is a variable flux machine, the field current being the load current and therefore varying with the load. For small loads magnetic saturation will not be appreciable and the flux will thus be proportional to the load current. Hence,

$$n_r \propto \frac{1}{I_a} \qquad . \qquad . \qquad . \qquad . \qquad (7.19)$$

Equation (7.19) shows that when the load current is small the speed will be very large, so that there is a danger of the series motor

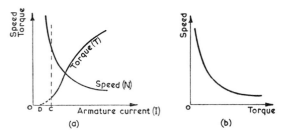

FIG. 7.37. CHARACTERISTICS OF THE SERIES MOTOR

reaching dangerously high speeds. It is normal to arrange that the series motor can never operate below a safe minimum load (say *OC* in Fig. 7.37(*a*)).

When saturation occurs the flux tends to become constant, and consequently the speed will also tend to a constant value. There will, however, continue to be a fall in speed due to the continued increase in the series volt drops.

TORQUE/CURRENT CHARACTERISTIC

From equation (7.11)

$$T \propto \Phi I_a$$

Before saturation is appreciable $\Phi \propto I_a$ and hence,

$$T \propto I_a^2 \qquad . \qquad . \qquad . \qquad . \qquad (7.20)$$

As magnetic saturation occurs the flux tends to become constant, and hence,

$$T \propto I_a \qquad . \qquad . \qquad . \qquad . \qquad (7.21)$$

From equations (7.20) and (7.21) the form of the torque/current curve will be initially parabolic but will finally straighten as the load current becomes large. This is shown in Fig. 7.37(*a*), where only the load torque is depicted. *OD* will be the no load current, but as has already been seen, it is unsafe to allow the series motor to run on no load. The speed/torque curve shown in Fig. 7.37(b) is easily derived from the curves of Fig. 7.37(a).

7.20. Characteristics of the Compound Motor

Fig. 7.38 shows the connexion diagrams for the long shunt and the short shunt d.c. compound motor. The symbols have the same significance as for the compound generator.

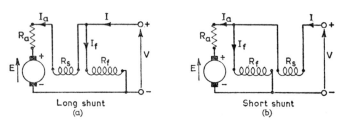

Fig. 7.38. The D.C. Compound Motor

In the long shunt compound motor—

$$I_f = \frac{V}{R_f}$$

$$I = I_a + I_f$$

$$V = E + I_a(R_a + R_s)$$

while in the short shunt machine,

voltage across the shunt field $= V - IR_s$

Therefore

$$I_f = \frac{V - IR_s}{R_f}$$

and

$$V = E + I_aR_a + IR_s$$

Speed/Torque Characteristic

Fig. 7.39 shows typical shunt and series motor speed/torque characteristics. With the cumulative compound motor almost any intermediate type of characteristic (e.g. the one shown) may be obtained. Because of the existence of the shunt winding for which the m.m.f. is practically independent of the load, there is always sufficient flux in the machine to ensure a stable speed even on no load.

In the differential compound motor an almost level speed/torque characteristic is obtainable. There are, however, a number of difficulties in operating this type of machine. In particular, at starting the series field may overcome the shunt field and so give a reverse flux tending to start the motor in the reverse direction.

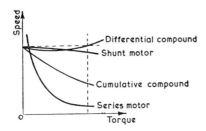

FIG. 7.39. CHARACTERISTICS OF THE COMPOUND MOTOR

Moreover, the machine tends to be unstable in operation, since after a certain load the motor is working on a rising speed/torque characteristic. This results in a tendency for a cumulative build up of speed and load which may be highly dangerous. For these reasons the differential compound motor is little used.

7.21. Choice of Motor

The d.c. shunt motor is a general purpose machine and is suitable for any constant speed drive which is not subject to heavy overloads. A further advantage of the machine is that speed control is simply and economically obtained by means of a resistance in the field circuit (see §7.22).

The series motor is suitable for fluctuating loads where constant speed is not necessary. If a sudden loading of the motor occurs the machine slows down considerably and excessive power is not drawn from the supply. The nature of the load must make it impossible for the motor to run unloaded (e.g. a belt-driven load is unsuitable).

The main application for series motors is in electric traction where there is almost no chance of the motor breaking free of the load. Other features of the series motor which recommend it for this purpose are (a) the fact that two or more series motors when mechanically connected to drive the same load will, owing to their sharply falling characteristics, share the load more evenly than will two shunt machines, and (b) the speed of the vehicle will automatically fall when it is ascending a gradient, thus preventing excessive power being taken from the supply. Other important applications are in cranes and for driving ventilating fans. Small series motors are also used as the starting motors of automobiles.

The compound motor is suitable for fluctuating loads and has the advantage over the series motor of a stable no load speed. It is particularly suitable for driving fluctuating loads which incorporate a flywheel to smooth out energy changes, since the moderate drop in speed on load allows the flywheel to give up energy to the load, and the motor is able to return this energy to the flywheel when the load becomes smaller. A typical application of the compound motor is the driving of steel rolling mills.

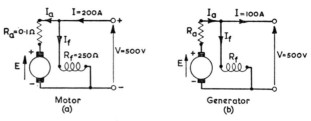

FIG. 7.40. CIRCUITS FOR EXAMPLE 7.11

Example 7.11

A 6-pole, d.c. shunt machine has a wave winding with 488 conductors, and a flux per pole of 0·04 Wb. The shunt field resistance is 250 Ω and the armature resistance is 0·1 Ω. The brush contact drop may be taken as 1 V per brush. Determine the speed of the machine when running (*a*) as a motor taking 200 A and (*b*) as a generator supplying 100 A. The terminal voltage in each case is 500 V.

In both cases the field current is,

$$I_f = \frac{V}{R_f} = \frac{500}{250} = 2 \text{ A}$$

(*a*) For a shunt motor, from equation (7.13),

$$E = V - I_a R_a - \text{brush drop}$$

The brush drop is 1 V per brush. In Example 7.8 it was pointed out that for a lap winding the total brush drop was twice the brush drop per brush. In the wave winding also there may be a number of sets of parallel brushes (although only two are essential in this case), so that by the same reasoning as was previously used the total brush drop for the wave winding is twice the drop per brush.

Total input current = 200 A

Therefore armature current = $I_a = I - I_f = 200 - 2 = 198$ A

Therefore $E = 500 - 198 \times 0·1 - 2 = 478·2$ V

From equation (7.8),

$$n_r = E \times \frac{1}{\Phi Z} \times \frac{a}{p} = 478·2 \times \frac{1}{0·04 \times 488} \times \frac{1}{3} = 8·17 \text{ r.p.s.} = \underline{\underline{490 \text{ r.p.m.}}}$$

(*b*) For a shunt generator—

$$E = V + I_a R_a + \text{brush drop}$$

Armature current = $I_a = I + I_f = 100 + 2 = 102$ A

Therefore $E = 500 + 102 \times 0\cdot1 + 2 = 512\cdot2$ V

Therefore $n_r = 512\cdot2 \times \dfrac{1}{0\cdot04 \times 488} \times \dfrac{1}{3} = 8\cdot73$ r.p.s. $= \underline{\underline{524 \text{ r.p.m.}}}$

Example 7.12

A 200-V series motor takes a current of 100 A and runs at 1,000 r.p.m. The total resistance of the motor is $0\cdot1\ \Omega$ and the field is unsaturated. Calculate (*a*) the percentage change in the torque and the speed if the load is so altered that the motor current is 50 A and (*b*) the motor current and speed if the torque is halved.

(*a*) From equation (7.11),

$$T \propto \Phi I_a$$

Since the field is unsaturated the flux per pole, Φ, will be proportional to the field current, which, in a series motor, is the load or armature current. Hence,

$$\Phi \propto I_a$$

and $T_1 \propto I_1{}^2$.   .   .   .   .   (*a*)

where I_1 is the initial armature current, and I_2 is the new armature current,

$$T_2 = T_1 \left(\frac{I_2}{I_1}\right)^2 = T_1 \times \left(\frac{50}{100}\right)^2 = \frac{1}{4}T_1$$

Therefore per cent change of torque $= \dfrac{T_1 - T_2}{T_1} \times 100 = \underline{\underline{75 \text{ per cent}}}$

From equation (7.9),

$$E \propto \Phi n_r$$

Therefore $n_r \propto \dfrac{E}{\Phi} \propto \dfrac{V - I_a R_a}{I_a}$ since $\Phi \propto I_a$

hence, $\dfrac{n_{r1}}{n_{r2}} = \dfrac{V - I_1 R_a}{V - I_2 R_a} \times \dfrac{I_2}{I_1}$

$$n_{r2} = \frac{V - I_2 R_a}{V - I_1 R_a} \times \frac{I_1}{I_2} \times n_{r1} \; . \quad\quad . \quad\quad . \quad (b)$$

$$= \frac{200 - 50 \times 0\cdot1}{200 - 100 \times 0\cdot1} \times \frac{100}{50} \times 1{,}000 = \underline{\underline{2{,}050 \text{ r.p.m.}}}$$

(*b*) From (*a*),

$$I_2' = I_1 \Big/ \sqrt{\left(\frac{T_2'}{T_1}\right)} = 100 \Big/ \sqrt{\left(\frac{1}{2}\right)} = \underline{\underline{70\cdot7 \text{ A}}}$$

From (*b*),

$$n_{r2}' = \frac{200 - 70\cdot7 \times 0\cdot1}{200 - 100 \times 0\cdot1} \times \frac{100}{70\cdot7} \times 1{,}000 = \underline{\underline{1{,}435 \text{ r.p.m.}}}$$

7.22. Speed Control of D.C. Motors

The speed of a d.c. motor is given by the relationship,

$$n_r \propto \frac{V - I_a R_a}{\Phi} \qquad . \qquad . \qquad . \quad (7.17)$$

The supply voltage V is usually fixed and the armature current I_a is dependent on the load imposed on the motor. Although R_a is a given constant it can be varied upwards by inserting an external resistance in series with the armature. Evidently, then, there are three general methods of speed control of d.c. motors—(i) variation of the supply voltage V, (ii) variation of the armature resistance R_a, and (iii) variation of the flux per pole Φ.

Variation of the supply voltage is not usually possible, and is in any case an unsatisfactory method of control unless the motor field is separately excited. Otherwise variation of supply voltage will also affect the field current and flux, rendering the method ineffective.

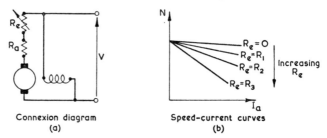

Connexion diagram   Speed-current curves
(a)   (b)

Fig. 7.41. Speed Control of a Shunt Motor by Variation
of the Resistance in its Armature Circuit

For effective speed control what is in fact required is a variation of the armature voltage without affecting the voltage across the field. This may be done by connecting an external resistance in series with the armature. Fig. 7.41(a) shows the method of connexion for a shunt motor. Since in this case the field is connected directly across the supply, the flux in the machine will not be affected by the variation in the external resistance, R_e, which is connected in series with the armature. In the case of a series motor (Fig. 7.42(a)) the current, and hence the flux, may be affected slightly by the alteration in the total series resistance.

From the proportionality (7.17) it may be seen that an increase in R_a (i.e. an increase in R_e in Figs. 7.41(a) and 7.42(a)) will decrease the speed, and therefore an increase of speed cannot be obtained by this means. One disadvantage of this method is that it wastes energy. A further disadvantage is that for a given value of R_e the speed reduction is not constant but varies with the load on the machine. Fig. 7.41(b) shows typical speed/current curves for a shunt motor with various values of added armature resistance, and Fig. 7.42(b) shows the same curves for a series motor.

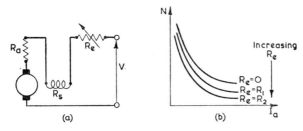

(a)   (b)

FIG. 7.42. SPEED CONTROL OF A SERIES MOTOR BY VARIATION
OF THE RESISTANCE IN ITS ARMATURE CIRCUIT

In the shunt motor variation of the flux is simply achieved by connecting a variable resistance R_c (Fig. 7.43(a)) in series with the field circuit. This reduces the field current and hence the flux. In the series motor the field current is reduced by a diverting resistance R_d, which is shunted across the field and so diverts a proportion of the current from the field winding (Fig. 7.44(a)). Since both these

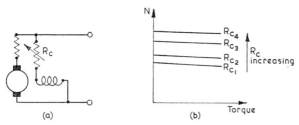

(a)   (b)

FIG. 7.43. SPEED CONTROL OF A SHUNT MOTOR BY
VARIATION OF FLUX

methods reduce the flux they will result in an increase in the speed of the machine. The methods are economical, and in the shunt case the constant speed characteristic is maintained. The shunt field rheostat is used for small adjustments of the normal speed, and the series field divertor is found in electric traction equipment. Figs. 7.43(b) and 7.44(b) give typical curves for shunt and series motors respectively, whose speeds are controlled by flux variation.

For separately excited motors, speed control is obtained by varying the voltage applied to the armature. In the Ward-Leonard system a constant-speed electric motor drives a d.c. generator whose field is separately excited from a d.c. exciter which is coupled to the same shaft. The output voltage of the main generator is controlled by a potentiometer in its field circuit, and is applied direct to the armature

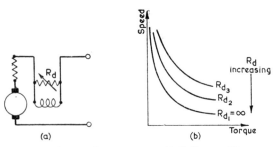

FIG. 7.44. SPEED CONTROL OF A D.C. SERIES MOTOR BY
VARIATION OF FLUX

of the main motor. The field of the main motor is supplied from the constant voltage output of the exciter. The speed of the main motor may thus be controlled over a wide range by the potentiometer (Fig. 7.45). This system of control is economical where high power machines require to have a large speed range, such as in colliery winders.

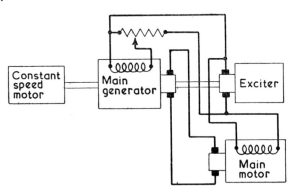

FIG. 7.45. WARD-LEONARD CONTROL

Example 7.13

A 200-V series motor takes a current of 100 A and runs at 1,000 r.p.m. when driving a certain load the torque of which is constant. The field resistance is 0·05 Ω and the armature resistance is 0·1 Ω. Find the resistance to be placed in series with the armature to reduce the speed to 800 r.p.m. Neglect the effect of armature reaction, and assume that the flux is proportional to the field current.

From equation (7.11),

$$T \propto \Phi I_a$$

and

$$\Phi \propto I_a$$

Therefore

$$T \propto I_a{}^2$$

$$\frac{T_1}{T_2} = \frac{I_1{}^2}{I_2{}^2} = 1, \text{ since the load torque is constant,}$$

giving

$$I_1 = I_2$$

Hence

$$n_r \propto \frac{V - I_a(R_a + R_s)}{I_a}$$

Hence,

$$\frac{n_{r1}}{n_{r2}} = \frac{V - I_1(R_a + R_s)}{V - I_2(R_a + R_s + R_e)} \times \frac{I_2}{I_1}$$

Therefore

$$V - I_2(R_a + R_s + R_e) = \{V - I_1(R_a + R_s)\} \cdot \frac{I_2}{I_1} \times \frac{n_{r2}}{n_{r1}}$$

$$= \{200 - 100 \times 0{\cdot}15\} \times \frac{100}{100} \times \frac{800}{1{,}000}$$

$$= 148 \text{ V}$$

Therefore

$$R_a + R_s + R_e = \frac{200 - 148}{100} = 0{\cdot}52 \ \Omega$$

The resistance to be connected in series with the armature must therefore be,

$$R_e = 0{\cdot}52 - 0{\cdot}15 = \underline{\underline{0{\cdot}37 \ \Omega}}$$

Example 7.14

A 500-V shunt motor has an armature resistance of $0{\cdot}1 \ \Omega$ and a field resistance of $250 \ \Omega$. When driving a load at 450 r.p.m. the armature current is 200 A. The speed of the machine is to be raised to 500 r.p.m. by inserting a resistance in the field circuit. The load torque is constant. Calculate the value of the resistance if the magnetization curve is assumed to be a straight line.

Let subscript 1 refer to values at 450 r.p.m., and subscript 2 refer to values at 500 r.p.m.

Then from equation (7.11),

$$T \propto \Phi I_a$$

Therefore

$$\frac{T_1}{T_2} = \frac{\Phi_1 I_1}{\Phi_2 I_2}$$

Therefore

$$I_2 = I_1 \times \frac{\Phi_1}{\Phi_2} \qquad \qquad . \qquad . \qquad . \qquad . \quad \text{(i)}$$

From equation (7.17),

$$n_r \propto \frac{V - I_a R_a}{\Phi}$$

Therefore

$$\frac{n_{r1}}{n_{r2}} = \frac{V - I_1 R_a}{V - I_2 R_a} \cdot \frac{\Phi_2}{\Phi_1} \qquad \qquad . \qquad . \qquad . \quad \text{(ii)}$$

Substitute in (ii) for I_2 and solve for $\dfrac{\Phi_1}{\Phi_2}$

Therefore
$$\frac{n_{r1}}{n_{r2}} = \frac{V - I_1 R_a}{V - I_1 \times \frac{\Phi_1}{\Phi_2} \cdot R_a} \times \frac{\Phi_2}{\Phi_1}$$

Therefore
$$\frac{450}{500} = \frac{500 - 200 \times 0\cdot 1}{500 - 200 \times 0\cdot 1 \times \frac{\Phi_1}{\Phi_2}} \times \frac{\Phi_2}{\Phi_1}$$

Therefore
$$\left(\frac{\Phi_1}{\Phi_2}\right)^2 - 25\left(\frac{\Phi_1}{\Phi_2}\right) + 26\cdot 6 = 0$$

Therefore
$$\frac{\Phi_1}{\Phi_2} = \frac{25 \pm \sqrt{(25^2 - 4 \times 26\cdot 6)}}{2} = 23\cdot 8 \text{ or } 1\cdot 1$$

Rejecting the higher value as impracticable,

$$\frac{I_{f1}}{I_{f2}} = \frac{\Phi_1}{\Phi_2} = 1\cdot 1, \text{ since the flux is assumed proportional to the}$$

field current.

$$I_{f1} = \frac{V}{R_f} = \frac{500}{250} = 2 \text{ A}$$

Therefore
$$I_{f2} = \frac{2}{1\cdot 1} = 1\cdot 82 \text{ A}$$

From this, the total field resistance when the speed is 500 r.p.m. will be

$$\frac{500}{1\cdot 82} = 275 \ \Omega$$

Therefore resistance to be added to the field circuit is,

$$R_c = 275 - 250 = \underline{\underline{25 \ \Omega}}$$

Example 7.15

A 200-V series motor takes a current of 100 A and runs at 1,000 r.p.m. The field resistance is $0\cdot 05 \ \Omega$ and the armature resistance is $0\cdot 1 \ \Omega$. At what speed will the motor run if the field is shunted by a resistance of $0\cdot 05 \ \Omega$? Assume that the flux is proportional to the field current, and the load torque is constant.

From equation (7.11),

$$T \propto \Phi I_a$$

$$\frac{T_1}{T_2} = \frac{\Phi_1 I_1}{\Phi_2 I_2} = 1, \text{ since the load torque is constant.}$$

Therefore
$$\Phi_1 I_1 = \Phi_2 I_2 \qquad . \qquad . \qquad . \qquad . \qquad . \qquad . \qquad . \quad \text{(i)}$$

Since the divertor resistance is equal to the field resistance only half the armature current will pass through the field when the divertor resistance is connected. Since the flux is proportional to the field current,

$$\frac{\Phi_1}{\Phi_2} = \frac{I_1}{\frac{1}{2}I_2} \qquad . \qquad . \qquad . \qquad . \qquad . \quad \text{(ii)}$$

From (i)
$$\frac{\Phi_1}{\Phi_2} = \frac{I_2}{I_1} \qquad . \qquad . \qquad . \qquad . \qquad . \quad \text{(iii)}$$

Equating (ii) and (iii) gives

$$\frac{I_2}{I_1} = \frac{I_1}{\frac{1}{2}I_2}$$

$$I_2{}^2 = 2I_1{}^2$$

$$I_2 = \sqrt{2} \cdot I_1 = \sqrt{2} \times 100 = 141 \text{ A}$$

Therefore

$$\frac{\Phi_1}{\Phi_2} = \frac{I_2}{I_1} = 1\cdot41$$

From equation (7.17),

$$n \propto \frac{V - I_a(R_a + R_s)}{\Phi}$$

Therefore

$$\frac{n_1}{n_2} = \frac{V - I_1(R_a + R_{s1})}{V - I_2(R_a + R_{s2})} \times \frac{\Phi_2}{\Phi_1}$$

Therefore

$$n_2 = \frac{V - I_2(R_a + R_{s2})}{V - I_2(R_a + R_{s1})} \times \frac{\Phi_1}{\Phi_2} \times n_1$$

$$= \frac{200 - 141(0\cdot1 + 0\cdot05/2)}{200 - 100(0\cdot1 + 0\cdot05)} \times 1\cdot41 \times 1{,}000 = \underline{\underline{1{,}390 \text{ r.p.m.}}}$$

7.23. Starting of D.C. Machines

For a shunt motor,

$$V = E + I_a R_a \qquad . \qquad . \qquad . \qquad (7.13)$$

and for a series motor,

$$V = E + I_a(R_a + R_s) \qquad . \qquad . \qquad . \qquad (7.18)$$

The currents taken by a shunt and series motor are thus given respectively by the equations,

$$\text{(shunt) } I_a = \frac{V - E}{R_a} \qquad . \qquad . \qquad . \qquad (7.22)$$

$$\text{(series) } I_a = \frac{V - E}{R_a + R_s} \qquad . \qquad . \qquad . \qquad (7.23)$$

Under normal operating conditions the terminal voltage V, and the generated e.m.f. E, differ by a comparatively small amount. At the instant of starting, however, the armature is stationary, and as a result there is no generated e.m.f. If the supply voltage were switched directly on to the stationary motor an excessively high armature current would flow. For example, in the case of a motor with an armature resistance of $0\cdot1\ \Omega$ switched to a 200-V supply directly, the initial armature current would be,

$$I_a = \frac{V - E}{R_a} = \frac{200 - 0}{0\cdot1} = 2{,}000 \text{ A}$$

In order to overcome this difficulty it is normal practice to incorporate a starter in d.c. motor circuits. The starter is, in effect, a resistance which will limit the initial current to a reasonable value, and which may be progressively cut out as the generated e.m.f. rises in value with the speed. "No-volt" and overload protective devices are normally incorporated in the starter.

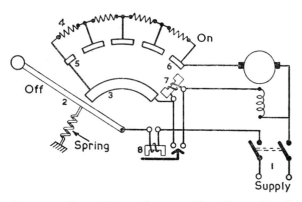

FIG. 7.46. SHUNT MOTOR STARTER (FACE PLATE TYPE)

A schematic diagram of a shunt motor starter showing the method of connexion is given in Fig. 7.46. Here (1) is a double-pole isolating switch connecting the motor and the starter to the supply. The starter arm (2) is connected to one side of the supply and makes contact with a brass arc (3) and the starting resistance section (4). Starting from the first stud (5) the starter arm is moved to the last stud (6) so cutting out the resistance sections connected between studs as the motor speeds up. When the supply is switched on the no-volt coil (7), which is in series with the field, and the shunt field are fully energized. This gives full flux and hence a high torque on starting.

The function of the no-volt coil is to protect the motor in the event of switching off, a failure of the supply, or a break on the field circuit. The starter arm moves to the "on" position against the action of a spring. When it makes contact with stud 6 a soft iron armature which is attached to the arm is attracted to the poles of the iron-cored no-volt coil with sufficient force to hold the starter arm in position against the force exerted by the spring. If the machine is switched off or the supply voltage fails the no-volt coil is de-energized and the starter arm is returned to the "off" position by the spring. In the absence of a no-volt release there is a danger that, on the restoration of the supply, the starter arm may be left on the "on" position with the resistance sections of the starter cut out. If this occurs a severe overload current will flow in the armature circuit. The overload release (8) is a relay which is designed to "pull in" at a predetermined overload current. When the relay operates it short circuits the no-volt coil, which is therefore de-energized. Hence the starter arm will then return to the "off" position under the action of the return spring. A similar arrangement may be used for a series motor but in this case the no-volt coil is connected in series with the armature. As in the shunt motor the no-volt coil is a protection against over-speeding of the motor. If the load on the machine is removed (i.e. when over-speeding is possible) the current will fall, and the no-volt coil may be arranged to be sufficiently demagnetized to release the starter arm, and so disconnect the supply.

7.24. Losses in a D.C. Machine

The losses in any rotating electromagnetic machine may be divided into three classes; (i) the mechanical losses, (ii) copper losses, and (iii) the magnetic or iron losses. All these losses appear as heat and will thus raise the temperature of the machine.

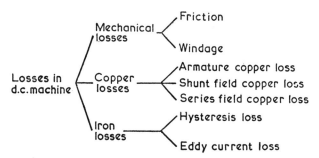

FIG. 7.47. LOSSES IN A D.C. MACHINE

Mechanical losses arise due to bearing and brush friction and also due to windage of the armature and the cooling fan. These losses are a function of the speed. Copper losses arise in the current-carrying parts of the machine, i.e. in the armature and field windings. The armature loss is $I_a^2 R_a$ and the field loss will be $I_f^2 R_f$. In the shunt machine the field loss is approximately constant. It should be noted that the copper losses must be calculated at the working temperature of the machine, since the resistance of the copper will increase with temperature.

Iron losses arise in the magnetic circuit of the machine and are of two types, namely the hysteresis loss and the eddy-current loss. Hysteresis loss occurs in the armature of the d.c. machine since any given part of the armature is subject to magnetic flux reversals as it passes under successive poles. Hysteresis loss depends on the maximum flux density in the iron and on the speed of the machine. Eddy-current loss arises due to the e.m.f.s induced in the iron parts of the machine which experience flux changes. The eddy-current loss depends on the square of the flux density, and on the square of the speed.

The losses in the d.c. machine are summarized in Fig. 7.47.

7.25. Estimation of Efficiency by Swinburne's Method

In the shunt motor the speed remains almost constant and, neglecting armature reaction, the flux also remains constant. Hence the windage and friction losses may be assumed to be constant, along with the iron losses. The shunt field copper loss is also constant since the supply voltage is constant.

The only loss which varies with the load will thus be the armature copper loss, all other losses being approximately the same at full load and at no load. Hence, using the assumption of constant speed and constant flux the full load efficiency of a machine may be estimated from a no load test.

Let $I_0 = $ no load current

$I_{0a} = $ no load armature current

$I_a = $ armature current for any other load current I,

where $I = I_a + I_f$ for a shunt motor

$V = $ supply voltage

Then the no load input power is VI_0 watts, and the no load armature copper loss is $I_{0a}^2 R_a$ watts.

Constant loss, $k = VI_0 - I_{0a}^2 R_a$

$= $ all losses except armature copper loss

Efficiency, $\eta = \dfrac{\text{output}}{\text{input}}$

$= \dfrac{\text{input-losses}}{\text{input}}$

$= \dfrac{VI - (k + I_a^2 R_a)}{VI}$.   .   . (7.24)

The load current which will make the efficiency of the machine a maximum may be calculated in the following manner—

If the field current is small compared with the armature current, the expression for the efficiency may be written as

$$\eta \doteqdot \frac{VI - (k + I^2 R_a)}{VI}$$

$$\doteqdot 1 - \frac{k}{VI} - \frac{IR_a}{V}$$

Therefore

$$\frac{\mathrm{d}\eta}{\mathrm{d}I} = \frac{k}{VI^2} - \frac{R_a}{V}$$

$$= 0 \text{ for maximum efficiency}$$

Therefore

$$k = I^2 R_a \qquad . \qquad . \qquad . \qquad (7.25)$$

That is the load current at which maximum efficiency occurs is the one which makes the variable loss equal to the constant loss.

The Swinburne method takes no account of stray losses in the machine on load. It should be noted that the value of armature resistance used in the above calculations should be the "hot" resistance.

7.26. Efficiency of D.C. Motors by Direct Load Test

The best method of determining the efficiency of d.c. motors is by a direct load test. This is normally done for small machines by loading the motor on to a brake which dissipates the output as heat. The electrical input and the mechanical output are measured. If n is the speed of the motor in r.p.m., and T is the torque applied by the brake, (lb-ft) then,

$$\text{mechanical output} = \frac{2\pi nT}{33,000} \text{ h.p.}$$

$$= \frac{2\pi nT}{33,000} \times 746 \text{ W}$$

If the input voltage and current are V and I respectively,

$$\text{electrical input} = VI \text{ W}$$

$$\text{Hence efficiency} = \frac{2\pi nT}{33,000} \times \frac{746}{VI} \text{ per unit}$$

The main difficulty associated with direct load tests occurs for large machines, when it may be difficult to dissipate the output at the maker's works. In such cases other methods must be used, such as the Swinburne method or the Hopkinson method. In this latter method, which it is not proposed to treat in detail, two similar machines must be available. These are mechanically coupled, one acting as a motor and driving the other which is connected as a generator. The output of the generator is fed back to the motor, and only the combined losses of the set are taken from the supply.

Example 7.16

A 500-V, d.c. shunt motor has an armature resistance when hot of 0·1 Ω and a field resistance of 250 Ω. When running on no load the motor takes a current of 8 A. Find approximately the maximum efficiency and the load current at which it occurs.

No load input $= 500 \times 8 = 4{,}000$ W

Field current $\qquad\qquad = \dfrac{500}{250} = 2$ A

No load armature current $= 8 - 2 = 6$ A

No load armature copper loss $= 6^2 \times 0·1 = 3·6$ W (i.e. negligible)

Therefore constant loss $k \doteqdot 4{,}000$ W

The maximum efficiency occurs when the variable loss is equal to the constant loss, i.e. approximately when

$$k = I^2 R_a \qquad . \qquad . \qquad . \qquad . \qquad . \quad (7.25)$$

Therefore $\qquad\qquad I = \sqrt{\left(\dfrac{4{,}000}{0·1} \right)} = \underline{\underline{200 \text{ A}}}$

From equation (7.24) the efficiency at this load is,

$$\eta = \frac{500 \times 200 - (4{,}000 + 4{,}000)}{500 \times 200} = \underline{\underline{0·92 \text{ per unit}}}$$

The expected efficiency will be slightly less than this value.

EXAMPLES 7

1. A 4-pole generator has a flux of 0·04 Wb per pole and a lap-connected armature having 740 conductors. Calculate the speed at which the generator should be driven if the open circuit e.m.f. is to be 494 V.

Ans. 1,000 r.p.m.

2. Deduce the e.m.f. equation for a d.c. machine.

A 4-pole, lap-wound, d.c. shunt generator has a useful flux per pole of 0·07 Wb. The armature winding consists of 220 turns each of 0·004 Ω resistance. Calculate the terminal voltage when running at 900 r.p.m. if the armature current is 50 A. (*O.N.C.*)

Ans. 459 V.

3. A 4-pole, short-shunt, compound generator has armature, shunt field and series field resistances of 0·4 Ω, 160 Ω and 0·2 Ω respectively.

The armature is lap connected with 440 conductors and is driven at 600 r.p.m. Calculate the flux per pole when the machine is delivering 120 A at 400 V. (*O.N.C.*)

Ans. 0·108 Wb.

4. Sketch typical speed-torque curves for d.c. shunt, series and compound motors. State the factors which influence their shapes.

The armature of a 4-pole motor has a wave winding with 556 conductors. Calculate the torque (in lb-ft) when the current input to the armature is 90 A and the flux per pole is $3·7 \times 10^6$ lines

(N.B. 1 Wb $= 10^8$ lines) (*L.U.*, 1949)

Ans. 434 lb(wt)ft.

5. (a) Explain in detail the function of the interpoles in a d.c. machine.

(b) A 240-kW, 230-V, 6-pole, d.c. generator has the data below. Estimate the number of turns needed for each interpole. Ignore the effect of iron parts of the circuit and of leakage.

Total number of armature conductors = 600

Type of armature winding— lap

Interpole air gap = 1 cm

Flux density in interpole air gap = 3,500 lines/cm² (0·35 Wb/m²)

Ans. 11.

6. Derive the e.m.f. equation of a d.c. machine.

A 4-pole, wave-wound, d.c. generator has 41 slots. There are ten conductors per slot, and the flux/pole is 0·05 Wb.

Calculate the speed required for a generated e.m.f. of 500 V. Also find the demagnetizing AT/pole produced by a brush rotation of 4 mechanical degrees when the load current is 20 A. (*O.N.C.*)

Ans. 732 r.p.m.; 45·5.

7. The relationship between the field current and the open circuit voltage of a certain d.c. generator driven at constant speed is given in the following table—

Field current (amperes)	0·5	1·0	1·5	2·0	2·5	3·0	3·5
Voltage (volts)	60	120	138	145	149	151	152

The resistance of the armature circuit is 0·1 Ω.

If the machine is connected as a shunt generator with the resistance of the field circuit adjusted to 53 Ω and is run at the same speed as before, calculate— (a) the open circuit voltage, (b) the load current when the terminal voltage is 100, (c) the terminal voltage when the load has a resistance of 0·4 Ω. Neglect the effect of armature reaction. (*L.U.*, 1941)

Ans. 150 V; 428·9A; 117 V.

8. Explain the conditions to be fulfilled for a d.c. shunt generator to build up to its normal voltage on no load and describe what tests should be made if a particular machine fails to excite.

A d.c. shunt generator running at 850 r.p.m. gave the following relation between field current and e.m.f. generated.

Field current (amperes)	0	0·5	1	2	3	4	5
Armature e.m.f. (volts)	10	60	120	199	232	248	258

If the resistance of the shunt field is 50 Ω determine the additional resistance required in the shunt field circuit to give 240 V at a speed of 1,000 r.p.m. State any assumptions made. (*L.U.*, 1949)

Ans. 64·3 Ω.

9. Sketch the load characteristic of a d.c. generator with (i) shunt (ii) series excitation. Give reasons for the particular shape in each case.

The open-circuit characteristic, at 700 r.p.m., of a series generator with separately excited field is as follows—

Field current (amperes)	20	40	50	61	75
Armature e.m.f. (volts)	190	360	410	450	480

Determine the current and terminal voltage as a self excited series machine when running at 600 r.p.m. with a load of 6 Ω connected to the terminals. Resistance of armature and series winding 0·3 Ω. Ignore the effects of armature reaction. (*L.U.*, 1949)

Ans. 369 V; 61·5 A.

10. Estimate the reduction in speed of a generator working with constant excitation on 500-V bus-bars to decrease its load from 500 kW to 250 kW. The resistance between terminals is 0·015 Ω. Neglect armature reaction and field current.

Ans. 1·46 per cent.

11. In a 10-kW, compound generator the resistances of the armature, shunt and series windings are 0·06 Ω, 25 Ω and 0·04 Ω respectively. The load consists of 200 lamps each rated at 55 W, 110 V. Find the total e.m.f. and armature current when the machine is connected (*a*) long shunt (*b*) short shunt. How will the ampere-turns of the series winding be affected if in (*a*) a divertor resistance of 0·1 Ω be connected in parallel with the series field winding? Ignore the effects of armature reaction and brush contact drop. (*O.N.C.*)

Ans. 120 V, 104 A; 120 V, 104 A; Ampere-turns reduced to $\frac{10}{14}$ of original value.

12. A 4-pole, d.c. shunt motor has a flux per pole of 0·04 Wb and the armature is lap-wound with 720 conductors. The shunt field resistance is 240 Ω and the armature resistance is 0·2 Ω. Brush contact drop is 1 V per brush. Determine the speed of the machine when running (*a*) as a motor taking 60 A and (*b*) as a generator supplying 120 A. The terminal voltage in each case is 480 V. (*O.N.C.*)

Ans. 972 r.p.m.; 1,055 r.p.m.

13. Derive an expression for the total torque developed by a d.c. motor. Using this expression draw graphs showing the relationship between the torque and the armature current for (*a*) a shunt motor (*b*) a series motor, assuming the supply voltage to remain constant.

A 460-V, series motor runs at 500 r.p.m. taking a current of 40 A. Calculate the speed and percentage change in torque if the load is reduced so that the motor is taking 30 A. Total resistance of the armature and field circuits is 0·8 Ω. Assume flux and field current to be proportional. (*L.U.*, 1946)

Ans. 679 r.p.m.; 43·8 per cent.

14. Deduce and sketch the shape of the speed-torque curve for a d.c. series motor working on constant voltage. Neglect all losses and magnetic saturation.

A d.c. series motor operates a crane at normal voltage and lifts a load of 2 tons at 150 ft/min. Neglecting saturation and losses (*a*) determine the speed at which it will lift a load of 4 tons and (*b*) explain how the motor may be arranged to lift a load of 1 ton at 300 ft/min. (*L.U.*, 1951)

Ans. 106 ft/min.

15. Explain how the speed of a d.c. shunt motor may be varied both above and below the speed at which it runs with full field current.

A 10-h.p., 230-V, shunt motor has a full load speed of 1,200 r.p.m. The resistance of the armature and field circuits are 0·3 Ω and 180 Ω respectively. The full load efficiency of the motor is 86 per cent.

Neglecting brush drop and the effects of armature reaction calculate (a) the speed at which the motor will run at no load if under these conditions its total input is 600 W; (b) the value of resistance to be added to the armature circuit to reduce its speed to 1,000 r.p.m. when giving full-load torque with full field current. (*L.U.*, 1950)

Ans. 1,255 r.p.m.; 1 Ω.

16. How may the speed of a d.c. shunt motor be controlled?

Explain in detail what happens when the flux is reduced by 10 per cent in a 220-V motor, having an armature resistance of 0·2 Ω, carrying a current of 50 A and running at 960 r.p.m. prior to weakening the field. The load torque may be assumed to remain constant; iron and friction losses may be neglected. (*L.U.*, 1940)

Ans. Speed rises to 1060 r.p.m., and current to 55·6 A.

17. A d.c. series motor runs at 1,000 r.p.m. with 20 A at 200 V. $R_a = 0.5 \Omega$. $R_f = 0.2 \Omega$. Find the speed for a total current of 20 A at 200 V when a 0·2 Ω resistor is in parallel with the field winding. The flux for a field current of 10 A is 70 per cent of that for 20 A. (*L.U.*, 1945)

Ans. 1,445 r.p.m.

18. Give a diagram of connexions of a starter fitted with protective devices suitable for a d.c. shunt motor and explain the function of each part.

The resistance for a starter for a 200-V shunt motor is such that the maximum starting current is 30 A. When the current has decreased to 24 A the starter arm is moved to the second stud.

Calculate the resistance between these two studs if the maximum current on the second stud is 30 A. The armature resistance of the motor is 0·4 Ω. (*L.U.*, 1950)

Ans. 1·33 Ω.

19. Discuss briefly the various losses of energy that occur in a d.c. machine.

A shunt motor running on no load takes 5 A at 200 V. Resistance of field circuit is 150 Ω; resistance of armature circuit is 0·1 Ω.

Determine the output and efficiency of the motor when the input current is 120 A, at 200 V. State the conditions assumed. (*L.U.*, 1940)

Ans. 21,560 W; 0·9 p.u.

20. A d.c. shunt motor running on no load takes 5 A at 200 V. The field resistance is 100 Ω and the armature resistance is 0·1 Ω. Find the approximate maximum efficiency and the load current at which it occurs. (*O.N.C.*)

Ans. 0·9; 100 A.

CHAPTER 8

Transformers

A TRANSFORMER is a piece of apparatus which without any moving part changes alternating voltages or currents from high to low values or vice versa. Transformers are necessary for the efficient distribution of electric power and are essential for the operation of many industrial processes and in electronics.

8.1. Principle

If two coils are wound on a common iron core as in Fig. 8.1 and one of them, the primary, is supplied with an alternating current,

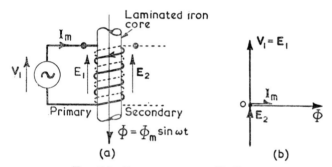

FIG. 8.1. TRANSFORMER ON NO LOAD

then an alternating flux will be produced in the iron core. This alternating flux will link both coils and will induce e.m.f.s in both of them. The second coil is called the secondary. The transformer is a form of mutual inductance. The iron core greatly increases the flux produced by a given magnetizing current and increases the proportion of main flux to leakage flux. The dot notation used for mutual inductance will also be employed for transformers.

Consider a perfect transformer which has no losses. If the primary voltage is sinusoidal, the flux produced will also be sinusoidal. Let the flux be $\phi = \Phi_m \sin \omega t$ Wb, where Φ_m is the peak flux.

274

If the primary coil has N_1 turns then the e.m.f. induced in the primary,

$$e_1 = \frac{d}{dt}(\Phi N_1)$$

$$= \frac{d}{dt}\Phi_m \sin \omega t \times N_1$$

$$= \omega \Phi_m N_1 \cos \omega t$$

e_1 has a maximum value, E_{m1}, when $\cos \omega t = 1$

$$E_{m1} = \omega \Phi_m N_1$$

and $$e_1 = E_{m1} \cos \omega t \qquad . \qquad . \qquad . \quad (8.1)$$

The r.m.s. value of the e.m.f. induced in the primary,

$$E_1 = \frac{\omega}{\sqrt{2}} \Phi_m N_1$$

$$= \frac{2\pi f}{\sqrt{2}} \Phi_m N_1$$

i.e. $$E_1 = 4 \cdot 44 f \Phi_m N_1 \text{ V} \qquad . \qquad . \qquad . \quad (8.2)$$

If the secondary winding has N_2 turns, the r.m.s. value of the e.m.f. induced in the secondary,

$$E_2 = 4 \cdot 44 \Phi_m N_2 \text{ V} \qquad . \qquad . \qquad . \quad (8.3)$$

dividing equation (8.2) by equation (8.3)—

$$\frac{E_1}{E_2} = \frac{N_1}{N_2} \qquad . \qquad . \qquad . \qquad . \quad (8.4)$$

Thus the ratio of primary to secondary e.m.f.s is the same as the turns ratio of the transformer. The back e.m.f. in the primary, E_1, will be exactly equal to the applied voltage V_1. Hence V_1, E_1, and E_2, will all be in phase in the vector diagram.

Equation (8.1) shows that the e.m.f. leads the flux by 90°. The vector diagram for the ideal transformer on open circuit (Fig. 8.1(*b*)) is completed by inserting the primary magnetizing current I_m in phase with Φ. For convenience E_2 is drawn below the origin.

Substituting $\Phi_m = B_m \times A$ where A is the iron cross-sectional area in metres², in the e.m.f. equation (8.2) gives

$$E_1 = 4 \cdot 44 f N_1 B_m A$$

or $$\frac{E_1}{N_1} = 4 \cdot 44 f B_m A \text{ volts/turn} . \qquad . \quad (8.5(i))$$

and
$$\frac{E_2}{N_2} = 4\cdot44fB_mA \quad \text{volts/turn} \quad . \quad . \quad (8.5(\text{ii}))$$

Example 8.1

A 100-kVA, 50-c/s, 6,600/500-V, 1-phase transformer operates at a peak flux density of 1·3 Wb/m² and has 4 V induced per turn. Calculate the core cross-sectional area, and the numbers of primary and secondary turns. If the transformer is to be used on a 60-c/s system, find the new value of core flux density for the same voltages.

From equation (8.5),
$$\frac{E_1}{N_1} = 4\cdot44f\,B_mA$$

$$4 = 4\cdot44 \times 50 \times 1\cdot3 \times A$$

Therefore
$$A = \underline{0\cdot0139 \text{ m}^2}$$

For the secondary, there are 4 V/turn, so that for 500 V, there are

$$\frac{500}{4} = \underline{125 \text{ turns}}$$

Then from equation (8.4)

$$N_1 = N_2 \times \frac{E_1}{E_2} = 125 \times \frac{6,600}{500} = \underline{1,650 \text{ turns}}$$

At 60 c/s, equation (8.2) gives

$$6,600 = 4\cdot44 \times 60 \times 1,650 \times B_m \times 0\cdot0139$$

Therefore
$$B_m = \underline{1\cdot08 \text{ Wb/m}^2}$$

8.2. Transformer on Load

If the secondary circuit is closed through a load, a current I_2 will flow through the secondary winding (Fig. 8.2(*a*)). This current will give rise to a secondary m.m.f. in the iron core, which will be in time phase with I_2 and will have a value I_2N_2 AT. This m.m.f. will naturally tend to alter the flux in the core from its original value. However, the flux in the core must remain at its no-load value for this is the flux, which, when linking the primary winding and changing at the frequency of the supply, gives rise to a primary back e.m.f. equal to the supply voltage. Thus, when the secondary m.m.f. tends to alter the flux and the primary back e.m.f. from equality with the supply voltage, an additional current must flow in the primary winding to give rise to an additional primary m.m.f. equal and opposite to the secondary m.m.f.

Let I_1 be the additional primary current to balance the secondary m.m.f. then

$$I_1 N_1 = I_2 N_2 \quad . \qquad . \qquad . \qquad . \quad (8.6)$$

I_1 and I_2 are represented on the space and vector diagram of Figs. 8.2(a) and 8.2(b) respectively. It will be seen that in the space diagram I_1 and I_2 are in the directions which will give rise to opposing m.m.f.s in the core. They have also the directions to give rise to energy intake by the primary and energy transmission from the

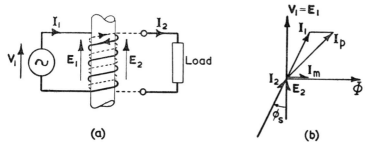

(a)   (b)

FIG. 8.2. TRANSFORMER ON LOAD

secondary. This follows since the foregoing argument regarding m.m.f.s is basically the law of conservation of energy. I_1 and I_2 are in time phase with one another, consequently the corresponding vectors will be in the same direction in the vector diagram.

It will be remembered that I_1 is not the total primary current. The total primary current, I_p, is the vector sum of I_1 and the magnetizing current I_m.

The current ratio is N_2/N_1 only when the total primary on load is much larger than the no-load current.

The approximate vector diagram is shown in Fig. 8.2(b) I_2 lags behind E_2 by the phase angle ϕ_s of the load. I_1 will be in phase with I_2, and hence will lag V_1 by ϕ_s. For clarity E_2 and I_2 are shown below the origin.

In a practical transformer the iron path is complete to give a low reluctance flux path. Fig. 8.3 shows a typical complete magnetic circuit for a 1-phase transformer. The iron must be laminated or serious eddy current losses will

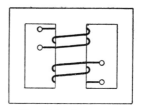

FIG. 8.3. COMPLETE MAGNETIC CIRCUIT

result. These losses were described in §2.28 and Example 5.8. A non-laminated transformer would be entirely unsatisfactory.

Example 8.2

A 20-kVA, 50-c/s, 250/110-V, 1-phase transformer has 125 primary turns. Calculate (a) the secondary turns, and (b) the approximate values of primary and secondary currents on full load. Also find the primary and secondary winding cross-sectional areas, for a current density of 1,000 A/in^2.

(a) From equation (8.4) $N_2 = \dfrac{E_2}{E_1} N_1 = \dfrac{110}{250} \times 125 = \underline{55 \text{ turns}}$

(b) Full-load $kVA = \dfrac{E_2 I_2}{1,000}$. Therefore $I_2 = \dfrac{1,000 \times 20}{110} = \underline{182 \text{ A}}$

Hence from equation (8.6) $I_1 = 182 \times \dfrac{55}{125} = \underline{80 \text{ A}}$

For primary, cross-section $= \dfrac{80}{1,000} \text{ in}^2 = \underline{0\cdot08 \text{ in}^2}$

For secondary, cross-section $= \dfrac{182}{1,000} \text{ in}^2 = \underline{0\cdot182 \text{ in}^2}$

EXAMPLES 8

1. The no-load voltage ratio in a 1-phase, 50-c/s, core-type transformer is 1,200/440. Find the number of turns in each winding if the maximum flux is to be 0·075 Wb. (*O.N.C.*)
Ans. 27 and 74 turns.

2. Calculate the peak magnetizing current in a 6,600/384-V, 1-phase, 50-c/s transformer. The cross-sectional area of the core is 775 cm^2 and the mean iron length is 250 cm. There are 378 turns on the high voltage side. The magnetization curve for the core material is—

B (Wb/m^2)	0·4	0·6	0·8	1	1·2	1·3
H (AT/m)	100	185	275	475	975	1,800

(*O.N.C.*)
Ans. 3·3 A.

3. Derive an expression for the induced e.m.f. in a transformer in terms of the frequency, the maximum value of the flux and the number of turns in the winding. Find the number of turns in each winding of a 1-phase, 50-c/s transformer with a maximum value of the flux of about 0·05 Wb and a no-load voltage ratio of 6,600/250. (*O.N.C.*)
Ans. 23 and 607 turns.

4. A 1-phase transformer has 500 primary and 1,200 secondary turns. The net cross-sectional area of the core is 75 cm^2. If the primary winding be connected to a 400-V, 50-c/s supply, calculate (i) the peak value of flux density in the core and (ii) the voltage induced in the secondary winding. (*O.N.C.*)
Ans. 0·48 Wb/m^2; 960 V.

5. A 1-phase transformer there are 400 primary turns and 200 secondary turns. Calculate the supply current and power factor when the primary is connected to a 240-V, 50-c/s mains and the secondary terminals are connected to a load of resistance 10 Ω and inductive reactance 7 Ω in series. The magnetizing current is 0·5 A. Neglect the effect of the resistance and reactance of the transformer windings. (*O.N.C.*)
Ans. 5·24 A; 0·77 lagging.

CHAPTER 9

Elementary Electronics

THE BRANCH of electrical engineering which studies the conduction of electricity through a vacuum or through a gas, and the circuits associated with this type of conduction, is called electronics. Most electronic circuits are built up round valves or electron tubes which consist essentially of a group of conducting electrodes in a sealed container. The electrodes are connected through air-tight seals to connexions outside the container, which is normally a glass envelope. The simplest type of valve has two electrodes and is called a diode. 3-electrode valves are called triodes; 4-electrode valves, tetrodes; 5-electrode valves, pentodes, etc. In addition there are more complicated types of electron tubes such as the cathode-ray tubes which are used in television.

In high-vacuum, or "hard" valves, the container is evacuated to as high a degree as possible, and conduction takes place by means of a stream of electrons flowing across the space between the electrodes. It will be recalled that electrons are small particles which are normally part of atoms but which can exist separately. It will be shown later how a supply of these free electrons may be produced inside a valve. Inside the valve the electrons (which have a negative electric charge) will be attracted towards whichever electrode is positive and will be repelled by any negative electrodes. This movement of free electrons constitutes a flow of current.

The outstanding features of valves are (i) the fact that current will pass through them in one direction only, and (ii) the ease with which the flow of electrons (and hence the current in the external circuits) may be controlled. The supply of electrons for the electron stream in high-vacuum valves is normally obtained by utilizing the fact that certain metals and oxides produce a copious emission of electrons when heated to a sufficient temperature. This is termed thermionic emission.

The mass of an electron is so small in relation to the electric charge which it carries that gravitational forces on electrons may usually be neglected in comparison with the electrostatic forces which are present in valves. Hence if a free electron is placed in the electrostatic field between two electrodes, the electron will be accelerated towards the positive plate.

The simplest arrangement for a valve is shown in Fig. 9.1, where the negative electrode (or cathode) is heated and emits electrons.

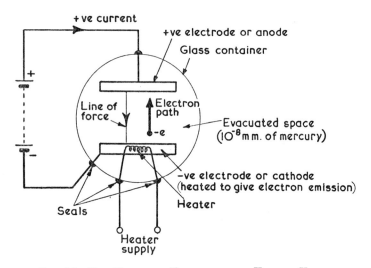

FIG. 9.1. THE ESSENTIAL FEATURES OF A VACUUM VALVE

These are attracted to the positive electrode (or anode), and pass round the external circuit through the battery and back to the cathode. The conventionally positive direction of current in the external circuit is, of course, in the opposite direction to the direction of electron drift, and hence will be as shown.

9.1. Thermionic Emission of Electrons

It may be verified that when certain materials are heated electrons are given off from the surface. There are only a few known substances which will provide a sufficiently large emission at a low enough temperature to be of much practical value in the production of free electrons in a valve. Commercially important emitters are—

(*a*) Pure tungsten which is generally operated at a temperature around 2200°C (i.e. white hot). It is often called a "bright emitter," and gives a total emission current density of order 0·1 A/cm² of heated surface.

(*b*) An oxide-coated emitter, particularly the mixture of barium and strontium oxides on a nickel plate (thorium on tungsten—thoriated-tungsten—is also found). The barium-strontium oxides give a good emission at about 700°C (i.e. dull red, hence a "dull emitter"), though the maximum emission current attainable varies considerably with surface conditions and the voltage applied.

The important differences between the two types are—

1. Tungsten as a pure material has a long reliable life, being resistant to chemical poisoning and bombardment by gas particles.

2. An oxide-coated emitter operating at a low temperature will require a very much smaller heating power for a given emission current.

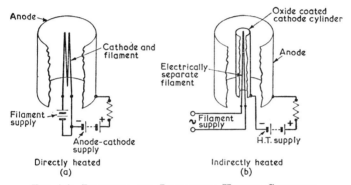

Fig. 9.2. Directly and Indirectly Heated Cathodes

In a valve it is arranged that the emitter is the negative electrode (or cathode), so that when a positive plate (or anode) is placed near it the electrons from the cathode will flow across to the anode.

In a small valve, e.g. a receiver valve, the capital cost is low and a replacement is easily made, so that it is most economical to take advantage of the low filament power consumption of an oxide coated valve and one of these is always used. In large valves (e.g. the power valves in a transmitter), the capital cost is very high, and the reliability factor is most important, hence a tungsten filament valve is used.

There are two types of thermionic cathode construction (*a*) the directly heated type (*b*) the indirectly heated type (Fig. 9.2). In the indirectly heated type, the heater wire (or filament) is run up the centre of the cathode which is in the form of an oxide-coated nickel cylinder. The filament is electrically insulated from the cathode by means of aluminium oxide.

Basic Electrical Engineering

The indirectly heated valve has the operational advantage of having the heater and anode supplies electrically separate. Thus an alternating current may be used to heat the cathode without affecting the anode current. If a directly heated valve has an a.c. filament supply, the filament current is liable to affect the operation of the rest of the circuit. For an indirectly heated valve the cathode cylinder must be oxide coated. Since most valves are heated from an a.c. supply, indirectly-heated, oxide-coated cathodes are most common. Battery-driven valves which are heated by direct current are required to use a minimum of heater-power, so that a directly-heated, oxide-coated filament is used. Large valves using tungsten filaments for long life are directly heated.

9.2. Electronic Conduction through a Vacuum

Consider the diode valve shown in Fig. 9.3(a). With the heater current at a constant value the cathode will attain a constant temperature and electrons will be emitted at a certain fixed rate. It might be thought on first consideration that if the anode of the valve (i.e. the positive electrode) were at any positive potential (even a

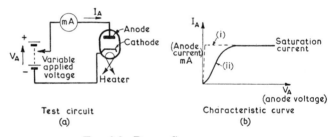

FIG. 9.3. DIODE CHARACTERISTICS

low one), then all the emitted electrons would move towards the anode so that the anode current at all values of anode potential would be the total emitted, or saturation, current for the given cathode temperature. This would be represented by the characteristic (i) in Fig. 9.3(b). In fact it is found that the characteristic is that shown by curve (ii). This shows that an appreciable anode voltage is required before the complete saturation current flows.

The explanation lies in the important factor of "space charge," i.e. the charge on the electrons which at any given instant are in the interspace between anode and cathode.

In the diagram of Fig. 9.4 a sample space charge of electronic charges is shown. It will be realized that an electron on the cathode side of the space charge will be under a reduced electrostatic force since the repelling effect of the negative space charges counters the attractive effect of the positive anode. Thus field strengths towards the cathode are reduced, while field strengths towards the anode are increased. Now the reduced field strength at the cathode will still cause all the emitted electrons to travel to the anode unless the space

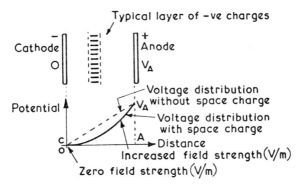

FIG. 9.4. EFFECT OF SPACE CHARGE ON VOLTAGE DISTRIBUTION
BETWEEN CATHODE AND ANODE IN A DIODE VALVE

charge reduces the field strength at the cathode to zero. This must therefore be the case, for all the emitted electrons do not move to the anode.

The operation of the valve should be viewed in the following manner—when the cathode is heated electrons are emitted to form a negative space-charge around the cathode so that any further emitted electrons are repelled and fall back into the cathode. With a positive potential applied to the anode some electrons are drawn from the space charge to the anode, so that temporarily the space charge is reduced and further electrons will leave the cathode to join the space charge. The current through the valve is said to be "space-charge limited" and in this condition obeys the law (three-halves law),

$$I_A \propto V_A^{3/2} \qquad . \qquad . \qquad . \qquad . \qquad (9.1)$$

If the anode voltage, V_A is sufficiently great to draw electrons from the space charge at the maximum rate at which they are emitted from the cathode then the space charge disappears and the current, I_a, is constant at its saturation value for the given cathode temperature. This high current range is rarely used, the valve being usually operated in its space charge limited region. The space charge may be assumed to collect very close to the cathode surface. A typical diode characteristic is shown in Fig. 9.5.

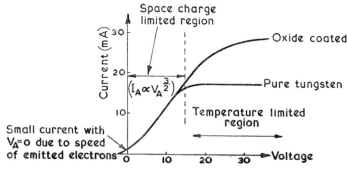

FIG. 9.5. CHARACTERISTICS OF VACUUM DIODES

9.3. Diode Rectification

Diodes are found in all sizes from the small valves used in communication receivers to rectify high frequency alternating currents, through the medium sizes used to rectify the 50-c/s alternating supplies to electronic equipment, to the large valves used as high voltage rectifiers at say 20 kV. The essential feature of the diode is the fact that electrons can only flow from the cathode to the anode, and not from the anode to the cathode, i.e. the conductivity is unidirectional.

(a) SINGLE-PHASE RESISTANCE LOAD RECTIFIER CIRCUIT

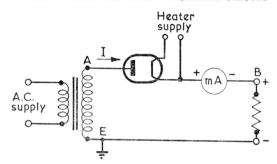

FIG. 9.6. USE OF A DIRECTLY-HEATED DIODE AS A SIMPLE 1-PHASE RECTIFIER

The circuit is shown in Fig. 9.6. The rectifying element (i.e. the diode) may be regarded as having an infinite resistance to current in the cathode-anode direction (i.e. to electrons in the opposite direction) and practically zero resistance in the forward or anode-cathode current direction. This assumption of zero forward resistance is usually sufficiently accurate since, as shown by Fig. 9.7, the anode characteristic may be approximated to by a straight line which corresponds with a resistance of the order of 1000 Ω, and the load

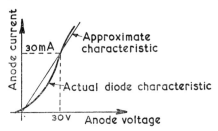

FIG. 9.7. To Illustrate that the Diode Characteristic is Nearly a Straight Line

resistance of the circuit for this valve will normally be about 10,000 Ω.

Let E be the reference (earthed) point in the circuit of Fig. 9.6. Then the potential of A is represented by a sine wave of peak value ($\sqrt{2} \times$ transformer secondary voltage). During the half periods when this potential would tend to give a diode reverse current, the diode resistance becomes infinitely high—no current flows, and the whole supply potential will appear across the diode. During the half periods when the supply potential gives rise to forward current the diode is almost a short circuit and the potential of the point B is almost that of A. It will be noticed that the diode volt drop is small during the conducting period but rises to the peak supply voltage value during the non-conducting periods. (A diode must not be used in circuits supplied from voltages in excess of the permissible reverse voltage for the particular valve.)

From Fig. 9.8 which shows the current and potential waveforms, it will be seen that the peak voltage across the load resistance is the peak supply voltage (neglecting any volt drops in the valve), and that the load voltage wave form is simply the positive half-cycles of the supply. This is called half-wave rectification.

If $V = $ r.m.s. supply voltage, then

$$\text{peak load voltage} = \sqrt{2}V,$$

and instantaneous load voltage $= \sqrt{2}V \sin \omega t$, for $0 < t < \dfrac{\pi}{\omega}$

and $\qquad\qquad\qquad\qquad = 0$ for $\dfrac{\pi}{\omega} < t < \dfrac{2\pi}{\omega}$

Mean load voltage
$$= \frac{1}{2\pi/\omega} \int_0^{\pi/\omega} \sqrt{2}V \sin \omega t \, . \, dt$$

$$= \frac{\sqrt{2}V}{\pi} \text{ V} \qquad . \qquad . \qquad . \quad (9.2)$$

This is the voltage which would be observed on a moving-coil voltmeter connected across the load resistance.

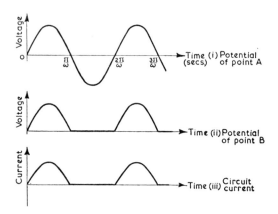

FIG. 9.8. CURRENTS AND POTENTIALS IN THE CIRCUIT OF FIG. 9.6

$$\text{Mean load current} = \frac{\sqrt{2}V}{\pi R} \text{ A} \qquad . \qquad . \quad (9.3)$$

This is the current which would be observed on a moving-coil ammeter in the load circuit.

(b) FULL-WAVE, RESISTANCE LOAD RECTIFIER

The circuit for a full-wave rectifier with resistance load is shown in Fig. 9.9(a). With respect to E the potential of A varies sinusoidally with a maximum value of $\sqrt{2}V$, where V is the r.m.s. voltage across half of the transformer secondary winding. The potential of C will also vary sinusoidally with a maximum value of $\sqrt{2}V$ but this wave will be in anti-phase to the first since it is derived from the opposite side of the secondary winding. The valve used in this circuit has two diodes inside the one envelope with a common cathode. It is called a double diode. The electrons emitted from the cathode will move to the anode which has the more positive potential and hence the current flow will change from one anode to the other at every half-cycle of the supply voltage. If the volt drop in the valve is neglected then the cathode potential must be the same as that of the instantaneously more positive anode. The output voltage and current waves are a series of positive half sine waves as shown in Fig. 9.9(*b*).

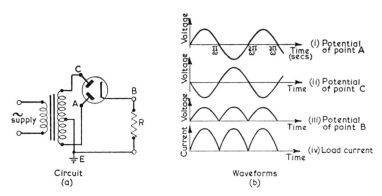

Circuit
(a)

Waveforms
(b)

Fig. 9.9. Full Wave Rectification with Resistance Load

The mean output voltage and the mean output current are twice the corresponding mean values found in the 1-phase case. The peak reverse voltage in this case is equal to the peak end-to-end transformer voltage, since the cathode potential is always that of the conducting anode.

(*c*) Single-phase Capacitance Load Rectifier Circuit

To illustrate the action of the circuit of Fig. 9.10(*a*) suppose that the sinusoidal supply is switched on at the instant when the voltage is passing through its zero value and is becoming positive. A charging current will then flow through the diode and charge the capacitor so that the point *B* attains a positive potential. The charging current is limited by the circuit resistances and the potential arising across the capacitor. The current will flow as long as the supply potential exceeds the capacitor potential. When the supply potential decreases after a quarter-cycle a point at which supply and capacitor potentials are equal is reached. There will be zero current at this instant and beyond this instant, when the capacitator voltage exceeds the supply potential, there will be a tendency for the capacitor to discharge through the diode in the reverse direction. Since this is impossible the charge will be maintained throughout the negative half-cycle and for a portion of the next positive half-cycle until the supply voltage again exceeds the capacitator voltage. Similarly, the capacitor voltage will be built up during each positive half-cycle until it effectively equals the peak supply voltage. It will then remain at the peak supply potential, and there will be no further charging current. Note that the current flows as a series of pulses (Fig. 9.10(*b*)). The initial pulses would have been greater had the initial "switch on" occurred at an instant during a positive half-cycle.

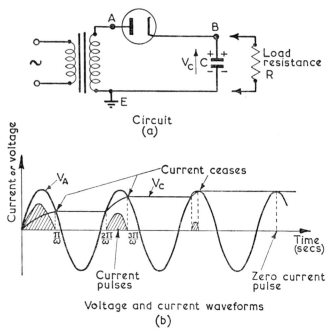

Circuit
(a)

Voltage and current waveforms
(b)

FIG. 9.10. CAPACITOR LOADED RECTIFIER

(*d*) SINGLE-PHASE CAPACITANCE—RESISTANCE LOAD RECTIFIER CIRCUIT

Consider that the load resistance R is connected across the capacitor C of Fig. 9.10(*a*). Assume that the resistance R is relatively high. After the first few cycles the capacitor will charge to the peak supply voltage but instead of maintaining this value the capacitor will discharge somewhat through R during each negative half-cycle and part also of the positive half-cycles. The capacitor will be recharged during each positive half-cycle. The action is illustrated by the wave forms of Fig. 9.11.

At each positive peak the capacitor (called the "reservoir capacitor") is effectively charged to the peak supply voltage, $\sqrt{2}V$. After this instant the supply voltage will be less than the capacitor voltage until the next positive half-cycle, and during this time, while

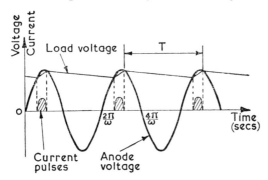

Fig. 9.11. Waveforms for Resistance Loaded 1-Phase Rectifier with Reservoir Capacitor

the diode current is zero, the capacitor, C, will discharge through the load resistor R.

It is usually sufficiently accurate to assume that at all instants the discharge current through R is approximately $\dfrac{\sqrt{2}V}{R}$, since in most practical cases a smooth output is required and this is obtained by arranging that the capacitor discharge shall be slight, so that its voltage (i.e. the voltage across R) will always be, at least nearly, $\sqrt{2}V$. If the output is "smooth" the discharge must last for almost the entire period T sec.

Therefore

(to a first approximation), discharge time $= T$ sec

and quantity in coulombs discharged in 1 cycle $\doteqdot \dfrac{\sqrt{2}VT}{R}$

Voltage fall across C during discharge period $= \dfrac{1}{C} \times$ charge lost

$$\doteqdot \frac{\sqrt{2}VT}{RC} \quad \text{V}$$

Therefore mean voltage $\doteqdot \sqrt{2}V - \dfrac{1}{2} \cdot \dfrac{\sqrt{2}VT}{RC}$

$$\doteqdot \sqrt{2}V\left(1 - \frac{T}{2RC}\right) \qquad . \qquad . \quad (9.4)$$

Therefore

peak voltage ripple = peak volts — mean volts

$$= \frac{T}{2RC} \sqrt{2}V \qquad . \qquad . \qquad . \quad (9.5)$$

e.g. if the ripple is not to exceed, say 0·5 per cent

$$\frac{T}{2RC} < \frac{5}{1,000}$$

i.e. $$RC > 100T$$

where T is the period of the supply voltage.

For a small discharge current the load resistance, R, will be large and the circuit is usually suitable for supplying currents up to 1 mA (mean). It would appear that by increasing the capacitor size larger currents could be dealt with but this is not so due to the large peak currents which would then be drawn from the rectifier valve. The "peak" nature of the rectifier current is shown in Fig. 9.11. The valve manufacturer usually states the maximum permissible capacitor size along with the valve ratings.

(e) FULL-WAVE, RESISTANCE—CAPACITANCE LOAD, RECTIFIER CIRCUIT

The circuit as shown in Fig. 9.12(a) operates in the same manner as its 1-phase prototype, the only differences being (i) the greater

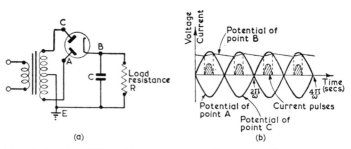

FIG. 9.12. FULL WAVE RECTIFIER WITH RESERVOIR CAPACITOR

current capacity and (ii) the shorter discharge time in this case (one half of the supply period). The output ripple will be at twice supply frequency. The relevant wave forms are shown in Fig. 9.12(b).

For large, well-smoothed currents a smoothing circuit consisting of a series inductor and shunt capacitor, or a series resistor and shunt capacitor, is added after the reservoir capacitor, as shown in Fig. 9.13 (π circuit). The inductor gives the better smoothing with

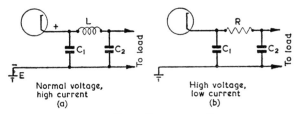

Normal voltage,
high current
(a)

High voltage,
low current
(b)

Fig. 9.13. π-Type Smoothing Circuits

less power loss, and is used for normal-voltage, high-current rectifiers. The resistor is cheaper, and is used in high-voltage, low-current circuits.

9.4. The Triode

In the triode valve a third electrode is introduced between the cathode and the anode. The function of this electrode is to control the flow of anode current in the valve. The construction of a typical triode is shown in Fig. 9.14(a). The third electrode is called a grid, although it is almost always constructed as the open wire spiral

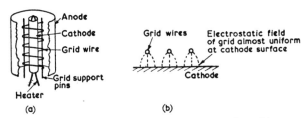

(a)

(b)

Fig. 9.14. Construction of the Triode and Grid Field at Cathode Surface

shown. If the grid is uncharged then it will intercept only a small proportion of the total electrons in the electron stream, and hence will have a negligible effect on the anode current. If, on the other hand, the grid is charged, then the electrostatic field which it produces will be almost uniform at only a short distance from the grid wires, so that the grid may then be considered to act as a charged plate. Fig. 9.14(b) shows the field between a charged grid and the cathode surface.

To examine the characteristics of grid control, suppose that a triode valve with a positive voltage maintained on the anode has its grid voltage varied with respect to the cathode. Commencing with the grid at a positive voltage with respect to the cathode the electrostatic field will resemble that illustrated in Fig. 9.15(*a*). Since both grid and anode are positive, lines of force will run from both to the cathode, and the electrostatic field at all points on the cathode will be in such a direction as to draw electrons from the space charge around the cathode. In this state there is both grid and anode current.

With the grid at the same voltage as the cathode (Fig. 9.15(*b*)), the grid will partly shield the electrostatic field of the anode from the cathode. The anode current is reduced and the grid current will be extremely small.

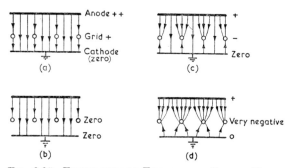

FIG. 9.15. ELECTROSTATIC FIELDS IN A TRIODE VALVE

With the grid voltage negative with respect to the cathode the field configurations are illustrated in Figs. 9.15(*c*) and (*d*). In (*c*), the grid is slightly negative, in (*d*) it is very negative. In both cases the grid shields the cathode from the electrostatic field of the anode. In the first case the shielding is partial, and in the second case it is complete, the electrostatic field at the cathode being then entirely "negative," so that there is neither anode nor grid current. The valve is then said to be "cut off". When the shielding is partial then these parts of the cathode opposite to a grid space still lie under the influence of the anode field, and electrons will leave the space charge at these points to give a small anode current. There will be no grid current, since a negative potential on the grid will repel electrons.

It is seen that the grid voltage controls the anode current and that there are three distinct states—

(*a*) High negative grid voltage—valve is "cut off", i.e. no anode or grid current.

(*b*) Low negative grid voltage—small anode current but no grid current. Since there is no grid current no power will be absorbed from the grid circuit which is the ideal requirement for an amplifier. Thus this is the most important and most common operating state.

(*c*) Positive grid voltage—large anode current and some grid current. Power is now absorbed from the grid circuit which is usually undesirable, and this state is only used when a particularly high power is to be delivered from the anode circuit.

9.5. Operation of the Triode Valve

Three modes of operation of a triode valve will be considered.

(*a*) OFF-ON CURRENT CONTROL

The probable purpose of such a device would be the operation of a switch or some other unit from a source with a very small power

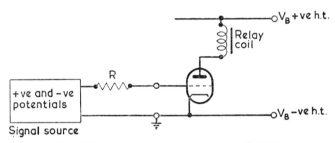

FIG. 9.16. SIMPLE APPLICATION OF A TRIODE

capacity e.g. a photo-electric cell, a telephone or radio signal, or some delicate measuring circuit. The circuit representation of a unit with a low power capacity is a generator with a high internal resistance, so that when the load impedance is low the output voltage is much below the generated e.m.f.

Fig. 9.16 depicts an arrangement in which it is desired to operate a relay from a low power source which gives positive and negative output voltages. When the output of the source is positive it is required that the relay operates, and when the output is negative the relay should release. The triode valve and h.t. voltage must be so chosen that the negative voltage of the source is sufficient to "cut off" the valve.

When the positive source voltage is applied, both grid and anode current will flow. The grid-cathode structure of the triode will then form an equivalent diode in which the grid acts as an anode. Due to the high series resistance, R, the volt drop across the equivalent diode tends to zero, i.e. the triode grid voltage is zero. The flow of grid current in the high internal impedance of the source keeps the grid from becoming appreciably positive. The relay should operate on a current which is less than the valve current at zero grid voltage.

(b) OUTPUT VOLTAGE CONTROL

The small voltage derived from the potentiometer and cell arrangement of Fig. 9.17 may control the much larger output voltage across the valve if the valve is connected in series with a resistor R to the h.t. supply. Assuming that the resistance of the

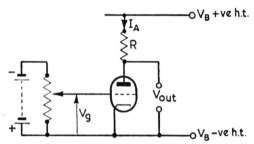

FIG. 9.17. CONTROL OF OUTPUT VOLTAGE IN A TRIODE

potentiometer is large, it will be useless to attempt to apply a positive voltage to the triode grid since the grid current which would then be drawn would give a volt drop almost cancelling the applied voltage. Thus only negative voltages need be considered.

If the grid is driven far negative the valve will become non-conducting, i.e. it is forced beyond "cut off." There is then no volt drop in the resistance R and the voltage across the valve (i.e. the output voltage), equals the h.t. supply voltage. The output voltage will remain at this value until the grid voltage is brought to a value less negative than the cut-off voltage. The minimum output or anode voltage occurs when the grid voltage is zero, i.e. the most positive grid voltage attainable.

Fig. 9.18 shows how the anode potential and current vary when the grid potential is reduced from a value beyond cut-off to zero. (Linear or "straight line" changes have been assumed). Note:

1. The anode potential variation is much larger than the grid potential variation, i.e. there is voltage amplification.

2. Whatever current (if any) is associated with the grid circuit is many times smaller than the anode current, i.e. there is power amplification.

3. The output power (if any) is entirely derived from the h.t. supply and not from the input.

4. The anode current varies "in phase" with the grid potential, i.e. the highest anode current coincides with the most positive grid potential.

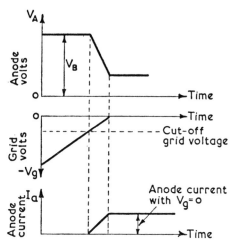

Fig. 9.18. Variations in Anode Current and Voltage with Variations in Grid Potential

5. The anode or output voltage varies "in anti-phase" with the grid potential, i.e. the highest anode potential occurs at the maximum negative grid potential.

6. The anode or output voltage is always a function of the anode current

$$V_A = V_B - I_A R$$

where V_B is the supply voltage (d.c.).

7. There are two distinct discontinuities—
   (a) the grid cut off potential, and
   (b) zero grid potential.

(c) Linear Voltage Amplification

The purpose of an amplifier is generally to give a faithful (i.e. undistorted) enlarged reproduction of a small voltage change. It is not usually required to deal with the large changes encountered in the previous sub-section. To obtain this faithful reproduction it is necessary to ensure that the changes in grid voltage occur within the range from zero to negative cut-off. The valve operation in this region requires further examination. The test circuit of Fig. 9.19(*a*) may be used, and the curves of Fig. 9.19(*b*) determined for any particular triode; these curves are called the anode characteristics of the triode.

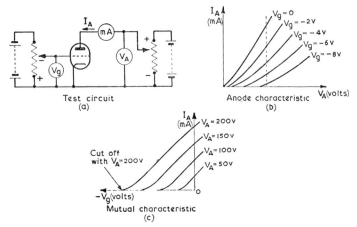

FIG. 9.19. CHARACTERISTICS OF A TRIODE

To obtain the characteristics, the grid voltage is set at a particular value and the anode voltage varied so that the corresponding current variation is obtained—the procedure is repeated for other values of grid voltage.

Each characteristic corresponds approximately to a $\frac{3}{2}$ power law and consequently is not straight. Nor are the characteristics evenly spaced with respect to grid voltage variations. These non-linearities lead to the virtual impossibility of obtaining amplification with zero distortion. However, by careful design, the distortion can be very small.

An alternative set of characteristics, called the mutual characteristics, displaying anode current against grid voltage for various constant values of anode voltage are shown in Fig. 9.19(*c*). These may be obtained either directly by experiment from the test circuit, or from the previously obtained anode characteristics, as follows— A vertical line across the anode characteristics is a line of constant anode voltage and will therefore correspond to a particular curve in the mutual characteristics. Thus if values of anode current are plotted to a base of grid voltage (taken from points on the vertical line) one curve of the mutual characteristic is obtained. If this is repeated for other values of anode voltage the whole family of mutual characteristic curves is obtained. The anode characteristics are generally the more useful in amplifier design.

For a voltage amplifier it is always necessary to have an impedance in the anode lead, e.g. the resistor R in the previous sub-section. The presence of this resistor makes the anode-cathode valve voltage dependent on the anode current. Thus if V_A is the valve anode-cathode voltage, V_B the supply voltage, and I_A the valve anode current, then

$$V_A = V_B - I_A R \qquad . \qquad . \qquad . \quad (9.6)$$

i.e.
$$I_A = \frac{V_B}{R} - \frac{V_A}{R} . \qquad . \qquad . \qquad . \quad (9.7)$$

which, on the anode characteristic graph, represents a straight line cutting the I_A axis at $\dfrac{V_B}{R}$ and the V_A axis at V_B as shown in Fig. 9.20(a). This line is drawn across the characteristics of Fig. 9.20(a), and then by point-to-point plotting, the corresponding line (now

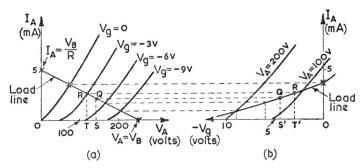

FIG. 9.20. LOAD LINE FOR A TRIODE WITH RESISTIVE ANODE LOAD

curved) is drawn across the equivalent mutual characteristics. The resistor R is called the anode load resistor, and such lines are called load lines.

The operation of the simple amplifier circuit of Fig. 9.21 may now be studied.

The input voltage (commonly called signal) is a small varying voltage, probably varying positively and negatively about a mean value of zero. In order that the grid-cathode voltage is always negative, the input signal is connected in series with a negative "grid-bias" voltage, which must be larger than positive peak value of the signal voltage.

A grid leak resistor (usually about 1 M Ω) is connected across the input terminals to provide a conducting path by means of which the grid bias voltage is applied to the grid in the absence of a path through the input circuit. It also gives a return path for stray electrons which may arrive at the grid in the valve.

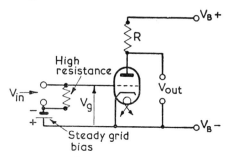

FIG. 9.21. SIMPLE AMPLIFIER CIRCUIT

With no input signal (i.e. the valve quiescent), the grid voltage is equal to the bias voltage, and the anode current and voltage are given by the point on the load line corresponding to this grid voltage. Point Q in the diagrams of Fig. 9.20 illustrates quiescent conditions. If the input signal increases the grid voltage, by say $S'T'$ volts (Fig. 9.20(*b*)) the point R is obtained on the load lines so that the increase in input voltage gives rise to a decrease in anode voltage from OS to OT volts. The voltage amplification is then $TS/S'T'$.

It will be seen that the corresponding changes in the grid and anode voltages of a triode are in opposition, i.e. when the grid voltage increases positively the anode voltage reduces and vice-versa.

Example 9.1

The anode characteristics of a triode are given in Fig. 9.22(*a*). (Mullard ECC33).

If the supply voltage is 300 V plot the anode load lines for anode resistors of (*a*) 10,000 Ω, and (*b*) 60,000 Ω. Plot the mutual characteristics for the valve for anode voltages of 150 V and 250 V. Across these, plot the load line for the 10,000-Ω resistor. Choose a suitable grid bias voltage for operation with each of the above resistors. Estimate the voltage amplification obtained with each resistor.

On the given anode characteristics of Fig. 9.22(*a*) the following load lines are drawn—

Load line (*a*) runs from ($V_A = 300$, $I_A = 0$)

$$\text{to } (V_A = 0, I_A = \frac{300}{10} = 30 \text{ mA})$$

Load line (*b*) runs from ($V_A = 300$, $I_A = 0$)

$$\text{to } (V_A = 0, I_A = \frac{300}{60} = 5 \text{ mA})$$

The mutual characteristics for $V_A = 150$ V, and $V_A = 250$ V correspond to the ordinates at 150 V and 250 V respectively on the anode characteristics. Point X at 150 V on the anode characteristics and $V_g = 0$, $I_A = 15$ mA, corresponds to point x on the mutual characteristics. Similarly Y to y, and Z to z. Hence the 150-V mutual characteristic may be drawn and the 250-V mutual characteristic in a like manner. The mutual characteristics are shown in Fig. 9.22(b).

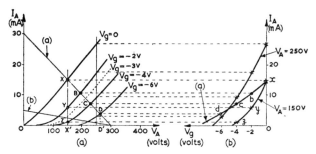

Fig. 9.22. Characteristics of the Mullard ECC33 Triode

The mutual load lines may be drawn by considering that point D ($V_g = -6V$, $I_A = 3 \cdot 6$ mA) on the 10,000-Ω anode load line corresponds with point d on the 10,000-Ω mutual load line. Similarly with B and b, C and c, X and x. Hence the 10,000-Ω mutual load line may be drawn. A grid bias voltage of -3 V is probably suitable for both of the anode load resistors. The -3 V characteristic is drawn by interpolation. Since the anode voltage changes are evidently greater when the grid voltage moves positively from -3 V than when the grid voltage moves negatively from -3 V, a better estimate of the amplification will be made by considering a grid voltage change from 0 to -6 V.

Amplification with 10,000 $\Omega = \dfrac{OD' - OX'}{6} = \dfrac{263 - 150}{6} = 18 \cdot 8$

Amplification with 60,000 $\Omega = \dfrac{222 - 47}{6} = \underline{\underline{29 \cdot 2}}$

9.6. Valve Parameters

For the majority of cases it is sufficiently accurate to assume that the characteristics of triode valves are straight lines which are evenly spaced from one another. If this is done the operation of valve amplifier circuits may be expressed in simple mathematical form by making use of the following constants or valve parameters.

(a) The "anode slope resistance" or "a.c. resistance" of a valve is defined as the rate of change of anode voltage with anode current for any constant value of grid voltage. It is represented by the symbol r_a, and may be taken as being the resistance of the valve to alternating currents or to changing currents. Mathematically,

$$r_a = \frac{\text{change in anode voltage}}{\text{change in anode current}} = \left(\frac{\partial V_A}{\partial I_A}\right)_{V_g \text{ const}} \Omega \quad . \quad (98)$$

In Fig. 9.23, which shows the linear portion of the anode characteristics of a valve, r_a may be interpreted as

$$r_a = \frac{AB(\text{volts})}{CD(\text{ampere})} \ \Omega$$

i.e. the reciprocal of the slope of a constant grid voltage line on the anode characteristic.

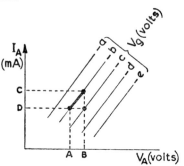

Fig. 9.23. Parameters of a Triode

(b) The "mutual conductance" (g_m) of a valve is defined as the rate of change of anode current with grid voltage for a constant anode voltage, i.e.

$$g_m = \frac{\text{change in anode current}}{\text{change in grid voltage}} = \left(\frac{\partial I_A}{\partial V_g}\right)_{V_A \text{ const}} \qquad . \quad (9.9)$$

It is usual to state this mutual conductance in mA/V. In Fig. 9.23 it may be written as

$$g_m = \frac{CD(\text{milliampere})}{(c-b)(\text{volts})} \ \ \text{mA/V}$$

(c) The "amplification factor" (μ) of a valve is defined as the rate of change of anode voltage with grid voltage for a constant anode current, i.e.

$$\mu = \frac{\text{change in anode voltage}}{\text{change in grid voltage}} = \left(\frac{\partial V_A}{\partial V_g}\right)_{I_A \text{ const}} \qquad . \quad (9.10)$$

From Fig. 9.23,

$$\mu = \frac{AB(\text{volts})}{(c-b)(\text{volts})}$$

Combining equations (9.8), (9.9), and (9.10) gives the following general relationship,

$$\mu = g_m \times r_a \ . \qquad . \qquad . \qquad . \quad (9.11)$$

The mutual conductance of a valve depends mainly on the control grid and cathode construction; it is normally in the range 1 to 10 mA/V. The anode slope resistance gives a measure of the effect of anode voltage on the anode current and is in the range of 1000 to 50,000 Ω.

Example 9.2

Determine the valve parameters for the triode whose anode characteristics are shown in Fig. 9.24.

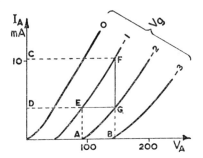

FIG. 9.24. CHARACTERISTICS FOR EXAMPLE 9.2

The horizontal line *DEG* is drawn on the characteristic at a point at which the curves are linear, to cut the −1 V grid line at *E* and the −2 V grid line at *G*. *BGF* is then drawn perpendicular to the axis of V_A to cut the −1 V grid line at *F*. Then,

$$r_a = \frac{AB}{CD} = \frac{140 - 90}{(10 \cdot 2 - 4) \times 10^{-3}} = \frac{50 \times 10^3}{6 \cdot 2} = 8,000 \ \Omega$$

$$g_m = \frac{(10 \cdot 2 - 4) \times 10^{-3}}{2 - 1} = 6 \cdot 2 \times 10^{-3} \ \text{mhos} = 6 \cdot 2 \ \text{mA/V}$$

and
$$\mu = \frac{140 - 90}{2 - 1} = 50$$

Note that $g_m \times r_a = 6 \cdot 2 \times 10^{-3} \cdot 8,000 = 49 \cdot 5$

$$\doteqdot \mu$$

It should be noted that similar constructions enable the valve parameters to be obtained from the mutual characteristics of the valve.

Example 9.3

Determine the valve parameters for the triode whose mutual characteristics are shown in Fig. 9.25.

The characteristics shown are approximately linear at the point *G*. The vertical line *GF* represents a change in anode current with a constant grid voltage,

Therefore $r_a = \left(\dfrac{\partial V_A}{\partial I_A} \right) = \dfrac{200 - 150 \ (\text{volt})}{CD \ (\text{milliampere})} = \dfrac{50 \times 1,000}{1 \cdot 3} = 38,500 \ \Omega$

EF represents a change at constant anode voltage,

Therefore $\quad g_m = \left(\dfrac{\partial I_A}{\partial V_g}\right) = \dfrac{CD \text{ (milliampere)}}{KL \text{ (volt)}} = 1\!\cdot\!3 \text{ mA/V}$

EG represents a change at constant anode current,

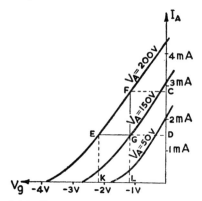

Fig. 9.25. Characteristics for Example 9.3

Therefore $\quad \mu = \left(\dfrac{\partial V_A}{\partial V_g}\right) = \dfrac{200 - 150 \text{ (volt)}}{KL \text{ (volt)}} = 50$

Note that $g_m \times r_a = 1\!\cdot\!3 \times 10^{-3} \times 38{,}500 = 50 = \mu$

9.7. Cathode Ray Tubes

Cathode ray tubes are used to study the wave forms of electrical voltages and currents, and have now an even wider application as the picture elements in television. They have also many other uses. Essentially, a pencil-like beam of electrons is directed at a fluorescent screen, where it produces a spot of light. The beam can be directed at any point on the screen by a deflecting system.

The construction of a typical cathode ray tube with electrostatic deflexion and focusing is shown in Fig. 9.26. It consists of (a) an electron gun, to give the beam of electrons (b) the deflecting system, and (c) the fluorescent screen, the whole being mounted in an evacuated glass envelope.

The source of electrons for the electron gun is an indirectly heated cathode in the form of a nickel cylinder the end cap of which is oxide coated. Surrounding and extending beyond the cathode is a second cylinder (the Wehnelt cylinder or grid) which is kept at a negative potential with respect to the cathode. A constriction at the end of this cylinder serves to concentrate the electrons into a rough beam before they pass through to the first or accelerating anode (*A*1). If the grid is sufficiently negative, the beam will be cut off, so that by varying the grid potential a brilliancy control is achieved.

The anodes *A*1 and *A*2 are in the form of discs with small central holes through which the electrons pass. Between them is a third anode in the form of a cylinder, the whole arrangement serving to

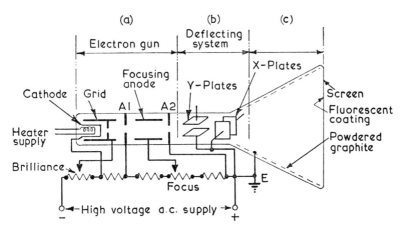

FIG. 9.26. CONSTRUCTION OF AN ELECTROSTATIC CATHODE RAY TUBE

focus the electrons into a narrow beam, and being termed an electron lens.

It is usual to have the final anode, *A*2, at earth potential, so that the deflecting plates and the screen may also be at earth potential. This means that the cathode is held at a considerable negative potential with respect to earth (from 800 to 4,000 V) and explains why the filament supply must be well insulated from earth.

After leaving the electron gun, the beam passes between two pairs of parallel deflecting plates, which are mutually perpendicular. If no potential is applied between the plates then the beam strikes the centre of the fluorescent screen. A potential applied between the *X*-plates produces a horizontal deflexion of the spot on the screen, and a potential between the *Y*-plates produces a vertical deflexion. Both deflexions may take place at once.

The funnel-shaped part of the tube leading to the screen is usually coated with graphite and earthed to form a shield. The screen itself is coated with a fluorescent powder, such as zinc sulphide (blue glow) or zinc orthosilicate (blue-green glow).

It is also possible to use magnetic focusing and deflecting systems. These are common in television applications.

The most common laboratory application for an oscillograph is the study of alternating voltage wave forms. For this application a special electronic circuit called a time base circuit is required and is commonly built into the oscillograph case. The time base circuit produces an output voltage with the saw-tooth wave form shown in Fig. 9.27.

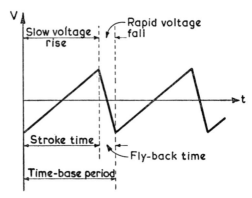

FIG. 9.27. VOLTAGE WAVE-FORM FOR A C.R.O. TIME BASE

This voltage is connected across the X-plates in such a direction that the spot is pulled across the screen from left to right relatively slowly, and is then returned to the left hand side very quickly, whereupon the cycle is repeated. The voltage whose wave form is to be examined is applied between the Y-plates so that the Y-deflexion of the spot will follow the wave form which is under examination. If the frequency of the time-base wave form is now adjusted until it is equal to the frequency of the signal on the Y-plates (or an integral sub-multiple of this frequency) then a steady trace of the required wave form will be displayed on the screen of the cathode ray tube.

EXAMPLES 9

1. The following readings were taken on a vacuum triode. Plot the mutual characteristics and determine (a) the alternating-current resistance, (b) the mutual conductance, and (c) the amplification factor for a region in the neighbourhood of zero grid voltage.

Grid voltage V	0	-2	-4	-8	-12	-14	-16
Anode current mA							
(for 130 V anode voltage)	15	13	11	7	3	1·5	0·7
(for 100 V anode voltage)	10	8	6	2·2	0·4	0·1	—

Ans. 6,000 Ω; 1 mA/V; 6.

2. A triode has the following mutual characteristics—

V_g	-1	-2	-3	-4	-5	-6	$V_A = 150$ V
I_a mA	4·7	3·0	1·7	0·8	0·3	0·05	
V_g	$+1$	0	-1	-2	-3	-4	$V_A = 100$ V
I_a mA	4·7	3·0	1·7	0·8	0·3	0·05	

Plot the mutual characteristics for anode voltages of $V_A = 125$, 75 and 50. Find the values of r_a and μ. Derive the anode characteristics for $V_g = 0$, -1, $-2 \ldots -6$ V, and draw a load line for a resistance R of 30,000 Ω, the anode supply voltage being 150 V. Hence plot the dynamic mutual characteristic.

Ans. 40,000; 25.

3. Draw sketches illustrating the construction of a triode and show how the indirectly-heated cathode differs from the directly-heated cathode. Enumerate the advantages and disadvantages of the two methods of heating the cathode.

Define the following terms and explain how they are related—(a) amplification factor (b) mutual conductance (c) anode slope resistance.

Describe how these quantities can be determined experimentally for a triode. (*L.U.*, 1952)

4. The static characteristic of a triode taken at an anode voltage of 120 V is as follows—

Grid voltage	0	-1	-2	-3 V
Anode current	20	10·5	3·3	0·3 mA

At an anode voltage of 100 V and a grid voltage of $-0\cdot5$ V the anode current is 10 mA.

The valve is used as an amplifier with an anode load resistor of 5,000 Ω and a grid bias of -1 V, the supply voltage to the anode being adjusted to give an anode current of 10·5 mA when the alternating voltage applied to the grid circuit is zero. Calculate (a) the value of the supply voltage, and (b) the variation of the p.d. across the load resistor when an alternating voltage of peak value 0·2 V is applied to the grid. (*L.U.*, 1954)

Ans. 172·5 V; 5 V.

5. A region of the anode characteristics of the Mullard EC52 triode are given in the following table. Estimate the values of r_a, g_m, and μ for the region.

$V_g = -2$ V	$\begin{cases} I_A \text{ (mA)} \\ V_A \text{ (V)} \end{cases}$	5	10	15
		150	205	245
$V_g = -3$ V	$\begin{cases} I_A \\ V_A \end{cases}$	4	10	15
		200	260	305
$V_g = -4$ V	$\begin{cases} I_A \\ V_A \end{cases}$	4	9	14
		260	310	360

Ans. 9,750 Ω, 6·0 mA/V; 57·5.

6. On the characteristics given in the previous example draw the load line for a supply voltage of 400 V and an anode load resistance of 14,000 Ω. From this determine the change in anode voltage for a peak grid voltage variation of 1 V about a steady grid bias of -3 V.

Ans. 35 V.

7. A half-wave, hard-valve rectifier without smoothing is to supply a pure resistance load with a mean voltage of 100 V. Calculate the r.m.s. voltage of the alternating supply. Neglect volt drops in the valve.

Ans. 222 V.

8. A full-wave, hard-valve rectifier without smoothing is supplied from a transformer with an output voltage of 250 V-0-250 V. Calculate the mean d.c. voltage and find the maximum peak inverse voltage from anode to cathode of the valve. Neglect volt drops.

Ans. 223 V; 990 V.

9. A cathode ray tube requires a d.c. supply of 100 μA at 2,000 V. Smoothing is provided by a single 0·2-μF capacitor. Calculate the 50-c/s, r.m.s. voltage required from the supply transformer and find the peak ripple voltage across the tube (neglect valve volt-drop).

Ans. 1,410 V; 5 V.

10. A 300-V d.c. supply is to be obtained from a rectifier with a π smoothing circuit. Neglecting volt drops calculate the necessary r.m.s. transformer voltage and the peak inverse voltage across the valve.

Ans. 212 V; 600 V.

Index